Selected readings in

The cultural, social and behavioural determinants of health

Edited by John C. Caldwell and Gigi Santow

HEALTH TRANSITION SERIES No. 1

National Library of Australia
Cataloguing-in-Publication entry

Selected readings in the cultural, social and behavioural
    determinants of health.

    Bibliography
    ISBN 0 7315 0799 1.

    1. Social medicine - Developing countries. 2. Public health - Social aspects -
    Developing countries. I. Caldwell, John C. (John Charles), 1928-   . II. Santow,
    Gigi. III. Australian National University. Health Transition Centre. (Series:
    Health transition series; no. 1).

306.461091724

Printed in Australia by the Highland Press, Canberra, for the
Health Transition Centre, National Centre for Epidemiology
and Population Health, The Australian National University,
GPO Box 4, Canberra, Australia 2601.

Distributed by Bibliotech, ANUTECH Pty Ltd
GPO Box 4, Canberra, Australia 2601.

Contents

iv

FAMILY BEHAVIOUR   Page Nos.

MECHANISMS - ANTHROPOLOGICAL INVESTIGATIONS

HEALTH PROGRAMMES

List of Tables

List of Figures

PREFACE

This book has been funded by the Rockefeller Foundation. The work has very largely been carried out in the Health Transition Centre in The Australian National University's National Centre for Epidemiology and Population Health. One editor also employed for a period the facilities of the Netherlands Institute for Advanced Study in the Humanities and Social Sciences.

The original idea and encouragement for the volume of readings came from Dr Kenneth Prewitt, Vice-President of the Rockefeller Foundation, and subsequent support continued to come from Dr Sally Findley and Dr Scott Halstead of the Foundation's Health Sciences Division.

The book of readings is now part of a larger programme that will provide a substantial amount of teaching and research material in the health transition field. The next publication in the Health Transition Centre's series will be a double volume, *What We Know About Health Transition: The Proceedings of an International Workshop, Canberra, May 1989, John C. Caldwell, Sally Findley, Pat Caldwell, Daphne Broers-Freeman and Wendy Cosford (eds)*, the list of contents of which appears as Appendix I to the present volume. Following this, as the third in the Health Transition Series, will be a volume on appropriate and emerging methodologies in the field, deriving from a workshop held in June 1989 at the Centre for Population Studies, London School of Hygiene and Tropical Medicine, University of London, the list of papers presented is included in this volume as Appendix II.

The work of production manager and coordinator was undertaken by Daphne Broers-Freeman; Wendy Cosford assisted with the editing; word-processing was by Andrea Fleming and copyediting by Gordon Sheldon.

We wish to thank the authors for agreement to republish and also to thank the following journals and organizations:

Social Science and Medicine for permitting republication of Edward C. Green, 'Can collaborative programs between biomedical and African indigenous health practitioners succeed?', *Social Science and Medicine*, 27(11), 1988: 1125-1130, Copyright 1988, Pergamon Press PLC; of John Cleland and Jerome van Ginneken, 'Maternal education and child survival in developing countries: the search for pathways of influence', *Social Science and Medicine* 27(12), 1988: 1357-1368, Copyright 1988, Pergamon Press PLC; and of John Caldwell, Indra Gajanayake, Pat Caldwell and Indrani Peiris, 'Sensitization to illness and the risk of death: an explanation for Sri Lanka's approach to good health for all', *Social Science and Medicine* 28(4), 1989: 365-379, Copyright 1989, Pergamon Press PLC. The Population Council for permitting the republication of Lincoln C. Chen, Emdadul Huq and Stan D'Souza, 'Sex bias in the family allocation of food and health care in rural Bangladesh', *Population and Development Review* 7(1), March 1981: 55-70; and of John C. Caldwell, 'Routes to low mortality in poor countries', *Population and Development Review* 12l(2), June 1986: 171-220. *Population Studies* for permitting the republication of J.C. Caldwell, P.H. Reddy and Pat Caldwell, 'The social component of mortality decline: an investigation in South India employing alternative methodologies', *Population Studies* 37(2), July 1983: 185-205. The University of Wisconsin Press for its republication from John C. Caldwell, P.H.Reddy and Pat Caldwell, *The Causes of Demographic Change: Experimental Research in South India,* University of Wisconsin Press, Madison, 1988, pp.132-160. *Social Biology* for permitting the republication of Alaka Basu, 'Household influences on childhood mortality: evidence from historical and recent mortality trends', *Social Biology* 34(3-4), 1987: 187-205. The International Union for the Scientific Study of Population for permitting the republication of W.Henry Mosley, 'Will primary health care reduce infant and child mortality? a critique of some current strategies, with special reference to Africa and Asia', in Jacques Vallin and Alan D. Lopez (eds), *Health Policy, Social Policy and Mortality Prospects,* Ordina, Liège, 1985, pp.103-137; of Samuel Preston, 'Resources, knowledge and child mortality: a comparison of the U.S. in the late nineteenth century and developing countries today', *International Population Conference, Florence, 1985,* IUSSP, Liège, 1985, vol.4, pp.373-386; and of Michel Garenne and Francine van de Walle, 'Knowledge, attitudes and practices related to child health and mortality in Siné-Saloum, Senegal', *International Population Conference, Florence, 1985,* IUSSP, Liège, 1985, vol.4, pp.267-277. International Centre for Diarrhoeal Disease Research, Bangladesh for the republication of Shirley Lindenbaum, with the assistance of Manisha Chakraborty and Mohammed Elias, 'The influence of maternal education on infant and child mortality in Bangladesh', Report for ICDDR,B, Dhaka, August 1983. International Labour Office for the republication of M.E.Khan, Richard Anker, S.K.Ghosh Dastidar and Sashi Bairathi, 'Inequalities between men and women in nutrition and family welfare services: an in-depth enquiry in an Indian Village', World Employment Programme Working Paper No.158, Geneva, June 1987. The Gujarat Institute for Area Planning for the republication of John Simons, 'Cultural dimensions of the mother's contribution to child survival', *Interdisciplinary Workshop on Explanations of the Observed Association between Mother's Education and Child Survival, Ahmedabad, 16-18 January 1989.* The Center for Advanced Study of International Development, Michigan State University for the republication of John C. Caldwell, 'Mass education as a determinant of mortality decline', *CASSID Lecture, October 25, 1988,* CASSID, Michigan State University, East Lansing, 1989.

INTRODUCTION

As employed in this book of readings, the term 'health transition' means *the cultural, social and behavioural determinants of health.* Thus, the focus of interest is on the role played by these factors, as distinct from the roles played by health interventions or economic or nutritional factors, in determining levels of morbidity or mortality. In addition, as the word 'transition' implies, there is also an interest in change, and particularly in the part played by these factors in the achievement of lower levels of mortality and improved conditions of health. In spite of the distinction just made, much of the interest in how cultural, social and behavioural factors work is in how they achieve their impact in combination with health interventions. The use of three separate adjectival terms is dictated less by the fact that they are completely distinct than that they grade into one another to form a continuum. Admittedly, there are different social patterns within a single culture: indeed, it is by such contrasts that the impact of social forces is usually determined and measured. Nevertheless, a culture is essentially a social pattern with a degree of stability over time. Similarly, there may be different individual or family patterns of behaviour within a society, but the overall balance of behaviour does much to define any specific society.

The impetus for much of the present health transition work was derived from a seminal Rockefeller Foundation workshop held at Bellagio in 1985 on the subject of *Good Health at Low Cost.* It was, however, at a second meeting at Bellagio that the term *health transition* was coined and the field was more exactly defined.

In some ways, health transition has had a long history, but researchers have presented more compelling evidence during the last decade than at any previous time. Although so much of this work is recent – indeed the earliest paper in this book was published only in 1981 – it was felt timely to draw together a collection of published articles that would further the definition of the field, provide a textbook for teaching, and provoke more and, hopefully, better research. There is an urgent need for carefully designed fieldwork and for historical research on both transition in the West and that in the Third World. There is a need for greater theoretical insights, especially on such matters of central concern as whether such analytical categories as female education, female autonomy, and individual rights within the family are distinct categories or merely facets of a larger, and imperfectly perceived, whole.

The papers presented in this collection were all available by January 1989. In addition they were all relatively brief and most took the form of journal articles. Nevertheless, it was felt that many were not easily accessible, especially to persons across a wide range of disciplines not accustomed to locating conference proceedings, United Nations working papers or published lectures in fields other than their own. The collection is, of course, intended to provide access to a much larger range of information, some already in books and some soon to appear in other collections. The following is a guide to a few of the more notable omissions. Any student or researcher in the field should read Halstead, Walsh and Warren (1985), *Good Health at Low Cost,* the book to emerge from the original Bellagio meeting. Equally, the most ambitious attempt yet to provide an analytical and theoretical framework for the analysis of the health changes was that provided in Mosley and Chen (1984). Much information appears in many of the publications originating from the World Fertility Survey, but an important analysis of both those data and also material from other surveys is found in Mensch, Lentzner and Preston (1985). A great deal of relevant information on the apparently single most important issue in health transition, the situation of women and its relation to demographic change, is found in Mason (1988). A book on a single area, the Western Sahel, which throws a great deal of light on many of these matters is Hill (1985), and perhaps particularly the chapter by Hilderbrand *et al.*

Some papers in this book are amplified by others written by their authors. Cleland and van Ginneken (Chapter 4) should now be read in conjunction with Cleland (1990); Preston (Chapter 3) should be supplemented with Ewbank and Preston (1990); and Khan, Anker, Dastidar and Bairathi (Chapter 10) benefits from being read in conjuction with an earlier ILO study in Africa, Anker and Knowles (1977). Material for the Caldwell chapters drew upon Orubuloye and Caldwell (1975), Caldwell (1982), Caldwell, Reddy and Caldwell (1988) and an unpublished paper on gender differentials in mortality in South Asia, Caldwell and Caldwell (1987). In addition, the argument with regard to identifying many apparently different social changes as a single change is carried further in Caldwell (1990). Other highly relevant papers in the new publications are Das Gupta (1990) on North India and Sushama (1990) on South India.

CHARACTERISTICS OF THIS BOOK

This collection is a product of The Australian National University's Health Transition Centre's research programme, and hence reflects a specific view of the nature of the field and of priorities within it. In order to argue that case, we have included several papers from this research programme. The central aim was to present a series of papers which demonstrated the importance of the research area by clear and straightforward examples. Research was chosen which produced definite, and often quantified, findings. As a result, the following are characteristics of the collection even though we do not argue that any of them should necessarily be characteristics of the field as it develops.

The emphasis is far more on the *social* than it is on the *cultural* or *behavioural*. The main reason is that so many data are the products of surveys. Such investigations are usually carried out within a single culture and hence do not allow inter-cultural comparisons. When comparison is made between survey findings from different countries, there is often unease as to whether some of the differences derive largely from the fact of their being separate and necessarily different investigations. An even more serious barrier is the feeling that most important aspects of a culture cannot be measured but can only be understood and described by an anthropologist. This is compounded by the fact that few anthropologists work concurrently in more than one culture, and there is some debate as to whether even those who do can make more than speculative comparisons. In contrast, there has been a growing acceptance of quantified social data as providing a representation of a society at any given time, although it might be argued that such crude measures not only fail to represent society as a whole but also distort even the characteristics they address.

The papers that follow inevitably give rise to a nagging worry about the adequacy of the years of full-time tuition as a measure, or even an index, of education. There must also be a worry about whether it is the existence of this measure that has made the study of the role of education in health transition so dominant and whether the relative scarcity of analyses on the impact of female autonomy or grass-roots radicalism is partly a reflection of the absence of a similar simple measure in these areas. This is not, of course, the whole problem. Female autonomy, and even more grass-roots radicalism, tend more to be characteristics of whole societies and less those of individuals, although, in this collection, Caldwell (Chapter 5) argues that education too should more frequently be treated as a characteristic of the entire society. The ease with which simple social measures can be used has allowed them to capture most of the analysis of fertility transition at the expense of historical and other approaches. It might be noted that the Indianapolis Survey of half a century ago was originally planned on the assumption that psychological characteristics would prove to be the key to explaining different fertility behaviours, but, in the analysis, social data were so easy to employ and demonstrated such clear fertility differentials that their use not only monopolized most of the subsequent survey analysis but that of fertility studies ever since.

With regard to behavioural measures, there has been an important shift relating to their identification as important in First World health studies. This, as the collection of papers demonstrates, has not yet been the case in the Third World, partly because there are both definitional and methodological problems with regard to the study of behaviour, and partly because such studies tend to be expensive in that they frequently require longitudinal and observational approaches. In the present collection, no article is largely behavioural and only two are predominantly cultural; in contrast, seven could be described as either social or social and behavioural and five as being in a complex class which could be described as general/ theoretical/historical/cultural/social.

As a result of employing our selection criteria, 17 out of 24 authors would probably describe themselves as either demographers or in the population field, three as anthropologists, and four as in the health field. This is probably because health transition studies will have to begin with testable demonstrations of significant relationships between health transition variables and health levels. This is clearly not where it should remain, and, although there will continue to be a demand for demographers to test propositions quantitatively, there is already an urgent need for anthropologists to identify and to explain the behaviour that actually leads to health or sickness; for health scientists to show why sickness occurs; and for economists to measure why individuals take certain options and to demonstrate why governments should opt for one choice rather than another.

The health transition emphasis is definitionally on health rather than on sickness, let alone death. Yet, as those attempting to implement the Alma Ata Declaration have found, the nature of good health, and even more its level or intensity, is difficult to define and much more difficult to operationalize. In contrast, it is possible to mount programmes to attempt to identify and reduce ill health or morbidity. Nowhere is morbidity easy to measure and in the Third World it is very difficult indeed. In contrast, there is no dispute about the nature of death and less difficulty in measuring its occurrence. Its identification admittedly leaves nothing for an action programme but its existence is conclusive proof of absolute failure which has to be guarded against, and its measure certainly provides an index of this failure and may provide an index of the level of ill health. The First and Second Health Transition Workshops (see appendix) were more dominated by mortality measures than had been anticipated. However, it might be noted that six of the 14 papers in this book of readings are predominantly on health or morbidity, while only eight are more concerned with survival or mortality.

Finally, in terms of geographic distribution, the papers all focus on either the Third World or the whole world. The richer countries are not regarded as having completed their health or mortality transitions, but they are far along that road and the needs of the Third World are clearly much greater. It is, of course, true that the world's expenditure on health appears to be based on exactly the opposite premise, namely that the real need is for disproportionately great expenditure to be made on pushing life expectancy in low mortality countries toward asymptotic levels with all the resistance and cost which this implies. The per capita expenditure per head on health in societies where life expectancy is already 75 years or more is 100 times what it is in countries with life expectancies of 50 years or less. Where studies with a particular-country focus have been chosen, namely in six papers, the decision was made   to concentrate on the major remaining areas of very high mortality, sub-Saharan Africa and South Asia. The fact that the latter is represented by twice the number of papers as the former is a measure of the current availability of studies.

THE PAPERS IN THE VOLUME

The first three chapters employ a range of data to examine mortality change over time or between societies at different stages in the transition. The measure is necessarily mortality change because no other health index is available across such distances in time and place. Each paper comes to conclusions which may be testable in individual countries at specific times. Caldwell (Chapter 1) develops work begun in the *Good Health at Low Cost* workshop and the WHO Programme on Intersectoral Health. It argues that, for an understanding of the health transition, as much attention should be paid to those countries that perform relatively poorly as to those that are relatively successful. It questions the ease with which countries can radically improve their health by acts of political will and argues that they are often prisoners of their cultures and histories. It identifies education, female autonomy, a radical and democratic tradition, and the success at controlling fertility, or even the attempt to control it, as major factors in explaining low mortality. But it also argues that the historical evidence demonstrates that these social inputs achieve health success only when interacting with adequate inputs from modern medical services – adequate more in their universal availability and low cost than in their level of technology. Basu (Chapter 2) presents evidence that infant and child mortality is peculiarly susceptible to social changes which influence not only the way mothers regard children but the way whole households or families do so. She argues that the decline in Western child mortality around the beginning of this century was very largely the product of the changing place in society of women and children. Preston (Chapter 3) seeks to show why the differentials in child mortality by occupation of father, and by implication education and social status of parents, were much smaller in the United States of a century ago than they are in today's Third World. He concludes that a major factor was a lack of knowledge and awareness of the transmission of disease and hence that an explosion in correct popular health knowledge has been an important factor in health transition.

The extent to which research on the role of education, and especially mother's education, in health transition has progressed more than any other line of inquiry is evidenced by four chapters in the second section of the book. Cleland and van Ginneken (Chapter 4) examine a mass of evidence to conclude that maternal education has a very substantial impact on child survival independent of economic influences. They believe that the evidence demonstrates that much of this impact is achieved through interaction with modern health services but find the present research inconclusive as to the extent to which health maintenance alone (or the prevention of illness) is important. Caldwell (Chapter 5) argues that education's impact on individual health is achieved as much by the way it changes whole societies as by the way it impacts on individuals within each society and that it is our analytical approach which tends to obscure this point. He adduces evidence that any Third World country which succeeds in educating nearly all its children right through primary school can attain mortality levels close to those of the industrialized countries within the succeeding 20 years. Lindenbaum, Chakraborty and Elias (Chapter 6) present a masterly field analysis of how maternal education actually achieves its impact in rural Bangladesh. The success of such research receives confirmation from many strikingly similar findings in Chapters 6, 10, 11 and even 12. In contrast, Simons (Chapter 7) expands the theoretical frontier, shows how highly relevant work on the internal and external locus of control has been largely ignored, and indicates how the rather diverse findings in the health transition field might be integrated.

The small third section begins to focus attention on the family in two very different ways. Chen, Huq and D'Souza (Chapter 8), in what has now become a classic article, report on a major structured investigation into the existence and impact of gender differentials in food and health care in rural Bangladesh. Garenne and van de Walle (Chapter 9) present the actual responses of 21 married rural Senegalese mothers during discussions on health and death.

The fourth section of the book shows that essentially anthropological methods, combined usually with the recording of vital events and small-scale surveys designed in the field, can demonstrate how behaviour determines levels of health and survival. The three chapters provide an interesting sequence through declining mortality and rising female education with progression from the North Indian village studies by Khan, Anker, Dastidar and Bairathi (Chapter 10) to the rural area in South India examined by Caldwell, Reddy and Caldwell (Chapter 12), and finally to the range of locations reported for Sri Lanka by Caldwell, Gajanayake, Caldwell and Peiris (Chapter 12). As well as providing a great deal of detailed information, the North Indian paper is one of the few to give considerable attention to adult mortality. The Sri Lankan paper demonstrates how dependent good health is on a high level of individual sensitivity to illness and an absence of constraints on quick reactions to the detection of illness, but it also shows that substantial health returns are likely to come only when interaction is possible with a modern health system.

The final section deals with health programmes and the attempt to carry out the recommendations of the Alma Ata Declaration in Africa and Asia. Both Green (Chapter 13) and Mosley (Chapter 14) show the need for health interventions to proceed in tandem with social research. Both demonstrate that effective programmes must be based on social reality and that such reality is often far more complex than official reports suggest.

QUESTIONS AND PROBLEMS

The papers indicate the general directions of needed research but they also raise a mass of questions. To take just a few: is there too much analytical emphasis on formal education rather than on the full range of knowledge and are the measures of education too simple? Are we talking about something broader than female education or autonomy, such as increasing self-directedness or even the transition from subsistence to market production? Is the development of individualism largely a measure of that transition, and, if so, is this sufficient explanation for the distinctive behavioural patterns found in Sri Lanka and Kerala? Has the focus on maternal education obscured the health importance of paternal education and of broader household and family change? Are we sufficiently researching the whole area of child dependency and care? Is it possible to develop a methodology for examining household health maintenance so that our major focus is the absence of illness rather than its treatment? Do families achieve higher levels of health maintenance when they are small or are similar social changes responsible for altered levels of both fertility and care? Do traditional health systems have any impact on mortality? In the contemporary Third World is modern medicine to be equated with health services, or is it something much broader including modern pharmaceuticals sold by stores and traditional healers and does it include changing referral practices by traditional doctors and changing attitudes in the home?

THE RELATIONSHIP BETWEEN HEALTH TRANSITION RESEARCH AND HEALTH IMPROVEMENT

Chapters in this book argue that, at least in the presence of some access to modern health services, the cultural, social and behavioural determinants of health are the primary forces in determining the levels of mortality, and probably of morbidity, in the contemporary Third World. Even if there were little possibility of employing such knowledge to improve health, the very magnitude of the phenomenon would warrant the investment of substantial research funds and time because the most marginal of resulting health benefits would be worthwhile. However, the benefits, in terms of accelerating declines in morbidity and mortality, are likely to be much greater for two reasons.

The first reason is that self-knowledge acts spontaneously to change human beings and their societies. Health transition research findings will inevitably diffuse from journals (and even selected readings) into magazines, newspapers and conversation. Old certainties will deteriorate and behaviour will begin to be based on new assumptions. Much of the health behavioural change occurring in the contemporary West has been based on half-remembered news items and discussions. Even governments are affected in this way. In countries where women live in a degree of seclusion, the knowledge that this jeopardizes their children's survival, even that of their sons, is likely to change behaviour subtly at all levels from the household to the national government.

The other reason is that a careful reading of this book alone would suggest dozens of changes in individual or family behaviour which could be induced or encouraged by community leaders or by government. It would also suggest changes in government programmes. It is not the purpose of this introduction to draw up these lists. However, when the readings are being used as a textbook, one can hardly devise a better assignment than the listing of these examples. This does not mean that authorities should always accept uncritically what appear to be the policy implications. Nevertheless, there may be very good reasons why health transition interventions should be devised and tested on an experimental basis with the collaboration of social scientists, health scientists and officials.

REFERENCES

Anker, R. and Knowles, J.C. (1977), *An Empirical Analysis of Mortality Differentials in Kenya at the Macro and Micro Levels*, Population and Employment Working Paper No. 60, International Labour Office, Geneva.

Cleland, J. (1990), 'Maternal education and child survival: further evidence and explanations', in Caldwell *et al.*, 1990.

Caldwell, J.C. (1982), *Theory of Fertility Decline*, Academic Press, London.

Caldwell, J.C. (1990), 'Cultural and social factors influencing mortality levels in developing countries', *Annals of the American Academy of Science*, forthcoming.

Caldwell, J.C., Findley, S., Caldwell, P., Broers-Freeman, D. and Cosford, W. (eds) (1990), *What We Know About Health Transition: The Proceedings of an International Workshop, Canberra, May 1989*, Health Transition Centre, Australian National University, Canberra.

Caldwell, J.C., Reddy, P.H. and Caldwell, P. (1988), *The Causes of Demographic Change: Experimental Research in South India*, University of Wisconsin Press, Madison.

Caldwell, P. and Caldwell, J.C. (1987), 'Where there is a narrower gap between female and male situations: lessons from South India and Sri Lanka', paper presented to Social Science Research Council Workshop on Gender Differentials in Mortality in South Asia, Dhaka, January.

Das Gupta, M. (1990), 'Death clustering, maternal education and the determinants of child mortality in rural Punjab, India', in Caldwell *et al.*, 1990.

Ewbank, D. and Preston, S. (1990), 'Personal health behaviour and the decline in infant and child mortality: the United States, 1900-1930', in Caldwell *et al.*, 1990.

Halstead, S.B., Walsh, J.A. and Warren, K. (eds) (1985), *Good Health at Low Cost*, Rockefeller Foundation, New York.

Hilderbrand, K., Hill, A.G., Randall, S. and van der Eerenbeemt, M.-L. (1985), 'Child mortality and care of children in rural Mali', in Hill, 1985, pp.184-206.

Hill, A.G. (ed.) (1985), *Population, Health and Nutrition in the Sahel: Issues in the Welfare of Selected West African Communities*, Kegan Paul International, London.

Mason, K.O. (1988), 'The impact of women's position on demographic change during the course of development: what do we know?', *Research Reports* No. 88-123, Population Studies Center, University of Michigan, Ann Arbor.

Mensch, B., Lentzner, H. and Preston, S. (1985), *Socio-economic Differentials in Child Mortality in Developing Countries*, United Nations, New York.

Mosley, W.H. and Chen, L.C. (1984), 'An analytical framework for the study of child survival in developing countries', *Population and Development Review* (supplement), 10:25-45.

Orubuloye, I.O. and Caldwell, J.C. (1975), 'The impact of public health services on mortality: a study of mortality differentials in a rural area in Nigeria', *Population Studies*, 29,2:259-272.

Sushama, P.N. (1990), 'Social context of health behaviour in Kerala', in Caldwell *et al.*, 1990.

MORTALITY TRANSITION

Chapter 1

ROUTES TO LOW MORTALITY IN POOR COUNTRIES*

John C. Caldwell

Since 1980 a spate of reports has appeared adducing evidence that in major areas of the world, mortality decline, far from accelerating, has been unexpectedly slowing down.[1] This interpretation has not gone entirely unchallenged: for instance, Samuel Preston and P.N. Mari Bhat (1984) argue that new evidence for India indicates that the mortality decline there did not suffer the previously reported check during the 1970s. Still, the possibility that anticipated health targets are not being met is particularly ominous in the circumstances of the poor performance of the world economy during the 1970s and early 1980s, because it suggests once again that the ultimate constraints on mortality decline are those of material resources, and hence of economic living standards, which Malthus discerned some two centuries ago and which were identified again by Thomas McKeown (1965; 1967a,b; McKeown and Brown, 1955; McKeown, Brown and Record, 1972; McKeown and Record, 1962) in a series of persuasive papers and books appearing from 1955 on. It appeared possible that the recent optimism in interpreting post-World War II Third World experience to suggest that the economic shackles could be loosened to a very marked extent by the application of new medical technologies and by social change was unfounded, or at least premature. The social change argument has not been abandoned; indeed, W. Henry Mosley (1983) has presented evidence to show that in Kenya, urban-rural residence and parental education can explain all recent changes in child mortality (and has generalized the finding), while Preston (1985a) has interpreted late nineteenth century American data to mean that the major effect on child mortality comes only when the educational message imparts a specific understanding of the scientific cause of disease.

Informing this debate are the findings of a report on a 1985 Rockefeller Foundation conference (Halstead *et al.*, 1985), which investigates the success in mortality reduction in four poor populations: those of Kerala, Sri Lanka, Costa Rica, and China. 'Low cost' turns out to be an absolute rather than a relative term; each of these governments devoted an unusually large proportion of their resources to health.

---

*First published in *Population and Development Review*, 12(2)1986.

[1]For example, Gwatkin, 1980; Arriaga, 1981; Sivamurthy, 1981; Ruzicka and Hansluwka, 1982; Hansluwka and Ruzicka, 1982; United Nations, 1982; Ruzicka, 1983, 1984.

However, from the viewpoints of experiment, analysis, and policy formulation, this is an advantage because it provides us with the critical Malthusian test: how binding are economic bonds, as measured by a society's resources, on the reduction of mortality?

China has a per capita gross national product of US$310 (23rd poorest),[2] while Kerala has a per capita gross domestic product of $160, which would place it economically higher than only four countries in the world (or possibly as high as $270, which would place 12 countries below it).[3] Nevertheless, China is shown as having reached an expectation of life at birth of 67 years, Sri Lanka of 69 years, and Kerala of 66 years. These compare with 75 years for the Industrial Market Economies (employing World Bank categories) with an average per capita GNP of over $11,000; 70 years for the East European Non-market Economies (per capita incomes not yet assessed by the Bank); and 59 years, with a per capita GNP of $1,720, for the other 99 countries (classified here as the Third World).[4] Costa Rica, with a per capita income of $1,430, is two-thirds of the way up the ranking order of 99 Third World countries; nevertheless, its case is of great interest because, with an expectation of life of 74 years, it has attained the level of the industrial market economies with little more than one-eighth of their per capita income.

Clearly, the constraint of material resources can be very largely overcome, at least in the contemporary Third World, which can import both medical technology and social institutions (it is not argued here that the industrialized countries could in the nineteenth century or later have devised strategies for rapid mortality declines).

The focus of this paper is on how the selected populations achieved such a low mortality and whether their routes could be followed by other poor populations. Except for some data and general propositions extracted from the Rockefeller Foundation report, its work will not be repeated here;[5] rather the attempt will be made to discover whether those lessons are more widely applicable. The report's conclusions are summarized by its front-cover logo, which shows Kerala, Sri Lanka, and Costa Rica having achieved good health by a combination of 'political and social will' while China did so by 'political will' alone. Furthermore, the route followed is shown as leading through exceptional inputs in the areas of education, health services, and nutrition. In the volume itself there is also emphasis on periods of exceptional advances against mortality – 'breakthrough periods' in the language of the present paper. The questions addressed here are then:

1. To what extent are these experiences exceptional? Are they balanced by other countries with exceptionally bad experiences, worse than one would anticipate from the simple viewpoint of economic determinism?

---

[2]Cf. Frederiksen, 1960; Meegama, 1967; Gray, 1974.

[3]The figure US$160 is from Krishnan, 1985:40, and was taken from Kerala, 1984:10.xiii; the figure $270 is an estimate made by Preston, 1985b:160. An impressionistic estimate, based on a comparison with Sri Lanka and from acquaintance with both societies, is that the true figure, relative to Sri Lanka, may lie halfway between these two estimates.

[4]All World Bank data are from World Bank, 1984. Where the averages are not those of the Bank, they are unweighted. This categorization of the Third World includes, for instance, Portugal, Yugoslavia, and Greece.

[5]Health data and other information are drawn from Halstead et al., 1985, while statistical data for 99 Third World countries are taken from the 'Annex: World Development Indicators' in World Bank, 1984. It is not claimed that all the figures in the latter compilation are unchallengeable or even accurately known, but it is felt that conclusions drawn from their overall patterns are not likely to be seriously astray. Finally, statistical and other conclusions are extracted from a larger report written for a study still in preparation.

2. In what ways do the countries with exceptionally good health records contrast with those with exceptionally bad ones? Can one predict which kind of country will be able to exert political and social will and, indeed, the preferred direction of the exerted will?

3. Was there really a breakthrough period in achieving good health? Does it account for all or most of the health advantages in these countries? How was it achieved?

4. Under what circumstances can political and social will be exercised? To what extent has the political leadership been uniquely shaped by the history and nature of its society?

5. For countries with vastly different histories from those with success stories, are there lessons to be learned or policies that can be put in place to accelerate mortality reduction?

Necessarily, much of the research for this paper lay in the area of social history and anthropology. Most of the work has been restricted to the three populations with open societies, Kerala, Sri Lanka, and Costa Rica, partly because of the greater availability of sources, but largely because the most important aim would seem to be to identify routes to low mortality available to such societies. The availability of a different route followed by China and some other countries will be examined later.

EXCEPTIONAL MORTALITY EXPERIENCES

The analysis here focuses on mortality experience that is markedly at variance with what might seem to be dictated by the economic determinism exerted by per capita income levels. For a range of characteristics the 99 Third World countries have been ranked from the lowest or worst to the highest or best. The Annex to the World Bank's *World Development Report 1984* provides three age-standardized mortality measures: the infant mortality rate, the child death rate, and the expectation of life at birth. The first and last have been chosen for the analysis, as the Report notes that child death rates were derived from infant mortality rates by the use of model life tables. We have employed as our critical test for identifying superior health achievers an infant mortality rank at least 25 places above the country's per capita income rank, and that for identifying poor health achievers one at least 25 places below the income rank. The infant mortality rankings are highly correlated with those of expectation of life at birth, and both rankings are shown in Table 1.[6] Kerala, although only one state of India and hence not included in the *World Development Report*'s compilation of national statistics, is shown in Panel A of the table with rankings indicating the level equivalent to the national rankings.

---

[6]The mortality measures in the Report are not wholly distinct. Many of the infant mortality rates were originally computed from estimates of survival from birth to two or three years (a kind of child death rate) and these have in many cases played a major role in the determination of life expectancies. The comparison of rankings prevents the richest of the 99 countries being identified as superior health achievers, but this is not a major drawback as their average infant mortality rate is 50 (with a majority under 40) and life expectancy 67 years (half over 70). Similarly, the poorest 25 cannot be poor health achievers, but their averages are 121 for the infant mortality rate and 49 years for life expectancy. Nevertheless, we searched for any exceptional performers of the type that could not be recorded in the rankings and found none. It might be observed that the statistics quoted above give evidence of significant economic determinism with regard to mortality levels.

TABLE 1: EXCEPTIONAL MORTALITY LEVELS RELATIVE TO INCOME LEVELS FOR 99 THIRD WORLD COUNTRIES, 1982: RANKINGS SEPARATED BY AT LEAST 25 PLACES AS MEASURED BY INFANT MORTALITY RANKINGS

Country	Per capita GNP ($)	Infant mortality rate (per 1000 live births)	Ranking of infant mortality relative to income	Expectation of life at birth (years)	Ranking of life expectancy relative to income
Panel A Superior health achievers					
(Kerala)	(160-270)	(39)	(+75)	(66)	(+73)
Sri Lanka	320	32	+62	69	+61
China	310	67	+46	67	+61
Burma	190	96	+39	55	+38
Jamaica	1330	10	+37	73	+32
India	260	94	+36	55	+33
Zaire	190	106	+31	50	+23
Tanzania	280	98	+31	52	+22
Kenya	390	77	+31	57	+22
Costa Rica	1430	18	+27	74	+29
Ghana	360	86	+26	55	+19
Thailand	790	51	+25	63	+14
Unweighted averages	501	64		61	
Panel B Poor health achievers					
Oman*	6090	123	-70	52	-57
Saudi Arabia*	16000	108	-61	56	-50
Iran*	6465	102	-52	60	-37
Libya*	8510	95	-50	57	-47
Algeria*	2350	111	-48	57	-32
Iraq*	6465	73	-35	59	-39
Yemen A.R.**	500	163	-34	44	-32
Morocco**	870	125	-32	52	-18
Ivory Coast**	950	119	-28	47	-37
Senegal**	490	155	-27	44	-30
Sierra Leone**	390	190	-25	38	-25
Unweighted averages					
All countries	4462	124		51	
*Oil producers	7647	102		57	
**Non-oil producers	640	175		45	

Sources: World Bank, 1984 and Krishnan, 1985.

Table 1 demonstrates clearly that some countries reach health levels far above those that would be dictated by their economies and others fall far below. Thus the superior health achievers are characterized by average per capita income levels one-ninth of those of the poor health achievers, but, nevertheless, record half the infant mortality level and an expectation of life at birth ten years higher. Even those oil-producing countries that are found among the poor health achievers, although their incomes are 15 times greater than the superior health achievers, cannot equal the mortality levels of the latter.

It is, then, possible to break the economic shackles. There are sufficient other comparable and supporting mortality data over time to be fairly confident of the correctness of including each country in Panel A with the possible exceptions of Burma and Zaire.[7] The state and countries under review here – Kerala, Sri Lanka, and Costa Rica – are characterized by breakthrough periods since World War II. In contrast, for instance, Jamaica has a long history of mortality reduction (indeed, its infant mortality rate was probably as low in 1895 as was that of Sri Lanka in 1935). It is notable how well India does when performance is compared with income (as is also the case in terms of family planning and fertility levels); its basic problem is simply poverty.

Two countries that probably should be included among the superior health achievers, but that have been omitted because of lack of World Bank income estimates, are Cuba and Vietnam.[8]

Table 2 records additional data from the *World Development Report 1984* for countries in the two categories (omitting Kerala, which is not included in the Report).

Probably the first contrast to strike the reader when trying to decide what determines that a country shall become a superior or a poor health achiever is the religions of the two groups. Nine of the eleven poor health achievers are wholly or largely Muslim, while the other two (Sierra Leone and the Ivory Coast) have large Muslim minorities. The situation is not primarily a lag effect from the recent acquisition of oil wealth. The oil producers were relatively well off even before 1973, and the rise in oil prices did remarkably little to alter their income ranking order among the 99 Third World countries. In no country in the superior health achiever list is Islam culturally or politically dominant (and in only one – Tanzania – do Muslims form more than one-eighth of the population). However, Muslims constitute over one-fifth of Kerala's population. In the superior health achiever group are found three of the four largest predominantly Buddhist countries in the world (Thailand, Burma, and Sri Lanka), while the fourth (Vietnam) undoubtedly belongs there too. It

---

[7]There are fewer reliable national demographic statistics for these two countries than for any others in the list. The United Nations Demographic Yearbook provides a 1975-80 life expectancy for Zaire of only 46 years, and its only figure for Burma is a 1974 estimate of 58 years for the urban population alone. The Zaire figure may also be misleading in that the 1982 income figures were derived from a year which was at the bottom of an economic trough. In most other years Zaire has not been the seventh poorest country in the world, poorer than either Rwanda or Burundi, but considerably higher in income rankings.

[8]Preston (1985b) estimates Cuba's per capita income as US$1,000, while the World Bank (1984) credits it with an infant mortality rate of 17 and a life expectation at birth of 75 years. This infant mortality ranking is 27 places higher than the income ranking (i.e., the same as Costa Rica) and hence earns Cuba a place among the superior health achievers. Jones (1982) provides for Vietnam per capita income estimates that would translate into 1982 figures of $120-$200. Given the World Bank's 1984 figures of 53 for the infant mortality rate and 64 years for the expectation of life at birth, this would place Vietnam second only to Kerala among the superior health achievers. It might be noted that the Rockefeller Foundation Conference originally intended to include not only Sri Lanka, Kerala, Costa Rica, and China, but also Cuba, while the World Health Organization Program on Intersectoral Action for health chose as successful Third World countries Sri Lanka, Kerala, Thailand, and Jamaica (Gunatilleke *et al.*, 1984:i).

TABLE 2: VARIOUS CHARACTERISTICS OF POPULATIONS WITH EXCEPTIONAL MORTALITY LEVELS

Country	Population density (persons per km2 in 1982)	Per cent of relevant age group at primary school[a]				Ranking of 1960 per cent of females in primary school relative to income	Number of persons in 1980 per		Per cent of married women of child-bearing age practising family planning in 1981
		Females		Males			Physician	Nursing person	
		1960	1981	1960	1981				
Panel A: Superior health achievers									
Sri Lanka	230	90	100	100	106	+56	7170	1340	55
China	105	na	106	na	130	–	1810	1790	69
Burma	52	52	81	61	87	+49	4660	4750	na
Jamaica	200	93	100	92	99	+20	2830	630	55
India	218	40	64	80	93	+36	3690	5460	28
Zaire	13	32	75	88	104	+32	14780	1920	na
Tanzania	21	18	98	33	107	+12	17560	2980	na
Kenya	31	30	101	64	114	+9	7890	550	7
Costa Rica	45	95	107	97	109	+19	1460	450	65
Ghana	51	25	60	52	77	+5	7630	780	10
Thailand	94	79	93	88	95	+21	7100	2400	59
Unweighted average	96	55	90	76	102	+26	6962	2095	44
Sex ratio of children at school[b]		1960 = 72	1981 = 88						

TABLE 2 (CONT.): VARIOUS CHARACTERISTICS OF POPULATIONS WITH EXCEPTIONAL MORTALITY LEVELS

Country	Population density (persons per km2 in 1982)	Per cent of relevant age group at primary school[a]				Ranking of 1960 per cent of females in primary school relative to income	Number of persons in 1980 per		Per cent of married women of child-bearing age practising family planning in 1981
		Females		Males			Physician	Nursing person	
		1960	1981	1960	1981				
Panel B: Poor health achievers									
Oman*	4	na	57	na	90	–	1900	500	na
Saudi Arabia*	5	2	51	22	77	-95	1670	2895	na
Iran*	25	27	71	56	111	-60	6090	2520	na
Libya*	2	24	119	92	128	-69	730	400	na
Algeria*	8	37	81	55	106	-37	2630	740	na
Iraq*	33	36	109	94	117	-53	1800	2160	na
Yemen A.R.**	38	na	5	14	82	–	11670	4580	1
Morocco**	45	27	60	67	97	-20	10750	1830	19
Ivory Coast**	28	24	60	68	92	-29	21040	1590	3
Senegal**	31	11	38	36	58	-14	13800	1400	4
Sierra Leone**	44	15	30	30	45	-8	16220	1890	na
Unweighted averages									
All countries	24	23	62	53	91	-43	8027	1864	7
*Oil producers	13	25	81	64	105	-63	2470	1536	na
**Non-oil producers	37	15	39	43	75	-18	14696	2258	7

Sex ratio of children at school[b]   1960 = 43   1981 = 52

[a]The percentage that numbers at school form of total numbers enumerated as of primary school age (the index may exceed 100 if children from other age groups attend school).

[b]Percentage of girls at school/percentage of boys at school x 100.

Sources: Same as Table 1.

also includes the world's largest Hindu society (India). The Buddhist societies have a concept of 'enlightenment' that is easily interpreted as formal education; and in India this is broadly true in the case of the influential Brahmanical and Jainist traditions.

These mortality differences are not necessarily inherent in the religions, nor immutable (as is noted below). They are important at present, however. The central aspect of the relationship between Islam and mortality levels is undoubtedly the separate and distinctive position of women operating partly through their access to education but also in many other ways. It is evidenced in Table 2 not only in the low levels of female schooling, but also in low levels of family planning and in limited access to employment outside the household (which is revealed by the fact that the oil-producers in Panel B have only half the ratio of nurses to doctors as do the Panel A countries – a fact that also has a direct effect on health services).

That distinctive position is based on the Koranic injunction for men to protect their womenfolk. Raphael Patai wrote that 'in the traditional Muslim view the education of girls was considered not merely unnecessary and superfluous but positively wrong' (1971:462). Hamed Ammar reported of his home village in upper Egypt that there were doubts about teaching girls even the Koran (1954:207-208), and George Lipsky said of Saudi Arabia at the end of the 1950s that 'Public opinion has never really sanctioned formal education for girls, either in or out of the house' (1959:278). Indeed, at that time girls were not allowed to attend any state schools, although some were enrolled in a few new private girls' schools in Mecca and Medina. Change in interpretation of religion and mores was coming. Lipsky (1959) reported in the late 1950s the beginning of a newspaper debate in Saudi Arabia on the need for girls' schooling, and, as Table 2 shows, by 1981 half of all girls of primary school age were in school. Throughout the Middle East there had long been resistance to girls coming into contact with male teachers or boy students; thus, the 1948 Education Act in Egypt set the morning aside for boys' schooling and the afternoon for that of girls (Ammar, 1954). The changes during the 1960s and the 1970s affected primary more than secondary schooling, for parents and society continued to be deeply apprehensive of girls who were approaching puberty being involved in schooling or other forms of participation in public life. Nevertheless, significant numbers of girls now attend secondary school in Kuwait, the United Arab Emirates, Libya, and Iraq, the solvent in the two latter countries being the administrations' socialist ideologies and in the former two essentially secular attitudes towards education remaining little changed from British colonial times (a situation similar, for instance, to that in Pakistan).

This discussion is not meant to give the impression that limited female autonomy acts wholly through restricted education in retarding the fall of mortality. There are many other mechanisms that will later be examined. Nor is it meant to imply that Islam is associated only with lower levels of *female* schooling than income rankings would suggest. In fact, the enrolment of boys in formal schooling is lower in most Muslim countries than in non-Muslim countries with similar income levels. One reason has undoubtedly been the long existence of Koranic schools concentrating on religious teachings. In terms of child survival there appears to be no equivalence between parental education in Koranic schools and more secular schooling with a broader syllabus; in fact, where this has been investigated the Koranic education had no impact at all.[9] This appears to show that the impact of schooling has little to do with institutionalization, and reinforces our finding in South India that much of the effect of 'modern' schooling has been to lead the pupils to identify with the whole modern system, including health centres and the treatments they recommend (Caldwell *et al.*, 1983).

---

[9]Data are from the Changing African Family Project: Nigerian Segment, 1973; and Mensch *et al.*, 1985:23-24, 32.

In any event, one of the most obvious differences between countries in Panel A and those in Panel B is the higher levels of schooling in the former; the most marked difference being that of female primary school enrolments in 1960 for which average rankings exceeded income rankings by 26 places (that is, of females who were aged 6-11 years in 1960 and 28-33 years – the prime maternal ages – in 1982, the year for which we have mortality estimates). For most countries in both lists the 1982 infant mortality rankings are very close to the 1960 female primary school enrolment rankings. It is instructive to note the circumstances in which the latter is not a fairly accurate predictor of the infant mortality level. Among the superior health achievers, Jamaica records lower infant mortality than would have been predicted, but not a lower life expectancy (which may be a reason for querying the infant mortality rate, which is lower than that of half the industrial market economies and all the East European non-market economies). Tanzania, Kenya, and Ghana also do better, although the explanation in the first two cases is almost certainly a rapid rise in female education in the 1960s and low ages at female marriage and the commencement of childbearing (the average of enrolment ratings for 1960 and 1981 proves to be an excellent predictor). Among the poor health achievers, Saudi Arabia, Libya, and Iraq all have much lower infant mortality rates than their 1960 female educational rankings would suggest – a combination of subsequent rapid improvements in female education and massive inputs into health services; while Senegal and Sierra Leone do worse, almost certainly because of the very low health inputs.

Health services clearly play a role, although the message is that health cannot simply be bought. By 1980 Libya had employed its wealth to attain a density of physicians to population greater than in Japan and Ireland and not much less than in New Zealand and the United Kingdom. Saudi Arabia and Iraq were nearing the level of Chile and were not far below Singapore and Hong Kong. Yet, on average, the three Arab countries fell 16 years behind these other countries in life expectancy and experienced infant mortality seven times as great. Among the superior health achievers (and, when compared with income, among the whole Third World), China and India stand out in terms of their density of physicians. Yet these statistics must be treated with great caution, for the two countries probably number among the physicians they report a higher fraction of persons without full-duration modern medical training than any other country. The remainder of the superior health achievers average almost 8,000 population per physician, which compares with 11,000 for all low-income and lower middle-income countries from which they come (World Bank categories – excluding China and India). Similarly, the superior health achievers' average of 2,000 persons per nurse can be contrasted with 3,000 for the low- and lower middle-income countries combined. There is evidence, then, that the superior health achievers owe some of their achievement to above-average health inputs (although Tanzania is an exception).

Family planning also may play a role, although causation, in terms of the relationship between fertility control and the reduction of infant and child mortality, may well flow in both directions and they may indeed reinforce each other. Where data are available (almost certainly biasing the figures upward), the superior health achievers were characterized in 1981 by an average of 44 per cent of married women of childbearing age practising family planning (42 per cent excluding China and India) compared with an average for low- and lower middle-income countries of 27 per cent (26 per cent without China and India). The greater care given by parents to young children when the size of the family has been restricted has been noted in Nigeria, India, and China.[10] Nevertheless, the relationship is far from clear; pronounced mortality decline may be independent of fertility decline, and each may

---

[10]Caldwell and Caldwell, 1978:16; Caldwell, Reddy, and Caldwell, 1984:201-202; Caldwell and Srinivasan, 1984:78.

TABLE 3: CORRELATION BETWEEN MORTALITY AND VARIOUS OTHER MEASURES, 99 THIRD WORLD COUNTRIES

| | 1982 mortality measures | | Expectation of life at birth | |
| | Infant mortality rate | | | |
Other measure	Correlation[a]	Ranking of correlation	Correlation[a]	Ranking of correlation
1960 per cent females in primary school	–.8563	1	.8744	1
1960 per cent males in primary school	–.8374	2	.8409	3
1981 per cent wives practising family planning	–.8234	3	.8660	2
1981 per cent females in primary school	–.7932	4	.7835	5
1981 per cent persons in secondary school	–.7917	5	.8404	4
1960 per cent persons in secondary school	–.7338	6	.7800	6
1981 per cent males in primary school	–.6219	7	.6236	9
1980 ratio physicians to population	–.6105	8	.6733	7
1981 calories per capita	–.6095	9	.6511	8
1980 ratio of nurses to population	–.4401	10	.4246	10
1982 per capita income	–.3109	11	.3862	11

[a]Pearson's correlation.

be associated with the same causal factor. While only one poor health achiever, Morocco, exhibited a significant level of family planning, the superior health achievers were dichotomized. Burma, Zaire, Tanzania, Ghana, and Kenya are all characterized by low levels of family planning and high fertility levels – indeed Kenya may have the world's highest national rate of natural increase.

One other point should be noted. Eight of the 12 superior health achievers are former British colonies, compared with 26 per cent of low- and lower middle-income countries and 29 per cent of all Third World countries. Of 21 countries in the Middle East and North Africa, eight are poor health achievers, but only two of the ten ex-British colonies are in this category (and both are unusual cases: Oman, which was no more than a British-protected Sultanate; and Iraq, which under the Treaties and A-Class Mandate between World War I and the end of World War II, was little more). The explanation for the British colonial impact probably lies in both education and health policies, although the important factor was probably that of attitudes and frameworks because in most cases the full development of the programmes and the major declines in mortality occurred after independence. The use of the English language either for administration or among many administrators may well have resulted in the maintenance of stronger links during the post-independence period with global initiatives in education and health fields.

Finally, an attempt was made to test some of these conclusions through the correlations between mortality measures and the available social and economic measures for the 99 Third World countries as shown in Table 3. The mortality measures correlate highly with education and the practice of family planning. With regard to schooling, 1960 is still more important than 1981 and females more than males. Physicians are of considerable significance (much more so than nurses) and so is nutrition. Income is of surprisingly little importance. The only correlation that is significantly higher with infant mortality than with life expectancy is that with the density of nurses (in marked contrast to the situation with regard to physicians), and this may be a telling indication of their importance in antenatal and postnatal care.

These findings are in line with our analysis of the characteristics of superior health achievers. Is it, however, all we need to know or have we just pushed the problem back one level, and do we really want to know how and why societies achieved these characteristics that promote low mortality? First, we identify the routes followed by the three chosen superior health achievers, Sri Lanka, Kerala, and Costa Rica, toward attaining low mortality. This is largely an exercise in firming up statistics; the forces behind these changes are investigated later.

MORTALITY DECLINE AND BREAKTHROUGH PERIODS

Table 4 attempts to summarize what is known about trends in mortality in the three populations during the present century.[11] The earliest figures are necessarily the most suspect. A good deal of effort has gone into confirming that there were indeed 'breakthrough periods' and determining their duration, although there is much of interest in the earlier period as well. For instance, the Sri Lankan and Costa Rican expectations of life at birth in the early 1920s were comparable with those in England a century and half earlier, while those of 1939 compared with English levels 40 years before (thus demonstrating a rate of mortality decline between the two world wars that was almost six times faster than the English historical experience) (Keyfitz, 1968; Wrigley and Schofield, 1981). Gains against mortality were persistent but modest, averaging 0.2-0.6 years of expectation of life at birth per elapsed year, lower in the

---

[11]Major sources were: WHO, 1978; World Bank, 1984; (for Costa Rica) Mohs, 1982; Rosero-Bixby, 1985; (for Kerala) United Nations, 1975; Ratcliffe, 1978; Panikar and Soman, 1984; (for Sri Lanka) CICRED, 1974; United Nations, 1976; Nadarajah, 1976.

TABLE 4: CHANGES IN EXPECTATION OF LIFE AT BIRTH DURING THE
PRESENT CENTURY FROM THE FIRST SATISFACTORY ESTIMATE UNTIL 1982 (ALL
LIFE EXPECTANCY DATA IN YEARS)

	Sri Lanka	Kerala	Costa Rica
Before the breakthrough			
Period covered	1900-46	1916-52	1927-70
Initial life expectancy	35	26	41
Final life expectancy	46	49	66
Total change	11	23	25
Average annual change	0.24	0.57	0.58
During the breakthrough			
Period covered	1946-53	1956-71	1970-80
Initial life expectancy	46	49	66
Final life expectancy	58	61	73
Total change	12	12	7
Average annual change	1.71	0.80	0.70
After the breakthrough			
Period covered	1953-82	1971-82	—a
Initial life expectancy	58	61	–
Final life expectancy	69	66	–
Total change	11	5	–
Average annual change	0.38	0.45	–
Impact of breakthrough			
Calculated at the rate of			
change before the breakthroughc			
Additional fall (years of life)	10.3	3.5	1.2 (4.2)b
Years of time saved in			
achieving fall	43	6	2 (15)b
Additional fall as a proportion			
of the total post-WWII mortality			
decline (in per cent)	52	14	6 (21)b
Calculated at the rate of			
change after the breakthroughd			
Additional fall (years of life)	9.3	5.3	–
Years of time saved in			
achieving fall	24	12	–
Additional fall as a proportion			
of the total post-WWII mortality			
decline (in per cent)	40	22	–

aPeriod too short for meaningful analysis
bFigures in parentheses calculated by employing 1960s as the baseline.
cAssuming continuation of linear trend through breakthrough period.
dAssuming linear trend through breakthrough period same as trend after that period.

case of Sri Lanka and higher for the other two societies than the 0.4 years that a United Nations (1956) study found to be the average for those years for countries in Latin America and South Asia for which at least two life tables existed (probably more advanced countries than most with faster rates of mortality decline). It is not necessary here to challenge individual figures, for, even if there has been some understatement of mortality (for instance, the World Fertility Survey's retrospective calculation of Sri Lanka's infant mortality rate for 1971-74 gave a rate of nine points above the official one for those years: Meegama, 1980:19), it is almost certain that the periods of change and relative magnitude of change have been approximately delineated.

The Sri Lankan mortality breakthrough is the classic one, adding over an additional decade to the expectation of life at birth in only seven years of elapsed time (1946-53), accounting for around half of the additional gains against mortality over nearly four decades since World War II (and over half of all gains, if the total gain during those seven years is taken as the measure, rather than the additional gains beyond the pre-existing trend). The only parallels to the 12-year gain in life expectancy between 1946 and 1953 are a similar increase in Japan over the same period (Taeuber, 1958) and the experience of China since 1949.[12] In his analysis of the Sri Lankan experience, N.K. Sarkar (1957) suggests that this is a lag effect after the retardation of health advance by depression and war (an argument seemingly supported by the experience of Japan), but, as we will see later, most of the post-World War II advances were, in fact, related to initiatives made at that time. The lag argument, seemingly so clear on a graph, receives support only from some food shortages during the war (probably counterbalanced, except in the area of infant supplements, by a more equal distribution through rationing) and from the correct but contentious postulate that pre-war social advance had already been sufficiently great to support more initiatives at that time.[13] The Kerala experience was little more than a somewhat faster episode in a long period of continuing change. The Costa Rican experience is still more debatable. The argument for impressive success there must be based on other evidence, largely that mortality advance was slowing down as was evidenced by decennial gains in life expectancy of only three years during the 1960s compared with nine years in the 1940s and seven years in the 1950s. Taking this earlier record into account and the fact that gains against mortality have historically proved to be more difficult at low levels of mortality, it would seem reasonable to argue that unusually successful initiatives were taken in Costa Rica during the 1970s.

It is clear from Table 4 that our main task is to explain the long-term decline in mortality in the three societies, including the life expectancy already reached in Sri Lanka by 1900 – ten years higher than in India at that time, probably higher than in Costa Rica, and almost certainly an explanatory factor in the subsequent relatively slow fall in Sri Lankan mortality. The importance of the breakthrough periods in Sri Lanka and Costa Rica (and to a much lesser extent in Kerala) is that they were sufficiently brief to permit little fundamental social change during the period; these are laboratory conditions during which rapid mortality decline, though doubtless conditioned by the existing nature of the society, must be explained by new and

---

[12]Similar gains may have been made in China. Ignoring the even more spectacular recovery from the 1959-61 famine, and concentrating only on the longer trend lines, Banister (1984:254) estimates a gain of 12.7 years over nine years from 1953 to 1962 (for a somewhat lower estimate see Caldwell, Bracher, Santow, and Caldwell, 1984 and also Brass, 1984) and a gain of 20 years over a 15-year period, 1953-68. Coale (1984:67) calculated a gain of 18.5 years between the 1953-64 and the 1964-82 life tables (14.5 years between the midpoints of the two periods).

[13]Between 1942 and 1945 the crude death rate rose in Sri Lanka 19 per cent and the infant mortality rate 17 per cent but 1945 was an exceptional year and is ignored in Table 4. Both rates in 1946 were well below those of 1939 (by nine and 15 per thousand respectively).

different inputs. It is probable, of course, that the same inputs played a significant, but not so dominant, role during the longer mortality decline. This analysis will be left until later, but it might be noted here that those involved in these breakthroughs (admittedly mostly medical personnel) are virtually unanimous in regarding the health inputs as decisive.

One further point is important if we are to understand the nature of mortality breakthroughs and why health programmes at those times achieve such success. Comparing mortality by age at the end of the breakthrough with the situation at the beginning, it appears that in Costa Rica the reduction in infant deaths can explain almost three-quarters of the mortality decline, and reductions in deaths to all children under five years of age can explain almost all the decline; in Sri Lanka the saving in infant deaths explained almost one-third and among all children under five years almost two-fifths of the decline. Kerala's savings were spread across all ages in similar proportions to pre-existing death rates. Thus the breakthroughs tend to obtain spectacular results partly by taking advantage of the opportunity for reorganizing the health approach to pregnancy, birth, and the very young.

THE UNUSUAL NATURE OF THREE SOCIETIES WITH EXCEPTIONALLY LOW MORTALITY

Historically and socially there are striking parallels between Sri Lanka, Kerala, and Costa Rica – so striking, indeed, that they give pause to any belief that low mortality will be achieved easily in most other countries. These parallels include a substantial degree of female autonomy, a dedication to education, an open political system, a largely civilian society without a rigid class structure, a history of egalitarianism and radicalism and of national censuses arising from political contest with marked elements of populism. The problem with any analysis is the degree of interrelation: for instance, a society where women have a good deal of equality is likely to approach parity by sex in schooling and probably likely to have higher overall numbers in school; and an egalitarian society is likely to maintain democracy. There is also a problem about where to begin the inquiry, but we will do so with the position of women, which plays a fundamental role in how the health, education, and possibly political systems work and may well be a basic cultural factor and not a product of decisions and events of the last century or two. First, however, a few general historical and locational facts are important.

All three populations are small, as is shown by the 1982 figures: Sri Lanka – 15 million; Kerala – 26 million; and Costa Rica – 2 million. More importantly, all are isolated. Sri Lanka is an island; Kerala, for most of its history, has been largely cut off from the rest of India by the Western Ghats and has looked out to sea; Costa Rica has land frontiers infrequently crossed until recent times and has been culturally linked mostly with Spain and Europe. The inhabitants of small Third World states, often islands, peninsulas, or coastal enclaves, have on the whole experienced much more cultural and demographic change than have larger societies (Caldwell *et al.*, 1980). Usually they have been in the path of European overseas expansion and have been to a considerable extent a product of that expansion. Sri Lanka and Kerala produced cinnamon and pepper, as well as other products that were traded with ancient Egypt; they attracted Roman and Arab ships and by the sixteenth century Portuguese colonization, followed in Sri Lanka by the Dutch and then the British, and in Kerala by the British. Missionaries with their churches and schools had converted to Christianity by the beginning of the present century 10 per cent of the people of Sri Lanka and 21 per cent of those of Kerala (partly because of a pre-existing Christian population probably dating back to the fourth century); Arab merchants had produced similar proportions of Muslims. Cultural nationalism struck back in the second half of the nineteenth century in Sri Lanka, but Western education and other institutions were embraced to fight Western religion, rather than being attacked with it, and in a more complex way, something similar was happening in Kerala. Costa Rica was a Spanish colony that achieved its independence without a struggle in the early nineteenth century. Because most Indians in the colony had died by the end of the sixteenth century, the population was largely of European origin (except for a black proletariat on the lowland sugar and banana plantations resulting from nineteenth century Jamaican migration), although they too, influenced by European 'liberalism' in the second half of the nineteenth century, encouraged secular education to reduce the hold of the Church.

One other point is probably important. Most of the rural areas in Kerala and Sri Lanka are densely settled, as is the Central Valley of Costa Rica. Furthermore, they have widely grown cash-export crops from at least the nineteenth century: in all three, coffee resulted in an economic leap forward in the last decades of that century as world demand rose rapidly. Dense settlement and widely diffused commercial farming and other non-subsistence activities in rural areas appear to favour a reduction in rural-urban mortality differentials – a reduction that is usually the key to the attainment of low national mortality rates. Many of these activities are non-agricultural – services, retailing, and some artisanship – spurred both by population densities and, apparently, by new demands created among an educated population. In both Kerala and Sri Lanka, land reform has established not a more firmly based peasantry but a rural population among which most families derive limited support from small plots of land, while also sending family members to seek other income often by long-distance daily or weekly commuting. Mick Moore (1985) has calculated that 20 years ago at least half of Sri Lanka's rural work force was in non-agricultural employment, and he argued that this explained the failure of radical politicians to focus discontent on issues that usually appeal to a peasantry. Education had been one factor in producing such rural economies, but the latter in turn made more education, even for girls, a more attractive proposition.

THE POSITION OF WOMEN AND CHILDREN

A marked degree of female autonomy is probably central to exceptional mortality declines, especially in poor but open societies. When there is no scandal about girls assuming roles outside the house even when they are unmarried but have reached puberty, or about older women appearing in public on their own initiative, then girls are more likely to remain at school, and mothers are more likely to take action about sick children or about themselves, and when necessary, will travel to health centres, wait in queues of mixed sex, and argue even with male physicians. When a woman's morality and behaviour in the widest sense are primarily her own responsibility rather than that of her male relatives, then she will assume broader responsibilities, including those of deciding early and with certainty that children are sick and need rest and treatment; she will not worry about waiting to consult her husband or his mother or brothers. Where women have a good deal of autonomy, they will not only be in a position to treat their daughters more like their sons, particularly in terms of equality of feeding and medical services, but will also, in keeping with the community's views on females, inevitably see their sons and daughters in a similar light. When there is less concern about women's virginity, they are likely to marry later, a tendency that has implications for their training, work outside the home, and decision-making powers with regard to child health.

In practical terms, women's positions count enormously in establishing an effective rural health service. Where there is substantial female autonomy, girls are far more likely to become nurses; where there is less autonomy, parents worry about their daughters being in training schools, working with male doctors or patients, and living without relatives in distant places (cf. Damle, 1959). Where many rural girls are educated, especially in conditions of rural surplus labour, and where parents and relatives are proud if they get jobs, especially those of a somewhat professional nature, it is possible to recruit in every village women to work cheaply as health auxiliaries or to be trained as midwives. Where such persons can be recruited to work in their home areas, as in Sri Lanka and Kerala, their effectiveness in house-to-house visits is far greater than where nurses and midwives must be brought from elsewhere: as we observed in rural Karnataka, a state adjoining Kerala, female health workers often came from Kerala or Bangalore city and remained largely strangers to the local population, while in many places the lack of local recruits meant that there were no female health workers.

Sri Lanka and Kerala are the only two societies in the great arc extending from North Africa to the Middle East and down through India in which premarital pregnancy virtually never results in death, either at the hands of others or self-inflicted.[14] The parallel in Costa Rica is that *machismo* probably afflicts its males less than is the case in any other Central American country.[15] Such differences are not the result of modern enlightened policies but have ancient roots.

In Sri Lanka every major analysis of the society, from that of Robert Knox (1681) in the seventeenth century (one of the world's first great anthropological works) to those of John Davy (1821) in the nineteenth century and Ralph Pieris (1956) and Edmund Leach (1971) more recently, has commented on the relaxed sexual morality of women before and after marriage. These studies concentrated on upland (or Kandyan) Sinhalese society, and there is no doubt that lowland or maritime Sinhalese society is more strait-laced[16] and Tamil society more so again. Yet, Paul Alexander, describing a south-western coastal village, found elopement quite common and went no further than concluding that 'Premarital chastity is the expressed norm and is probably adhered to in most cases' (1982:23). Neither patriarchy nor patrilocality is strong among the Sinhalese, and the World Fertility Survey in 1978 household data collection found as many Sri Lankan young couples living immediately after marriage with the wife's as with the husband's parents.

In Kerala the position of women is even more significant, in that it has probably been the most important single determinant not only of demographic behaviour but also of the nature of society and even of its modern political history. Half its population was traditionally matrilineal, particularly the influential Nayar caste (a kind of *samurai* by profession) and the Ezhavas (a backward toddy-tapping caste who have for long been economically rising). Their girls were formally married just after puberty but thereafter had many liaisons that, in the case of the Nayars, fitted in well both with the movements of their armies around the country and with the important sexual and childbearing relations that some of their women had with the younger sons of the powerful landowning Nambudri families. De facto polyandry existed, and, among some groups, institutionalized polyandry. Foreign observers were startled by the contrast with the rest of India. Marco Polo concluded, 'They regard no form of lechery as a sin' (1958 edition:288), and two centuries later Duarte Barbosa, resident between 1500 and 1517, wrote of the Nayar woman, 'the more lovers she has, the greater is her honor' (1918 ed., vol.2:42). A nineteenth century observer concluded

---

[14]The Sri Lankan situation has been explored by the 1985 fieldwork in Sri Lanka directed by the Caldwells and Indra Gajanayake.

[15]This observation draws on published work on Costa Rica, especially Biesanz and Biesanz, 1944, as well as on other South American countries; it also draws on fieldwork undertaken by the Caldwells and Susana Lerner in Mexico for El Colegio de Mexico in 1981.

[16]Obeysekere, 1967:55; Alexander, 1982:23; Obeyesekere, 1984, *passim*; S.A. Meegama, personal communication. Obeyesekere places emphasis on the cult of the goddess Pattini, while Meegama stresses the impact of Dutch Roman law denying divorce and of British Victorian morality.

that there was less female seclusion than anywhere else in India, and claimed that, among the lower castes, female concubinage was common even among patrilineal groups (Mateer, 1883). The Nayar reform movement of the late nineteenth century and the Malabar Marriage Commission of 1891 were to employ even stronger language, pointing out that 'no religious element enters into the performance of a marriage' (Panikkar, 1900). Keralite marriage and female behaviour now conform more closely to the Indian pattern. Indeed John Ratcliffe (1978) dismissed the matrilineal factor in explaining why Kerala is different, and P.G.K. Panikar (1979) has argued that the larger Nayar family compounds that were part of the matrilineal system were headed by males – not fathers but usually senior brothers. It is, however, impossible to deny that the whole complex that went with matrilinearity, including a woman's right to decide with whom she consorted and for how long, meant that the female situation in Kerala was very distinctive indeed. It remains the basic reason that Keralite women, like those of Sri Lanka, have today a very considerable measure of freedom. In both societies early observers related such freedom not only to easy sexual relations but also to a significant incidence of polyandry.[17] The situation of females in Kerala was also of fundamental importance in another way. It did not conform to other Indian (or European) religious and social views, while matrilineal inheritance was at odds with European law, and the associated communally owned wealth of the compounds restricted individual entrepreneurship. Without this social and economic discordance, the Nayar reform movement of the late nineteenth century would not have developed and much of the radicalism of the present century would not have been generated.

The situation of Costa Rican women is not nearly so distinctive, but it has probably been helpful in reducing mortality. It was probably the best in Central America because of the lack of a conquistador tradition: even independence was achieved peacefully. A racially fairly homogeneous society of peasants and smallholders (with no Indians for labour, there was no hacienda system) produced a fairly liberal and modernizing Catholic society emerging from Spanish colonization. Women's position reflected the nature of the society, whereas Sri Lankan and Keralite society, to a very considerable extent, was moulded by the position of women.[18] In their classic social study of Costa Rican society, published over 40 years ago, John and Mavis Biesanz (1944) repeatedly drew attention to the restrictions within which women lived, but the contrast was always made with American women. However, they did emphasize the important decision-making role played by women within the family. Even in the early 1940s and among the middle class, chaperonage was declining and parents felt that they could not oppose their children's marriage choice (in contrast, the majority of marriages in Sri Lanka and nearly all in Kerala are still arranged). In their survey of bridal characteristics desired by male university and high school students, 'chastity' achieved only eighth place, just above 'neatness'. Middle-class families were still distressed if their daughters became the mistresses of

---

[17]For polyandry in contemporary Sri Lanka, see Yalman, 1967:108-110; Prince Peter, 1955:179-181.

[18]Dyson and Moore (1983:45), citing a paper by Safilios-Rothschild (1982), have applied the concept of female autonomy to India, defining it as 'the capacity to manipulate one's personal environment. Autonomy indicates the ability – technical, social and psychological – to obtain information and to use it as the basis for making decisions about one's private concerns and those of one's intimates. Thus, equality of autonomy between the sexes in the present sense implies equal decision-making ability with regard to personal affairs'. Both this definition and the indexes they employ are in general agreement with our usage. However, we are concerned about their north-south dichotomy of India, because we believe that the contrast between Kerala and the major states of South India is greater than that between the latter and North India. Possibly one should postulate a continuum: North Indian states; South Indian states except Kerala; Kerala and Sri Lanka.

rich men, but the poor were likely to encourage much less satisfactory liaisons and one-quarter of all births were illegitimate. Women did not achieve the vote until 1950, but the first girls' high school had been established in 1888.

When women's position is relatively good, so usually is that of children. One reason is that mothers are generally closer to children than are fathers and identify more closely with them. This is not the only reason. Inequality in the family is usually a contrast between patriarchal adult males and everyone else. In patriarchal societies, daughters may be ignored or treated as inferior, while sons may be treated roughly as preparation for man's estate, neither case being likely to result in the lowest mortality. Changes in the position of either wives or children usually affect the other, and, because of this, the reversal of wealth flows is rarely a simple intergenerational phenomenon. John Davy reported in the early nineteenth century that the Sinhalese treated their 'children with extraordinary affection' and were attentive to them when sick. P.N. Sushama reports from ongoing fieldwork in Kerala that many young rural women give up paid employment when they have babies, specifically to safeguard the health and well-being of the infants.

One measure of a child's position is parental willingness to send him or her to school. It can be argued that children were most readily put into school in those societies with economies peculiarly unsuited to the employment of children. The most specialized form of child labour in South Asia is animal tending, and larger domestic animals, such as cattle, sheep, or goats, are relatively scarce where farming has invaded the wet forest as in Kerala and much of Sri Lanka, or perhaps of lesser importance in coastal areas where fish provides an alternative to meat. Almost 200 years ago Francis Buchanan (1807) noted that there were few domestic animals on that part of the Malabar coast that is now Kerala. This is certainly now true of south-west Sri Lanka, although some of the older people claim that in their childhood there were more cattle looked after by boys, but subsequently the schools claimed the boys and the adults were reluctant to substitute for them. Panikar (1981) has pointed out that children in Kerala are now less likely to work than any other Indian children and that this situation was clearly recorded by the 1961 census. The pressures are not all one way: Joan Mencher (1980) reports that, in those parts of Kerala where there is more work for women, fewer older children attend school. In this case we are clearly discussing the demand for child labour for domestic child care, but the observation does suggest an interesting possibility: is it in the wet, densely settled parts of Kerala and Sri Lanka, where there is a great shortage of land and consequently a relatively low demand for either children's or women's labour, that parents are most ready to send their children to school because they are needed neither for agriculture nor for child-minding? This may well be part of the story, but not the major part. For instance, in Costa Rica Biesanz and Biesanz (1944) reported that in the early 1940s children still made a valuable contribution to family labour in remote rural areas, and were less likely to go to school, and that decades earlier this had been the case in the Central Valley but was no longer so because of profound attitudinal and behavioural changes, in keeping with both the parents' and children's expectations, that occurred from the time when the government, spurred by its secular liberal ideology, made increased provision for schooling.

THE DEMAND FOR SCHOOLING

The demand for schooling is a response both to long-established features of the society and to successive political and administrative events.

Buddhism, with its emphasis on enlightenment, which is easily identified with education, rendered Sri Lanka peculiarly receptive to education. There was an ancient tradition of temple schools, or *pirivenas*, that taught monks and some lay persons. The pupils were mostly, but not exclusively males. The fact that Buddha had come to accept the female right to enlightenment, and that there were some women monks in his own lifetime, has always exerted an important influence on the position of women and their right to education. The potential demand for education and the opportunity that demand presented for religious and cultural conversion was clear to all colonial powers. The Portuguese (the colonial power from the sixteenth century) established schools associated with churches; the Dutch (from the mid-seventeenth century) set up a network of parish schools; while the British (who acquired power in the early nineteenth century and for the first time ruled the whole island) developed both fee-paying English-medium schools and free vernacular ones.

Educationally and politically the most important event in modern Sri Lankan history was the resurgence of Sinhalese cultural nationalism, known as the Buddhist Revival, in the second half of the nineteenth century. Although linguistic nationalism was an important element in the movement, the Revival as a whole tended to compete in terms of Western values rather than to reject them. One reason was the long history of outside contact, a second was the fact that most of the leadership was mission-educated, and a third was the role played by the American Henry Olcott (the founder of theosophy). The revival of the Sinhalese people was seen as requiring an educational renaissance, and this ideological orientation has played a major role in inducing families to strain to educate their children, so that, by 1960, 95 per cent of the relevant age groups were enrolled in primary school and 27 per cent in secondary school (the latter being higher than in Czechoslovakia, Romania, Hungary, Switzerland, or Spain). For later generations the most influential writer was the movement's great moral leader, Anagarika Dharmapala, who has been described as 'a reformer of the Buddhist Church, infusing that institution with the puritan values of protestantism' (Obeyesekere, 1975:250). Significantly, he argued that sanitation, education and work had made Europe great, and his frequently reprinted *Daily Code for the Laity*, first published in 1898, contained 11 rules for teachers and even four on the use of the latrine. The reform movement set up an education fund and a Buddhist national fund (later, and significantly, merged), and school teachers became increasingly important as leaders of the movement. Nationalist, linguistic, religious, educational and health objectives became intertwined.

The colonial government was also active in the educational field and, enriched by coffee revenues and knowing that the society was interested, it, in contrast to most colonial governments in Asia and Africa (but with parallels to the independent government of Costa Rica), saw the movement toward universal compulsory schooling in the West during the last decades of the nineteenth century as providing a local goal. This was legislated at the beginning of the present century,[19] so that by the 1921 census 56 per cent of males and 21 per cent of females were literate (comparable with Pakistan at the 1971 census). Yet, one of the world's most interesting examples of social engineering was yet to come. In 1928 the British government sent a constitutional committee of inquiry to Ceylon, the Donoughmore Commission, which recommended internal self-government, and, noting the near-stagnation in mortality decline, advocated the franchise for women as well as men on the grounds that mothers alone cared sufficiently about their children's health to place health services high on the political agenda at each election (Ceylon, 1928:62-64). Thus in 1931 all males and females over 21 years of age were eligible to vote in the elections of that year (only two years after this had been the case for the first time in Britain). Over the next half-century, in a country given to changing the government at each election, the voters forced the political parties to place not only health but also education prominently among their political aims. As early as 1927 the Education Department had notified all schools: 'It is essential that every teacher should be an

---

[19]This was done with full recognition of the different position of women in various cultures, even within Sri Lanka; the minimum female school-leaving age was set at 14 years for Sinhalese, both Buddhist and Christian, but at ten years for Muslims and Tamils.

example of cleanliness and neatness'. In the 1930s a Rural Scheme of education was established, in which, after eight years of basic schooling, programmes were subsequently built around local needs, with the building of protective walls around wells and other public health schemes playing a central role. Finally, in 1947 free education, defined as forbidding any school to charge fees, was enacted.

The Kerala educational experience had strong parallels, especially in the missionary experience and in the impetus various social and political movements provided. Kerala, like Sri Lanka, and to a greater extent than anywhere else in India, had traditional schools, said to date back to Buddhist and Jain influences. In more recent times the rural people have run village schools on their verandahs, while lower castes have been taught by astrologers, who have traditionally been local teachers because their professional need of literacy has meant that they have always been the most literate of these castes. Kathleen Gough (1968) has claimed that a substantial proportion of the population was literate in the eighteenth century, an assessment that has been strongly challenged by P.K. Tharakan (1984), although it should be noted that Sir Thomas Munro, Governor of Madras, concluded in 1822 that schooling and home teaching in Malabar had probably resulted in about one-third of boys being able to read and write. Partly because of the pre-existing Christian base (although there was interdenominational conflict) and partly because of the educational demand, Protestant missionaries set up schools throughout the nineteenth century, opening the first girls' school in 1819 and the first female teacher training college in 1887. The Princely Governments of Travancore and Cochin reacted both to the demand for schooling and to the inroads of the missionaries; in Travancore an 1817 rescript stated that the state must defray all costs of providing education, while an 1844 proclamation made English the criterion for appointment to the much-prized positions in government services.

The origins of contemporary near-universal schooling, however, lie in the social upheavals of the late nineteenth and early twentieth centuries. Both the Nayars and the Ezhavas (who had found a leader and prophet in Sri Narayana Guru) saw education, and jobs of a type for which education was a necessity, as a solution to their problems, and female education as a way of changing the contentious situation of their women. Both groups organized to press government to expand its educational system, to establish their own schools, and to provide help to children of their castes to make it possible to stay at school. By 1901 Travancore and Cochin were the most literate places in India − by far the most in terms of women. In Travancore the students' numbers and the age structure of population suggest that two-thirds of children were enjoying some schooling. So great was the demand for education that only one-quarter of schools were fully supported by the government, while another quarter were aided, and a full half were completely private. Because of the number of schools and density of the population, there was one school to every 1.9 square miles, so that the great majority of the population would have been within three-quarters of a mile of a school. When A. Aiyappan carried out field research in an Ezhava village in 1955, he found that the families primarily sent their children to school because 'knowledge is good' and because 'a person without education is a beast'. He noted that newspaper reading in tea shops and *beedi* (local cigarette) shops had increased tremendously over the previous 20 years. A decade later, literacy was mandatory for membership within the state's Communist Party. In fact, schoolteachers had long made up a disproportionate number of the left-wing activists in rural areas, and from 1935 the left radicals (still within the Congress Party) laid stress on involvement in teaching the agricultural population to read and write. When the Communist Party gained political power in 1957, unable to implement land reform quickly, it gave major attention to education, doubling expenditure on primary schools. By 1978, among 6-to-10-year-olds, probably 82 per cent of boys and 86 per cent of girls were attending school, while the proportions for 11-to-13-year-olds were 80 and 74 per cent respectively (the last figure being more than double that for all-India) (Nag, 1985).

Costa Rica more closely resembles the Western experience, with largely successful attempts to create a mass elementary educational system in the late nineteenth and early twentieth centuries. The 1869 Constitution declared elementary education free and compulsory, and the Liberal regime of the late nineteenth century promoted education, partly as a secular movement divorced from the Church. By 1892, 28 per cent of the population over ten years of age was literate (a level Mexico and most of the other small Central American countries did not reach until the mid-twentieth century) and, by 1972, 66 per cent. A major attempt to complete and improve the school system was made in the 1940s and 1950s as social democratic politicians outbid those further to the left, and by 1970 illiteracy was confined mostly to the old in remote rural areas.

The conditions for unusual educational advance are fairly clear. One is a basic reverence for enlightenment or education, with a feeling that it is rarely a danger even to girls but almost invariably a lifting of the human spirit. This attitude is evident throughout Sri Lanka even among the poor and remote rural populations. (One of the most instructive aspects of our field research was the shock produced by our probing into the reasons for sending children to school when it was realized that we were asking about the economic rather than spiritual justification). Costa Rica was spurred more by its determination to remain a Europe (and increasingly a northern Europe) overseas. The countries that advance most rapidly in this area are those in which parents achieve as much satisfaction at seeing their daughters at school as their sons. Almost certainly the provision of schooling is likely to be greater when women vote and play a significant role, if only at the local level of convincing aspirants for election where their priorities lie. Education is likely to proceed furthest when it is seen as protecting and bolstering indigenous culture (even if that culture has had to experience a profound transformation before this interpretation can be applied). It may also proceed further when there is real political competition and when parties of the centre and left are vying in offering social reform packages to the electorate. Such has been the political history of Costa Rica for much of the last 100 years, of Sri Lanka for over half a century, and of Kerala for almost four decades. Finally, we might note that universal extensive education not only produces a surplus of girls willing to be nurses or midwives, but ultimately may produce an adequate number of men and women trained as doctors and – as the labour market becomes saturated – willing to accept rural appointments on modest pay scales.

EGALITARIANISM, RADICALISM, AND POLITICAL ACTIVITY

The education reforms in the three countries have been promoted as radical measures, usually justified on grounds of equality, and achieved through political activity. Much the same has been true of the expanded health systems. There are horse-and-cart problems in the analysis, for egalitarianism, radicalism, and political activism, as well as the demands for health services and even education itself, are ascribed by many observers to the educational levels already achieved. Clearly each aspect of the societies reinforced the others, and there were historical reasons for the egalitarianism and for the failure of privileged groups to check the radicalism. As we will see later, grass-roots political activism and radicalism are key elements in making health systems work, probably more important than governmental radicalism in establishing the programmes.

In Sri Lanka the basis for a continuing moderate radical tradition was laid by the nineteenth century Buddhist Reform Movement, which can also be interpreted as the social uprising of the newly prosperous low castes of the maritime districts (Roberts, 1982). Subsequently, as in the movement for universal free education in the mid-1940s, religious and nationalist pressures were harnessed for radical ends. External influences before World War II were paramountly from Britain and included those of the Labour Party and socialist movement, which fitted well with the established reform movements. During the 1928 hearings by the Donoughmore Commission on constitutional change, it was not the cautious major party, the Ceylon National Congress, that presented the case for the full franchise as an instrument for achieving social and economic change, but A.E. Goonasinha, who established the All-Ceylon Trade Union Congress and the Ceylon Labour Party in the same year and played a role in the organized strikes of the 1927-31 period. The non-parliamentary left gained strength both as a result of the crises in the export sector during the depression of the 1930s and in the years of full employment but of global tumult during World War II; indeed, K.M. de Silva (1981:495) writes, 'The social welfare schemes of the Donoughmore era were continued beyond 1947 [i.e., into Independence], partly as a means of blunting the challenge from the Marxist left'. In the half-century after the attainment of internal self-government in 1931 there were 11 elections, won by the party in power on only three occasions. It was this persistent competition that continually pushed up social welfare expenditure as a proportion of the budget, from 16 per cent in the late 1920s to 56 per cent by 1947. The major modification in this picture was the victory of the right in the elections of 1977, with, for the first time, a determination to reverse the trend in social welfare expenditure. This stance was made possible partly by the extent of the economic problems during the early 1970s but largely because of the global emergence of new political ideologies providing a moral basis for such action. In fact, the new government, while substantially changing economic policy, has done little to dismantle the social welfare system that has overwhelming support in the electorate.

In Kerala, an unusual social system was unstable once external intrusions had occurred and successive crises spurred radicalism. In some ways it took the society up to two centuries to assimilate all the changes starting from the disbandment of the Nayar armies beginning in Travancore in the mid-eighteenth century. The movements of the Nayars and the Ezhavas in the late nineteenth and early twentieth centuries helped to politicize the society. The latter were further radicalized by struggles over rights of temple entry and tenancy rights in the 1920s and by the six-month strike in the coir industry in 1938. The stage was thus set for the left to form a powerful faction within the Congress Party in Kerala during the 1930s and for the Communist electoral victory in 1957. In fact it was to be another 12 years before a later left-wing coalition government enacted major land reform. There is considerable debate as to whether these reform programmes did much to alleviate poverty: Ratcliffe (1978) argues that they did and Mencher (1980) that hard-core poverty remained largely untouched, while Panikar and C.R. Soman (1984) conclude that the 'changes have ... favourably affected the occupation pattern and vertical mobility'. Significantly, there is no dispute about the impact on individual attitudes and behaviour, and the fact that these social changes go far beyond those elsewhere in India. Donald Zagoria (1973) concluded that radical political consciousness had made far deeper inroads among the rural poor in Kerala than even in West Bengal, and Moni Nag (1985) confirmed this assessment. Even before 1957, Aiyappan found in his village study that, 'if any area of thought has been affected, it is that which affects the rights of workers which the Communists have been emphasizing in their propaganda' (1965:92). Mencher (1980) argued that poverty had not lessened but that human dignity had greatly gained because of the interwoven effect of radical politics and education. In Kerala the political left remains almost as effective out of power as in, because no other politician wants to allow them to argue that the social reform consensus has been broken or that the rights of the poor have been disregarded.

Costa Rica had no hacienda system and when the overseas coffee market grew in the 1840s, the government divided state land to create a class of middle-sized landowners. Without a military struggle for independence, the army, although significant up to its abolition in the 1948 Constitution and controlling the government for half the time between 1835 and 1899, had never formed a separate dominant class. State intervention for public ends became familiar during the Liberal dictatorship of the late nineteenth century and in the democratic period, 1905-14. Between the two world wars, the electorate, now largely literate, established the pattern of grass-roots participant organizations that has since characterized the country. These included trade unions, with a considerable Communist Party influence among the black proletariat of the coastal banana fields during the 1930s, and from 1940 a communist-led farmers' union organizing meetings on the central plateau. Nevertheless, modern Costa Rica has been largely the creation of a social democratic movement, the National Liberation Party (at first the National Liberation Front), which in 1948 overthrew an unlikely alliance of coffee aristocrats, social Christian reformers, and communists. As in Sri Lanka and Kerala, the competition has been between groups offering different routes (or just different leadership) to social reform.

John Booth has described the subsequent development of a highly participant society, seeking compromises and consensus: 'Development programmes have prompted popular organizations by the thousands to work for community improvement, health, nutrition and education – almost all of them making demands upon the state' (1984:164-165). From the 1930s European ideas were no longer completely dominant; other models originated in the American New Deal. The philosophy of the National Liberation Party was provided by the writing of José Figueres, thrice head of state, who preached government involvement in redistributory policies sufficient to remove the poor from a situation of real want. The presidency alternated between parties at every election save one after 1948, although, except for a brief period, the NLP maintained a majority in the Assembly. Coffee and banana prices remained high until the late 1970s, and continuing prosperity (with an average annual growth in real gross domestic product between 1960 and 1980 of 5.8 per cent) meant that successive administrations had to seek new proposals for attractive social reform. Ironically, the mortality breakthrough in the 1970s occurred during NLP administrations that most political observers described as lacklustre (most political histories fail even to mention the successful health programme). In the early 1980s Costa Rica suffered disproportionately from the world slump, and there was a substantial decline in per capita income. Democracy has been maintained, and, although the social welfare programme is under critical examination and has experienced a considerable decline in expenditure, its major elements and its effect on health have held so far (as in Sri Lanka under similar circumstances).

The historical parallels in the three locations are close. Social welfare programmes, including massive extensions of the education and health systems, were established in circumstances of close competition between parties of the centre and left because of campaign promises during successive elections. These were unmarred by coups or army interventions largely because of the nature of the societies and because of the absence of powerful entrenched classes feeling threatened by the education of the poor, the expenditures needed, or electoral enthusiasm for populist parties. In Sri Lanka the large estates had been foreign-owned, while in Kerala the huge Nambudri lands were of complex tenure and were being dissolved by social change into components controlled by those working them (in Travancore they were being dissolved by royal acquisition as early as the eighteenth century). In Kerala there was no possibility of a communist coup because of the powers of intervention of the central Indian government.

Yet the efficient health and education systems owed the attainment of their aims less to the central administrations than to local and individual determination to secure promised and just rights (far greater in Sri Lanka and Kerala than anywhere else in South Asia, with the possible exception of the Indian Union Territory of Goa, which also has effective education and health systems). This grass-roots democracy is partly the product of political history, but it is also a deeper product of society and a major explanation of the type of political change.

THE BUILDING OF THE HEALTH SYSTEM AND THE BREAKTHROUGH PROGRAMMES

The success of the 'breakthrough' health programmes in our three settings does not establish the primacy of medical intervention.   The value of studying breakthroughs, especially when mortality change occurred over such a short period that neither educational nor social attitudes could alter greatly, is that of a controlled experiment. There is a high probability that most of the change in mortality level can be attributed to the additional health inputs. Nevertheless, those gains presuppose the existing social and economic levels and imply little as to the likely gains in the absence of these factors.[20] All the breakthroughs occurred in societies with below average mortality levels relative to income even at the outset and all took their start in the existing health infrastructure.   There are, then, three issues: what had been already put in place and why; what new efforts constituted the breakthrough programme; and, finally, how had the breakthrough been effected?

Sri Lanka's years of prosperity, based on export crops, had permitted health programmes in limited areas from the late nineteenth century, so that by 1945 a great deal was known about what was actually effective if there were the resources and political will. Sri Lanka contained cholera ever more successfully from the 1870s, mostly through quarantine measures for arrivals from India, and from 1887 Colombo began to build its piped water system. S.A. Meegama (1981) lays stress on the great increase in food imports from the 1870s, and particularly for the middle class, easily washed cotton clothing.[21] In the first years of the century, trained midwives forced down neonatal tetanus rates in Colombo and between 1935 and 1941 their employment halved infant and maternal mortality in the estate sector of the society. After 1911 deaths from diarrhoea and respiratory diseases fell steeply in Colombo. 'The hookworm campaign, begun in 1916 [with Rockefeller Foundation assistance], was important in that it stressed the need for public health, sanitation and personal hygiene and for strengthening the preventive health system' (Perera, 1985:94). As a result of this experience, preventive and curative medicine was amalgamated under the Ministry of Public Health and the first health unit was established in 1926, staffed, as was to be the pattern, with a physician, nurses, midwives, and a sanitary inspector. The health units were supposed to spend much of their time on preventive services, but the evidence suggests that most of the activity was curative or obstetric. By the end of the 1930s there was clear evidence that midwives were far more effective when part of an organized unit under the direction of a physician (Meegama, 1981).

The more specific origins of the 1946-53 breakthrough were threefold. First, the spectacular malaria outbreak of 1934-35, with the death rate almost doubling to 37 per thousand, led to plans to cover all rural areas with cottage hospitals (primary health units). The plans were postponed by World War II but received top priority at its end. During the next five years the number of such centres increased by 117 per cent in the endemic malarial zone and 67 per cent elsewhere. During this expansion, free treatment was provided for the poor and after 1950 for everyone.   Second, the wartime food rationing system guaranteed a minimum level of nutrition for the poor

---

[20]Similarly, a period of social advances at constant levels of health inputs can establish the effect, at that level of health services, of social change. Mosley (1983) showed for Kenya that changes in parental education and level of urbanization 'fully explained' the mortality change between two dates and interpreted these findings as showing the relative unimportance of the health inputs. The correct interpretation, I believe, would be that the recorded mortality change measured accurately the impact of social change given the existing health structure and that the mortality levels achieved would not have been as low with a more rudimentary structure, let alone with none.

[21]Meegama, 1967, 1979, 1980, 1981 and 1985. Meegama is an important source for much of the Sri Lankan information on health history in the text that follows.

and established a structure for subsidizing staples thereafter. Subsidized food was supplemented by free school meals. Infant mortality fell dramatically – by almost 30 per cent between 1946 and 1947 – as large quantities of imported milk products again entered the country (seemingly significant evidence on the importance both of supplementation and a nutritional floor). Third, these years witnessed a tremendous leap in the availability of new health technology such as penicillin and greater use of sulpha drugs. It was the period when malaria was, for the time being at least, eradicated through DDT spraying. The question of the contribution of the campaign against malaria to the total mortality decline produced one of the most famous debates in the history of demography, with estimates ranging from 100 to 12.5 per cent, the latter probably being closer to the truth.[22] By 1950, in a population of 7.5 million, hospitals were treating 12.3 million patients a year, an increase of 61 per cent over the figures five years earlier, or, more significantly, of 150 per cent if malaria cases are excluded (World Bank, 1952, part 2:383). It was essentially a clinical service and in 1950 over 90 per cent of treatment was given to outpatients (although, during that year, one in nine of the population was an inpatient being treated and accommodated free for an average of nine days). The population readily accepted the expanded services. The anthropologist Edmund Leach (1971) reported that, in the dry-zone village he studied, washerwomen had a time-honoured and ritually important role as midwives and authorities on pregnancy; but, when a cottage hospital was established seven miles away (supplemented by weekly visits to the village by the doctor), all pregnant women enthusiastically made regular seven-mile journeys to the prenatal clinic there and gave birth in the hospital. It is unlikely that such a complete break with the past would have happened in South Asian societies with lower female educational levels.

Postwar Sri Lankan health expenditure did not rise above 1.5 per cent of the gross domestic product or 5 per cent of all government expenditure (although there was also a considerable foreign-aid component). Of this outlay, curative services accounted for about 60 per cent (with drugs explaining one-sixth of this cost). The total expenditure on health, food subsidies, housing and education continued to climb after 1950, from 5.0 per cent of gross domestic product in that year to 12.4 per cent in 1965-65, only to fall by 1983 to 3.9 per cent (Perera, 1985). There are now widespread complaints that the free-market government is allowing health services to deteriorate. Free school meals have been reduced to biscuits, and subsidized food for all has been replaced by a food stamp scheme intended for the really poor (although misstatement of incomes allows half the population to receive stamps). Nevertheless, between 1977 and 1980 the infant mortality rate fell by eight points, at almost double the average rate of change of the preceding quarter of a century, probably because the basic system remained while the economy grew and unemployment fell.

The Kerala population (like that of Sri Lanka) has long been known for its cleanliness: Marco Polo was astonished to find that even the poorest bathed twice daily. One reason may be the easy availability of water. There was still room for improvement, and in this century it came: Aiyappan, comparing the 1955 village situation with that 20 years earlier, concluded, 'The standard of personal cleanliness of the villagers seems to have gone up considerably ... The use of soap ... has also become common. The reduced social distance and the increased participation in common activities are the source of motivation for better dress and cleaner persons' (1965:102). In 1865 the Travancore Government enunciated a policy embracing a governmental role in the health field. However, major mortality declines awaited the coming of the present century. The expectation of life at birth increased persistently

[22]Cf. Frederiksen, 1960; Meegama, 1967; Gray, 1974.

in the first decades of the century, one reason being the containment of epidemics: deaths from cholera and smallpox constituted one-sixth of all deaths in the first decade of the century but never rose above 3 per cent for any decade after World War I.

T.N. Krishnan (1985), identifying the breakthrough period as having been 1956-66, explained it partly by the catch-up effect of the new Kerala State attempting to raise Malabar health provision toward the levels of Travancore and Cochin and partly by a strong emphasis during this period on the immunization of children. Indeed,he argued that infant mortality decline had been steep in only two periods, the decade after 1956 and the years since 1979, and that both had been associated with renewed vigour in immunization programmes. The evidence of the significance of health inputs in Malabar is convincing: in 1956-57 there were only 42 per cent as many hospital beds in proportion to population as was the position in the rest of Kerala (Travancore and Cochin), while the latter exhibited a crude rate 50 per cent of that found in Malabar; by 1970-71 Malabar's proportion of beds had climbed to 65 per cent and Travancore and Cochin's death rate was 76 per cent of that in Malabar. An even more intriguing comparison can be made for the latter date in terms of the health provision between the lowland, midland, and highland regions of Kerala, where the numbers of hospital beds per 100,000 population were 142, 87 and 46 respectively and the average areas served by each health facility were 11, 25, and 40 square miles. Presumably as a direct result of these differentials, the proportions of births with medical assistance were 59, 44 and 36 per cent respectively, and the proportion of deaths with previous medical care were 80, 72, and 53 per cent. The infant mortality rates were 47, 47, and 78 respectively (Kirshnan, 1976). Several points should be noted. If service areas are approximately squares with the health institution at the crossing point of the diagonals, then the maximum distances of any population from a facility are 2.5, 3.5, and 4.5 miles respectively and the majority of the population live within approximately 2, 2.5, and 3 miles of a facility. These differences are apparently great enough to cause significant differentials in accessibility to medical care, although infant mortality was similar in the two most densely served areas. However, it should be noted that the differential in infant mortality accounted for the whole mortality differential, suggesting that it is only infants who are endangered by not having adjacent health facilities. These densities of services are made possible by Kerala's dense population and are beyond the reach of most of the rest of India and much of the Third World for many years to come. The density of population is one reason that urban-rural distinctions are not great in Kerala (Reddy, 1978). In the lowland country there is no such thing as remoteness. Thus in the state as a whole the ratio of the urban to the crude death rate is only 1.2. Until recently, ratios were much higher in the other states, even the most advanced ones (Panikar, 1979; India, Registrar General, 1983); but the most recent measures show the same ratio in Gujarat, ratios of 1.4 in Maharashtra and the Punjab, and 1.6 in Haryana (India, Registrar General, 1985).

Attendance at government health facilities in Kerala is easily the highest in India in spite of a government level of expenditure that is not atypical among Indian states. The explanation is greater employment of existing facilities. In addition Kerala's population has long spent more on private medical care (both modern and Ayurvedic) than the state government spends (Panikar, 1985) – probably a unique situation in India. One explanation may be that, although Ayurvedic medicine has its origins in North India, its greatest employment for a millenium or more appears to have been in Kerala, which achieved fame throughout the subcontinent for its medical expertise and the use made of it by the people (there is another parallel here with Sri Lanka). Now, the population is largely covered by modern health care. By 1979 only 1.2 per cent of births were delivered by non-professionally trained birth attendants (Panikar, 1985:54). Furthermore the actual delivery has been an increasingly small part of the total package, which includes antenatal advice and care, food supplementation, strong pressure toward immunization, repeated home visits, and clinic referrals.

In Kerala (as in Sri Lanka) an integral part of the system has been the provision of a nutritional floor. A comprehensive free meal system was begun in primary schools (which almost all Kerala children attend) during the breakthrough period, in 1961, and three-quarters of the children, including the vast majority of the poor, take these meals (the refusals come from religious high-caste families fearing pollution or from the better-off claiming their children have superior meals at home). India's most comprehensive system of subsidized food outlets, the Fair Price Shops, expanded in the early 1960s. Food supplements are distributed through the health centres to expectant and nursing mothers and to pre-school children, while there are special programmes for tribal and slum children. Kerala's average nutritional levels are not high by Indian standards, nor have they improved, but the value of the nutritional floor is shown by the fact that by 1975-79, physiological tests of school children showed Kerala to have the lowest state level of severe malnutrition (Panikar and Soman, 1984).

Krishnan (1985) is almost certainly correct in his identification of two important elements of the breakthrough period, the extension of dense services to Malabar and the drive for more complete immunization. He probably underestimates the placing in position of the nutritional floor and the considerable expansion in funding for pre-existing services, which allowed more frequent home visits especially during pregnancy and after childbirth (it was these extra home visits that made the immunization campaign successful, but they inevitably improved other health inputs too). Most of all he lays insufficient stress on the increased awareness of the poor after 1957 that health services were their right and not a boon conferred upon them. Everyone in Kerala – from very different viewpoints – attests to the rapid growth of self-confidence among the poor in the late 1950s and 1960s. Mencher has described how this affected the health service: 'In Kerala, if a PHC were unmanned for a few days, there would be a massive demonstration at the nearest collectorate led by local leftists, who would demand to be given what they knew they were entitled to .... [T]he availability of doctors at a primary health facility, and public knowledge that something will be done at any time of the day or night if it is an emergency, has gone a long way to lowering child death' (1980:1781-1782). She emphasized the importance of politicization of the many and the poor, and stressed that any problems with the health services led to articles in the newspapers and questions in the State Assembly. She contrasted this, from her experience, with the very different popular expectations and demands in Tamil Nadu, as we can do similarly with Karnataka (Caldwell et al., 1983) (both adjoining states). There is, in Kerala, some threat of violence. Doctors and others who provide village services (for instance, bus drivers plying regular routes) know stories of their fellows who were treated violently or hurt in protests about their having failed their duty.

Costa Rica, again, provides something of a contrast, for the breakthrough occurred subsequent to the waves of populist enthusiasm but when a mechanism had evolved for financing effective public health intervention in remote and poor areas. Private health expenditure has grown steadily for a century, and by the 1950s there was one physician for every 2,700 population, by far the best ratio in Central America. Social security legislation paralleled the introduction of a liberal labour code in 1942, affected this time less by European innovations than by the American New Deal. Implementation was slow, but even in 1943, the Biesanzes judged that government health services were clearly helping to reduce child mortality. Under President Figueres, social welfarism increased during the 1950s. The pattern was one that has been widely employed in Latin America: social insurance, with a major employer's contribution, becoming mandatory first for those working with government or in larger private business. In these schemes not only are medical costs covered but medical services are provided, climbing in Costa Rica from a coverage of one-eighth of the population in 1956 to half in 1971. Most of those not covered were the self-employed rural population and the transitorily employed urban poor, the two groups least likely to use private medical services. The legal basis for adequate social security covering the entire population was enacted in 1961, but the law contained inadequate provision for financing the expansion of health services to allow everyone to exercise these rights. Figueres won the 1970 presidential election, promising 'a war on poverty and hunger' and stating: 'Having achieved the goal of free and compulsory education, the aim of the government now is to feed all the children'. The administration supplemented the Office of Social Security with the Combined Institute of Social Assistance, the latter intended 'to assist those who could not assist themselves'. These aims could be achieved only if there was money for the expansion of the governmental social security health apparatus. This was begun in a limited way in 1971 by lifting the ceiling on social service salary payments so that the higher earners paid more. The real breakthrough occurred only in 1974, when Figueres's successor by a Presidential Decree shifted most of the now enlarged social security contributions to the employer (which, concludes Mark Rosenberg (1979) in his excellent analysis, alone made the rural health programme possible) and made contribution by the self-employed obligatory. The government undertook to finance the contributions of the indigent, and also legislated for a sales tax that was especially important in helping to establish a nutritional floor through supplementary feeding for pregnant and nursing women and for infants. Since this time, around 20 per cent of the budget has been devoted to health. Between 1970 and 1980 the allocation for health rose from 5.1 per cent to 7.6 per cent of gross domestic product (but, because of the subsequent economic crisis, it had fallen to 5.7 per cent by 1983).

The Costa Rican breakthrough was provided by outlaying money to provide health services that were already known to work. The Ministry of Health and Social Security Office succeeded in inspiring a pioneering enthusiasm and a spirit of community collaboration among the health workers in the new rural programmes, which were not largely complete until about 1980. Nevertheless, it was essentially a bureaucratic achievement. There was no popular crusade, and political histories of the national Liberation Party's achievement in the 1970s generally describe their efforts as pale compared with their earlier administrations and make little reference to health initiatives. The primary success was in the area of infant and child mortality. This was achieved by the methods we have noted in Sri Lanka and Kerala: providing a universal free health service (even if paid for by compulsory contributions), ensuring easy neighbourhood access to services for all, organizing community-based house visits with a strong focus on pregnancy and infancy, interlinking this with a vigorous immunization programme, providing food supplements for pregnant and nursing women and their infants, and using schools to provide free or cheap meals. Costa Ricans were already sufficiently well educated and egalitarian for these facilities to be used fully as soon as they were provided; there was by the 1970s little need for a political revolution to teach them their rights, for that learning process had been under way for decades.

THE CONDITIONS OF BREAKTHROUGH

The provision of health services, where these are otherwise unavailable or unaffordable, can have – at least in a society with some education – a dramatic effect on the reduction of mortality. No one who has worked with these programmes during their expansionary phase has apparently ever doubted this. Furthermore, the success depends little on new and expensive technology: instead it depends on density of service; on efficiency of service (whether self-induced or caused by the client's insistence), often under a physician's leadership; on household visits, especially around the time of birth (with decisions on health actions at least partly being taken by the health workers); on immunization campaigns; and on the establishment of nutritional floors by means of subsidized and supplementary food, especially associated with maternal and child health programmes and school meals. What is striking is how similar was the range of successful interventions in the three countries. The evidence for the breakthrough periods carries conviction that such measures are also effective in the longer slower mortality declines. Yet notes of caution should be sounded. The first is that new sanitary interventions play a minor role during a limited period but may well be more important over a longer span. The second is that many of the measures bringing spectacular short-term results involve a focus on infants, young children, and their mothers; over the longer haul attention to those of all ages is necessary. The third is that continued contraction on health inputs may bring limited returns unless the need for continuing social inputs – especially in the areas of education and the position of women – is recognized.

The heart of the systems, at least in rural areas, is the primary health centre, which serves as a base for midwives and health auxiliaries, almost invariably female, who regularly visit individual households. When the systems are working most efficiently, these visits allow the identification of pregnant women and their referral for antenatal services, the delivery, any subsequent treatment of the infants and their immunization, as well as the identification of other sick persons, especially children. Three aspects of the system are of particular importance. The household visits are the base of a pyramidal referral system whereby the really sick can eventually reach a doctor or a hospital. The health visitors often make treatment decisions, and, because babies are delivered by trained personnel and usually in institutions, sick infants are not left solely to their parents' care. Antenatal and postnatal care are frequently associated with food supplements for both mothers and babies. In both Sri Lanka and Kerala the sick follow the long-established practice of also consulting Ayurvedic healers (now supported in Sri Lanka by a government department), but such consultations are usually either for minor children's complaints or for chronic incurable conditions.[23] Where Western medicine is needed to save lives, it is usually employed, not infrequently by referral from a traditional practitioner.

Participants in these breakthrough programmes seem to agree that much of the success was due to the fact that they were dealing with an educated, capable, and demanding public.[24] In rural Karnataka, Caldwell, Reddy and Caldwell (1983) showed that some education was necessary for a person to feel any identification with modern as distinct from traditional curative measures and that with increased schooling parents were more likely to bring sick children to health services, more likely to follow the suggested treatment properly, much more likely to persist sufficiently long with treatment, and much more likely to report back to the health service if a cure was not being effected. In Kerala, Nag (1985) added a lesser fear by females of medical examination. In Costa Rica, Claudio Gonzalez-Vega (1985) concluded that 'Education and concern for human rights result in a more trusting and respectful doctor-patient relationship'. However, education does more than this. Outside the ambit of the health system, educated parents are more likely to feed children adequately (even than uneducated parents at the same income level) and to treat them when sick in an appropriate way (especially by allowing them to rest rather than work). They are more likely to be clean and hygienic and to insist on such standards from their children. On the community and national level education does more again. There is repeated evidence from each of three case studies that it was because of its relatively high education levels that the society demanded fuller, more efficient health systems.

There is, then, a strong case for searching for the conditions leading to the greater provision of schooling. These appear to be a culture or religion that places greater emphasis on the achievement of enlightenment than on preserving an exact

---

[23]Information for Sri Lanka is derived from continuing research and from Obeyesekere, 1976. For South India see Caldwell *et al.*, 1983; Beals, 1976.

[24]Cf. World Bank, 1952; Aiyappan, 1965; Nag, 1985; Gonzalez-Vega, 1984.

interpretation of the world of the book (Buddhism, Hinduism, and much contemporary Christianity, as well as secular societies), a society that is not afraid of publicly educating its girls, and one where entrenched economic and social elites or autocracies do not feel that education of the poor threatens the political status quo.

An interrelated but distinguishable issue is that of female autonomy. Greater autonomy makes it likely that education differentials by sex will be narrow – an important point no matter whether the singularly strong influence of maternal education on infant and child mortality arises from the fact that it is the parent with the least schooling who retards parental endeavours to keep their children healthy or whether it arises from the uniquely close relationship between mother and child. Greater female autonomy also renders it more likely that a mother will make her own decision that something must be done when she identifies a child as sick (it also seems to lead her to make that identification at an earlier time), that she will venture outside the home to seek help, that she will struggle for adequate treatment with doctors and nurses, and that (at the same educational level) she will understand the advice and take responsibility for carrying it out. Such autonomy also makes it more likely that little girls will receive treatment similar to that given to their brothers: it is no accident that Kerala is the only part of South Asia where female expectation of life has been above that of males since the earliest life tables, or that Sri Lanka was subsequently the only other locale in the region to attain this situation. Several important points should be underlined. Female education is not the same as female autonomy, although the former may contribute to the latter. Extended female education may be more acceptable to some cultures than a direct cultural intervention affecting the female position more broadly – but sometimes with the consequence that substantial inputs into education do not result in the impact of female autonomy or on child and female health that might be anticipated from experience elsewhere. Ultimately, fundamental change in the female position depends more on ideological shifts than on either educational or occupational change. Demographers may have begun to concentrate too much on maternal education rather than on its larger context. Female autonomy is certainly not the same as female status, at least as measured by the potential for respect or reverence; indeed, it may be close to the opposite. Female autonomy exists at only a low level in Mediterranean cultures, where there is great respect for the mother-wife ideal. Female autonomy is greatest where both society and women themselves have little doubt about a woman's right to make decisions and to battle for her and her children's rights in the public arena.

The political issue is more complex still. All evidence suggests that continuing political activity is important, especially if there is a dominant populist or radical element, and that such activity hastens the emergence and the spreading throughout the community of adequate educational and health systems. However, such politics are often encouraged by educating the electorate, and this has an impact at the grass-roots as well as the upper level. The inefficiency of much of the health infrastructure in rural India is explained by both the low educational levels and the political passivity of the poor. Radicalism may also be a component in moves to reduce differences between males and females.

The most important aspect of radicalism (or populism or egalitarianism), and possibly the single most important factor in achieving health breakthroughs, is making existing health services work at their greatest efficiency. The Alma-Ata Declaration recognized the importance of this: 'Primary health care ... requires and promotes maximum community and individual self-reliance and participation in the planning, organization, operation and control of primary health care, making fullest use of local, national and other available resources; and to this end develops through appropriate education the ability of communities to participate' (WHO, 1978:4). Mosley (1983) has expressed scepticism as to whether this is possible in many cases, arguing that 'existing power structures at the local level' can frustrate 'true community involvement' (citing research by Ronaghy and Solter, 1974, in Iran; Chowdhury, 1981, in Bangladesh; and Rienks and Iskandar, 1981, in Indonesia) and that vertical programmes directed at the masses will probably be starved of funds by the bureaucracy (citing Egypt), thus retaining the urban bias in health services. He is basically right in indicting the Declaration for appearing to suggest that these are matters of planning and perhaps central decision making. Nevertheless, he did not go to the root of the matter, namely that there is no effective route except through community involvement, and that hostile existing power structures will be overcome only by movements stressing basic rights and women's rights. Such movements are essentially ideological and political and need support from national movements and political parties. Clearly, governments with specific commitments can play a role. According to a personal communication from K. Srinivasan, substantial recent declines in mortality in rural West Bengal are now reported, not because the state's communist government has succeeded in making the population aware of their rights as is the case in Kerala, but because they have used the party system to appoint cadres at every health centre to report on doctors or nurses who do not put all their time and effort into their services or who discriminate between patients.

Finally, it is likely that steep fertility declines give rise to greater parental worries about child survival and hence encourage greater infant and child care and consequently mortality transition, while ultimately the increasing likelihood of children surviving as mortality falls may well encourage fertility control except (but not necessarily always) where children are clearly an economic asset. Kerala, Sri Lanka, and Costa Rica have all experienced recent periods of unusually steep fertility decline: the first from about 1956 and the other two from around 1962. Thus, only in Costa Rica is the effect likely to have run from the fertility to the mortality decline; if there were any interaction in Sri Lanka, it must have been the other way around. In Kerala, faster political and social change may have had a simultaneous impact on both mortality and fertility.

The central finding of this paper, then, is that the provision of health services (and, better still, its accompaniment by the establishment of a nutritional floor and perhaps a family planning programme) can markedly reduce mortality. Much depends on the level of education, and education could be said to catalyse that change. There is, in fact, a symbiosis between cultural and health inputs. A good deal also depends on the level of political activity and the position of women, but these are more difficult changes to plan and achieve. The interaction between the provision of education and that of health services is probably in many conditions quite spectacular. A reanalysis of the data from two Nigerian villages reported in 1975 by I.O. Orubuloye and Caldwell suggests that the equivalent gain in expectation of life at birth (equivalent to changes in infant and child mortality) was 20 per cent when the sole intervention was easy access to adequate health facilities for illiterate mothers, 33 per cent when it was education (as measured by mother's schooling) without health facilities, but 87 per cent when it was both (Caldwell and Caldwell, 1985). It should be noted that this combined improvement is neither merely additive (which would have resulted in a 53 per cent improvement) nor multiplicative (which would have been 60 per cent) but greater than either.

THE ROAD TO 2000 AND BEYOND

The conclusions reached above have in recent years been of declining popularity in the social science literature, and this raises a number of questions. Why did McKeown (1967a) almost entirely discount health inputs in favour of rising incomes and Mosley (1983) in favour of social change? Why has Preston (1985a) argued that high mortality in nineteenth century America can largely be explained in cultural terms, namely by ignorance of the nature of disease?

THE CONTEMPORARY DEBATE

In regard to McKeown's thesis the simple answer is that he was examining a different situation in a different period with a different analytical approach. He identified potential change in health inputs with medical discoveries and attempted to show that these were of little consequence in Britain during the second half of the nineteenth century and the early part of the twentieth century. He implicitly included everything else, from better food and housing to the attainment of universal schooling, as material advance, and probably would also have included in the same category a greater density of private medical practitioners. Thus, education and many of the other factors we have considered here were subsumed under material progress. Similarly, he did not consider the expansion of the health infrastructure, although admittedly there was probably little in the way of additional medical technology to import and no political thought of creating a universal free health service. His analysis has little relevance to the contemporary situation in the Third World, although it is often treated as relevant in the sense that nineteenth century Britain was similar in many ways to today's Third World.

Mosley analysed child survival from birth to two years of age in Kenya to show that changes in mortality over time and between regions could largely be explained by differences in maternal education and family incomes. He argued that there was little left to explain after these two factors had been taken into account and that medical interventions do not work in many specific situations. Even immunization is self-selective according to the education and other characteristics of the family. He said that his analysis was supported by the negligible effects of urban-rural residence on infant and child mortality, once maternal education was controlled (a finding that had been reported for Ghana by S.K. Gaisie (1969) and from Nigeria by Caldwell (1979)). He also drew evidence from other parts of Africa and Asia.

Much of this argument may be widely true, for we have been focusing on what can happen and what has happened in selected countries. Yet it should be noted that his description of the Kenyan situation does not reveal the mechanisms whereby the educated and better-off reduced their children's mortality. In contemporary Kenya, with an expectation of life at birth nearing 60 years and an infant mortality rate around 75, it is almost certain that one way parents prevent their children from dying is by using the existing services – exactly as they did in the lower mortality Nigerian village described by Orubuloye and Caldwell (1975). Kenya's medical services are not equal to those we have been examining; nevertheless, by 1980 the ratio of physicians to population had reached the level attained by Sri Lanka during its breakthrough period in 1946-53 (and its mortality levels those of Sri Lanka at the end of the breakthrough). The interpretation of low infant and child mortality among educated parents in rural Africa is still unsatisfactory. Where educated parents were almost completely isolated, as in the village without health facilities described by Orubuloye and Caldwell, their children had lower mortality than those of uneducated parents, but not of the same order as in another village where the educated parents had access to health facilities. In much of rural Ghana and Nigeria educated parents do get modern health treatment for sick children even by travelling considerable distances: it is their education that convinces them that the journey is necessary and the fact that they are usually better-off that makes it easier to undertake it. Mosley did not deny that health interventions could be effective, but he concluded: 'the effectiveness of primary health care will be very much dependent upon the degree to which the population comes to accept the scientific basis of disease causation', citing, as supporting evidence, Caldwell, Reddy and Caldwell (1983) on Karnataka. Our interpretation of the Karnataka findings is that they show that primary health care can be effective if the population is willing to employ it, to follow instructions carefully, and to persist with recommended treatment. We found that this arose primarily from an identification with the whole modern system, increasingly likely as education rose, rather than from any understanding of bacteriology; and from an ability to do what was recommended – again, made easier by education. This interpretation has been greatly reinforced by our more recent experience in Sri Lanka, where a plurality of beliefs about causes and treatment of disease does not interfere with employing modern medicine properly where it is effective.

Preston (1985a) employed unique American data on child survival by parental literacy, occupation, and income in the late nineteenth century and found child mortality differentials by parental literacy to be much smaller than in the contemporary Third World. He addressed the question why the relatively high educational and income levels in the United States at that time did not translate themselves into a higher expectation of life at birth. His answer, employing material from contemporary newspapers and periodicals, was ignorance: a lack of knowledge of germ theory and hence a toleration of unhygienic conditions. He identified in this earlier America 'some combination of ignorance about personal health and ignorance about what public institutions could accomplish in the area of health. That this ignorance has largely disappeared is vividly suggested by the fact that urban residents in developing countries no longer suffer the excessive mortality that their dense living arrangements would otherwise foster' (vol.4:383). This is a rather extreme educational and cultural interpretation of the nature of mortality change. We have examined the evidence for a very similar late nineteenth century society, Australia, and have found that in general there was a striking aversion to dirty and unhygienic conditions and to contact with sickness; and a fear of infection, which was based on a tradition older than Pasteur's germ theory but was reinforced by it (although not by everyone understanding the mechanisms) in the last decades of the century. Among the more educated and richer there was undeniably a strong desire to buy better defence against mortality risks for both themselves and their children and a frustration about their inability to do so adequately. The reason they could not do so was that put forward by McKeown: medicine had little to offer. Thus mortality differentials were modest even though treatment differentials were not: the rich frequently called the doctor to their children while the poor were unable to afford his services. Parents did keep their children separated from others with infectious diseases and away from school when infection broke out. Pots and pans were washed in boiling water to an extent that is rare in the contemporary Third World. Admittedly, infant supplementary feeding may have involved more risks than occur today at least once the breakthrough programmes have been implemented. The Australian, and doubtless American, individual reactions were paralleled on the national stage and by experts. Sir Edwin Chadwick carried through his momentous revolution in sanitation in Britain on the intellectual foundations of the 'epidemic atmosphere' theory, namely, as he put it, that 'All smell is disease', or, in the words of one of his intellectual leaders, Southward Smith, that 'Wherever animal and vegetable substances are undergoing the process of decomposition, poisonous matters are evolved which, mixing with air, corrupt it, and render it injurious to health and fatal to life' (Finer, 1952:297-298). The health revolution in contemporary Sri Lanka has been carried through with probably the majority of the population believing not in the bacteriological source of many diseases but in demonic origins.

Other substantive research appears to support the position taken in this paper. Preston (1980) showed that expectations of life at birth in 1970-75 were for all developing countries about 8.6 years higher than would have been predicted from their 1940 levels on the assumption that the 1940 relationship between life expectancy and literacy, income, and calorie consumption had prevailed. The change was exogenous, presumably largely related to an extension of health services and a growth in the medical technology available. It is noteworthy that, while the excess gain in Asia averaged nine years, that recorded by Sri Lanka was 21 years, while Costa Rica's 12 years compared with a Latin American average of ten years. A.T. Flegg (1982) also examined all developing countries, focusing on the determinants of infant mortality, and concluded that the greatest impact on mortality came from raising the income of the poor (thus moving toward greater equality), the education levels of mothers, and the density of physicians (nurses being much less significant, possibly because of definitional and measurement problems), while fertility levels were not of importance. Davidson Gwatkin, J.R. Wilcox, and J.D. Wray (1980) reported on ten experimental health and nutrition projects showing generally marked declines in infant and child mortality. Anrudh Jain (1985) has recently analysed infant mortality differentials by state in India and has come to conclusions on social and health inputs very similar to those in this paper. Meegama (1985) has extended his analysis of historical trends in Sri Lanka, comparing them with those of Cuba, but his treatment concentrates on how the health services were able to achieve their advances rather than on why they existed and were effectively used. Alberto Palloni (1985, vol.2:348) has employed an 'epidemio-demographic analysis' to compare countries with rapid and slow mortality decline, concluding that 'mortality differentials across significant social groups cannot be explained by differentials in levels of economic growth or by income inequalities. It appears that the factor accounting for such differentials and, *mutatis mutandis*, for their trends over time, is the existence of highly mobilized and integrated population as reflected, for example, in high literacy rates'.

ALTERNATIVE ROUTES TO LOW MORTALITY

We have concentrated in this paper on open societies and have shown how, in Sri Lanka, Kerala, and Costa Rica, successive elections resulted in electors demanding educational and health services and in competing political parties offering to provide such services. There is, however, another proven route to low mortality, that followed by China, Cuba, and Vietnam, and based on earlier Soviet policies in devoting large resources to the health sector.[25] By 1982 the expectation of life at birth was around 75 years in Cuba, 67 years in China, and 64 years in Vietnam, in each case about 15 years higher than was typical of countries with similar incomes, and evidencing rates of mortality decline in previous decades similar to those found during the breakthrough years of the three populations analysed in this paper. How different was the route and why was it effective?

For the purposes of analysis, we will first summarize the conclusions reached in this paper from the experience of Sri Lanka, Kerala, and Costa Rica. Unusually low mortality will be achieved if the following conditions hold: (1) sufficient female autonomy; (2) considerable inputs into *both* health services and education, both essentially of the modern or Western model, and with female schooling levels equalling or being close to male levels; (3) health services accessible to all no matter how remote, poor, or socially inferior to those providing them; (4) ensuring that the health services work efficiently, usually because of popular pressure (and, in addition, disciplining rural health workers by having a physician in charge); (5) providing either a nutritional floor or distributing food in some kind of egalitarian fashion; (6) achieving universal immunization; and (7) concentrating on the period before and after birth, usually by providing antenatal and postnatal health services and having deliveries performed by persons fully trained for this purpose, and often by health visitors calling on households so frequently that they not only provide advice and services but also play a decision-making role in treatment (with decisions about infant treatment and survival after birth being, because of the institutionalized setting, almost completely out of parental hands).

Taking China as the representative case, it is clear that from the time of the first communist autonomous areas in the late 1920s, education, health services, and improving the position of women were central ideological aims. Indeed, if all the

---

25See Lorimer, 1946:120-121; Sigerist, 1939.

human and other resources devoted to health are totalled, it could well be concluded that the allocation in this area was inefficiently large in terms of achieving economic development (perhaps because it is easier to achieve health aims once firm decisions are made). The emphasis on education and health was not solely a matter of communist policy; China has long had respect for education and has placed an emphasis on traditional medicine that evidences similarities to the situation in Sri Lanka and Kerala. The Chinese employed modern medicine and well-trained medical personnel as much and as soon as possible (supplementing them with the much-publicized traditional medicines and barefoot doctors only to the extent that existing gaps could not otherwise be filled). Nor did the Chinese have any qualms about intrusive health services or health personnel assuming decision-making authority with regard to treatment. The key question is why the health services worked at the local level. There is probably a two-part answer. The first is that activism and pressure by individuals and community representatives is usually safe enough if it is in the direction of stated policies – and there is a good deal of spontaneity about such matters in the first years after a revolution. At the level of the brigade or commune, much spontaneity remained, for decentralized budgetary policies meant that the expenditure allocations in these areas were local decisions, as is clearly shown by markedly different allocations throughout China.[26] The second part of the answer is that the parallel party and bureaucracy administrations were effective in the health area, in that the reporting of lazy or inefficient health personnel by party members ensured that the existing machinery was used to its full potential.

There are also signs that some of the countries with mortality in excess of the levels that their per capita income would lead one to expect may be making strides. The majority of these countries are predominantly Muslim, but clearly religion is not an absolute bar to escaping from this position but rather the cultural context that has traditionally accompanied it. By 1982, of 29 predominantly Muslim countries among the 99 Third World countries analysed here, one (Bangladesh) had achieved a mortality ranking much better than its income ranking (a life expectancy of 48 years but better than most countries with twice its per capita income), and six more (Mali, Syria, Indonesia, Malaysia, Pakistan, and Lebanon) were recording somewhat better health performances than their incomes would imply (and an eighth, Tunisia, was doing better in terms of infant mortality). Bangladesh, Mali, and Lebanon have achieved better health by having both female schooling and health inputs (measured by the density of physicians) above income rankings, Indonesia by a superior female schooling ranking alone, and Pakistan and Tunisia by superior health inputs alone. Clearly, geography, cultural area, and the related position of women are important: the eastern wing of Islam – Bangladesh, Malaysia, and Indonesia – constitute almost half of these eight countries (and 70 per cent of the total population). The comparison between Bangladesh and Pakistan is instructive: by the beginning of the 1980s Bangladesh was educating 47 per cent of girls of primary school age and Pakistan only 31 per cent (but Pakistan was educating the higher proportion of boys), while Bangladesh had only one physician for every 11,000 people compared with one per 3,500 in Pakistan; both had life expectancies close to 50 years. Other explanations are: in the case of Lebanon and Malaysia, that they are plural societies (so the education and mortality figures are not only those of Muslims); in the case of Tunisia, a more secularized society; and in the case of Syria and Mali, left-wing governments. This last point is brought out more clearly if we focus on changes in the proportions of girls in school: Libya and Iraq achieved the world's greatest increases in rankings between 1960 and 1981, raising the proportions in primary school from one-quarter and one-third respectively to universal enrolment, and reaching secondary school proportions for both sexes (with females making up a substantial fraction) of 67 and 59 per cent respectively (with Kuwait at 76 per cent and the United Arab Emirates at

---

[26]Penny Kane, personal communications; cf. Prescott and Jamison, 1984.

61 per cent also doing well). These advances have not yet been translated into low mortality, as revealed by expectations of life at birth under 60 years and infant mortality rates near 100, but they may bode well for the future provided that the changes in the position of females are not largely confined to education.

LOW MORTALITY FOR ALL

These findings are out of step with today's dominant economic and political ideologies in the development field. They show that low mortality is indeed within the reach of all countries. Few countries are poorer than China and Sri Lanka, and very few indeed poorer than Kerala. Average sub-Saharan incomes are above those of China and Sri Lanka, while even those of the Sahelian countries may be higher than Kerala's. China, Sri Lanka, and Kerala are societies with life expectancies nearing 70 years. These health conditions have been bought by devoting unusually high proportions of national income to education and health (including such programmes as food subsidies for the poor). They have been bought more cheaply, and by a more certain route, than substantial advances in manufacturing or agriculture usually can be. Furthermore, in terms of development both the health and the educational advances are achievements that most of the population of Sri Lanka, Kerala, and Costa Rica regard as signs of progress and would not readily forgo.

The important point is not that these societies achieved remarkable levels of education and health by an act of political and social will but that they took it for granted that their political and social energies should be devoted to these goals. Most of the poor health achievers have ample political and social will for other goals; what they lack is a broad social consensus that top priority should be given to education – particularly female education, which is widely regarded with emotions that range from feeling that it is not a matter of great consequence for subsequent adult roles, to deep apprehension. With regard to political will, we have identified the necessary condition as there being no major social – and resultant political – schism in the society. There must be a broad social consensus as to the value of educational and health goals, and as to their cost, for successive governments to accept most of their adversaries' innovations instead of nullifying them.

There is no reason why a much wider range of countries should not, over the next decade or two, substantially raise the proportion of budgetary allocations to both education and health, although the latter expenditure will only be most productive if the emphasis in education is given to raising female schooling levels to parity with those of males.

The really striking needs are the furtherance of female autonomy and the rendering efficient of local health services. In many countries greater female autonomy is necessary just to gain family and community approval for girls' attending school or staying there for any sustained period, especially beyond puberty. In terms of health and other social advances, the movement toward greater autonomy will be inefficient and lengthy if its major instrument is seen only as female education. Fundamentally it must be an ideological movement, although clearly political parties, and even international organizations, have roles to play. Making community health services work is probably also less a bureaucratic or a planning decision than it is a cultural or ideological one in terms of perceived rights and attitudes toward equality. Nevertheless, this is an area where bureaucratic mechanisms, such as inspection, reporting, and following up complaints, may also be of some value.

What is clearest is that low mortality for all will not come as an unplanned spin-off from economic growth. Further, much international advice on maximizing the rate of economic development may minimize mortality decline and other desirable social advances. Certainly this is an area, at least in poor countries, where government intervention is more effective than allowing individuals to use the market, for, given the choice, they might decide to allocate their expenditure on something other than education or health. One problem is that education and health are purchased separately for each family member, and the patriarch may allocate insufficient amounts for his daughters or his wife.

ACKNOWLEDGEMENTS

This work on the conditions of mortality decline has been assisted at various stages by funding from the Australian National University, the Population Council's International Research Awards Program on the Determinants of Fertility in Developing Countries, the Ford Foundation (Delhi Office and New York), the Rockefeller Foundation, and the World Health Organization, as well as by other non-financial support from the Population Centre, Bangalore, India, the Demographic Training and Research Unit, University of Colombo, Sri Lanka, and the Australian National University. It benefits from field experience in Karnataka, Kerala, and Sri Lanka with Pat Caldwell, P.H. Reddy, Indra Gajanayake, Bruce Caldwell, and P.N. Sushama.

REFERENCES

Aiyappan, A. (1965), *Social Revolution in a Kerala Village: A Study of Cultural Change*, Asia Publishing House, Bombay.

Alexander, P. (1982), *Sri Lankan Fishermen: Rural Capitalism and Peasant Society*, Monographs on South Asia, no.7, Australian National University, Canberra.

Ameringer, C.D. (1978), *Don Pepe: A Political Biography of José Figueres of Costa Rica*, University of New Mexico Press, Albuquerque.

Ammar, H. (1954), *Growing up in an Egyptian Village: Silwa, Province of Aswan*, Routledge and Kegan Paul, London.

Arriaga, E.E. (1981), 'The deceleration of the decline of mortality in the LDCs: The case of Latin America', in *IUSSP International Population Conference, Manila 1981*, IUSSP, Liège, pp.21-50.

Arriaga, E.E. and Davis, K. (1969), 'The pattern of mortality change in Latin America', *Demography*, 6, 3:223-242.

Banister, J. (1984), 'An analysis of recent data on the population of China', *Population and Development Review*, 10, 2:241-271.

Barbosa, D. (tr. Dames, M.L.) (1918), *The Book of Duarte Barbosa: An Account of the Countries Bordering on the Indian Ocean and their Inhabitants, written by Duarte Barbosa, and completed about the year 1518 AD*, Hakluyt Society, London.

Beals, A.R. (1976), 'Strategies of resort to curers in South India', in C. Leslie (ed.), *Asian Medical Systems: A Comparative Study*, University of California Press, Berkeley, pp.184-200.

Bhat, P.N.M., Preston, S.H. and Dyson, T. (1984), *Vital Rates in India, 1961-1981*, Panel on India, Committee on Population and Demography, Report No.24, National Academy Press, Washington DC.

Biesanz, J. and Biesanz, M. (1944), *Costa Rican Life*, Columbia University Press, New York.

Booth, J.A. (1978), 'Are Latin Americans politically rational? Citizen participation and rationality in Costa Rica', in J.A. Booth and M.S. Seligson (eds), *Political Participation in Latin America*, Holmes and Meier, New York, pp.98-113.

Booth, J.A. (1984), 'Representative constitutional democracy in Costa Rica: Adaption to crisis in the turbulent 1980s', in S.C. Ropp and J.A. Morris (eds), *Central America: Crisis and Adaption*, University of New Mexico Press, Albuquerque, pp.153-188.

Brass, W. (1984), 'Mortality in China over the past fifty years: indirect estimates from the 1982 Census', paper presented at the International Seminar on China's 1982 Population Census, Beijing, 26-31 March.

Buchanan, F. (1807), *A Journey from Madras through the Countries of Mysore, Canara and Malabar Performed under the Orders of the Most Noble the Marquis Wellesley Governor General of India for the Express Purpose of Investigating the State of Agriculture, Arts and Commerce; Religion, Manners and Customs, the History Natural and Civil and Antiquities in the Dominions of the Rajah of Mysore and the Countries Acquired by the Honorable East India Company*, T. Cadell and W. Davies, London.

Busey, J.L. (1962), *Notes on Costa Rican Democracy*, University of Colorado Studies: Series in Political Science, no.2, University of Colorado Press, Boulder.

Caldwell, J.C. (1979), 'Education as a factor in mortality decline: an examination of Nigerian data', *Population Studies*, 33, 3:395-413.

Caldwell, J.C. (1982), *Theory of Fertility Decline*, Academic Press, London.

Caldwell, J.C. (in prep.), 'Introduction', in J.C. Caldwell and L. Ruzicka (eds), *Conditions of Mortality Change in South Asia*, Australian National University, Canberra.

Caldwell, J.C., Bracher, M., Santow, G. and Caldwell, P. (1984), 'Population trends in China: A perspective provided by the 1982 Census', in C. Li, D. Tie, H. Wu and J. Sun (eds), *A Census of One Billion People: Papers for International Seminar on China's 1982 Population Census*, Population Census Office, Beijing, pp.352-391.

Caldwell, J.C. and Caldwell, P. (1978), 'The achieved small family: early fertility transition in an African city', *Studies in Family Planning* 9,1:2-18.

Caldwell, J.C. and Caldwell, P. (1985), 'Education and literacy as factors in health', in Halstead *et al.*, 1985, pp.181-185.

Caldwell, J.C., Harrison, G.E. and Quiggin, P. (1980), 'The demography of micro-states', *World Development*, 8:953-967.

Caldwell, J.C., Reddy, P.H. and Caldwell, P. (1983), 'The social component of mortality decline: an investigation in South India employing alternative methodologies', *Population Studies*, 37, 2:185-205, (Chapter 11 of this book).

Caldwell, J.C., Reddy, P.H. and Caldwell, P. (1984), 'The determinants of fertility decline in rural South India' in T. Dyson and N. Crook (eds), *India's Demography: Essays on the Contemporary Population*, South Asian Publishers, New Delhi, pp.187-207.

Caldwell, J.C., Reddy, P.H. and Caldwell, P. (1985), 'Educational transition in rural South India', *Population and Development Review*, 11,1:29-51.

Caldwell, J.C. and Ruzicka, L.T. (1978), 'The Australian fertility transition: an analysis', *Population and Development Review*, 4,1:81-103.

Caldwell, J.C. and Ruzicka, L.T. (1986), 'The determinants of mortality change in South Asia', in K. Srinivasan and S. Mukerji (eds), *Dynamics of Population and Family Welfare 1985*, Himalaya Publishing House, Bombay.

Caldwell, J.C. and Srinivasan, K. (1984), 'New data on nuptiality and fertility in China', *Population and Development Review*, 10,1:71-79.

Ceylon, Director of Medical and Sanitary Services (1932), *Administrative Report, 1931*, Government of Ceylon, Colombo.

Ceylon, Government of, (1928), *Report of the Special Commission on the Ceylon Constitution* (the Donoughmore Commission), Ceylon Government Press, Colombo.

Ceylon, Ministry of Education and Cultural Affairs (1969), *Education in Ceylon (from the Sixth Century B.C. to the Present Day): A Centenary Volume*, Government Press, Colombo.

Changing African Family Project, Nigerian Segment (1973), Directed by J.C. Caldwell and F.O. Okediji, Department of Demography, Australian National University, and Sociology Department, University of Ibadan.

Chowdhury, A.O. (1981), 'Gonoshasthaya Kendra (People's Health Center)', *Link*, 1:3-5.

CICRED (1974), *The Population of Sri Lanka*, Department of Census and Statistics, Colombo.

Coale, A.J. (1984), *Rapid Population Change in China, 1952-1982*, Committee on Population and Demography, National Research Council, Report no.27, National Academy Press, Washington DC.

Damle, Y.B. (1959), 'Auxiliary nurse midwives: a study in institutional change', *Bulletin of the Deccan College Research Institute*, 19, 3/4:237-279.

Davy, J. (1821) (reprinted 1969), *An Account of the Interior of Ceylon and of its Inhabitants with Travels in the Island*, Tisara Prakasakayo, Colombo.

De Silva, K.M. (ed.) (1977), *Sri Lanka: A Survey*, Hurst, London.

De Silva, K.M. (1981), *A History of Sri Lanka*, Oxford University Press, Delhi.

Dumont, L. (1961), 'Les mariages Nayar comme faits indiens', *L'Homme*, 1.

Dyson, T. and Crook, N. (eds)(1984), *India's Demography: Essays on the Contemporary Population*, South Asian Publsihers, New Delhi.

Dyson, T. and Moore, M. (1983), 'On kinship structure, female autonomy, and demographic behavior in India', Population and Development Review, 9, 1:35-60.

Egypt, Government of, Ministry of Health, n.d. *Egyptian Experience in Primary Health Care, Cairo*.

Fagg, J.E. (1977), *Latin America: A General History*, 3rd edn., Macmillan, New York.

Fakhouri, H. (1972), Kafr El-Elow: *An Egyptian Village in Transition*, Holt, Rinehart and Winston, New York.

Fernando, D.F.S. (1985), 'Health statistics in Sri Lanka, 1921-1980', in Halstead *et al.*, 1985, pp.79-92.

Fic, V.N. (1970), *Kerala, Yenan of India − Rise of a Communist Power: 1937-1969, Nachiteka, Bombay*.

Fields, G.S. (1980), *Poverty, Inequality and Development*, Cambridge University Press, Cambridge.

Finer, S.E. (1952), *The Life and Times of Sir Edwin Chadwick*, Methuen, London.

Flegg, A.T. (1982), 'Inequality of income, illiteracy and medical care as determinants of infant mortality in underdeveloped countries', *Population Studies*, 36, 3:441-458.

Frederiksen, H. (1960), 'Malaria control and population pressure in Ceylon', *Public Health Reports*, 75.

Fuller, C.J. (1976), *The Nayars Today*, Cambridge University Press, Cambridge.

Gaisie, S.K. (1969), *Dynamics of Population Growth in Ghana*, Ghana Population Studies no.1, University of Ghana, Legon.

Gonzalez-Vega, C. (1984), 'Fear of adjusting: the social costs of economic policies in Costa Rica in the 1970s', in D.E. Schulz and D.H. Graham (eds), *Revolution and Counterrevolution in Central America and the Caribbean*, Westview Press, Boulder, pp.351-419.

Gonzalez-Vega, C. (1985), 'Health improvements in Costa Rica: The socio-economic background', in Halstead *et al.*, 1985, pp.147-158.

Gough, E.K. (1961), 'Is the family universal? – The Nayar case', in N.W. Bell and E.D. Vogel (eds), *A Modern Introduction to the Family*, Routledge and Kegan Paul, London.

Gough, E.K. (1968), 'Literacy in Kerala', in J. Goody (ed.), *Literacy in Traditional Societies*, Cambridge University Press, Cambridge.

Gray, R.H. (1974), 'The decline in mortality in Ceylon and the demographic effects of malaria control', *Population Studies*, 28, 2:205-229.

Gunatilleke, G. (1985), 'Health and development in Sri Lanka: An overview', in Halstead *et al.*, 1985, pp.111-124.

Gunatilleke, G., Wanigasekera, E., Namasivam, P. and Asirwatham, S.R. (1984), *Intersectoral Action for Health: Sri Lanka Study*, Marga Institute, Colombo.

Gwatkin, D.R. (1980), 'Indications of change in developing country mortality trends: the end of an era?', *Population and Development Review*, 6, 4:615-644.

Gwatkin, D.R., Wilcox, J.R. and Wray, J.D. (1980), *Can Health and Nutrition Intervention Make a Difference?*, Overseas Development Council, Washington DC.

Haines, M.R. and Avery, R.C. (1982), 'Differential child mortality in Costa Rica: 1968-1973', *Population Studies*, 36, 1:31-43.

Halstead, S.B., Walsh, J.A. and Warren, K.S. (eds) (1985), *Good Health at Low Cost: Proceedings of a Conference held at the Bellagio Conference Center, Bellagio, Italy, April 29-May 2, 1985*, Rockefeller Foundation, New York.

Hansluwka, H. and Ruzicka, L.T. (1982), 'Conclusion', in L.T. Ruzicka and A. Lopez (eds), *Mortality in South and East Asia: A Review of Changing Trends and Patterns, 1950-1975*, World Health Organization, Geneva.

Herrick, B. and Hudson, B. (1981), *Urban Poverty and Economic Development: A Case Study of Costa Rica*, Macmillan, London.

India, Registrar-General (1983), *Sample Registration System: 1976-78*, Government of India Press, New Delhi.

India, Registrar-General (1985), *Sample Registration System: 1981*, Ministry of Home Affairs, New Delhi.

International Union for the Scientific Study of Population (IUSSP)(1981), International Populaton Conference, Manila, 1981, Ordina, Liège.

International Union for the Scientific Study of Population (IUSSP)(1985), International Populaton Conference, Florence, 1985, IUSSP, Liège.

Isaac, T. (1983), 'The emergence of a radical working class movement in Alleppy, 1922-1938', *Working Paper* No.175, Centre for Development Studies, Trivandrum.

Jain, A.K. (1985), 'Determinants of regional variations in infant mortality in rural India', *Population Studies*, 39, 3:407-424.

Jeffrey, R. (1976), *The Decline of Nayar Dominance: Society and Politics in Travancore, 1847-1908*, Sussex University Press, London.

Jones, G. (1982), 'Population trends and policies in Vietnam', *Population and Development Review*, 8, 4:783-810.

Kerala, Government of (1984), *Statistics for Planning 1983*, Directorate of Economics and Statistics, Trivandrum.

Keyfitz, N. (1968), *World Population: An Analysis of Vital Data*, University of Chicago Press, Chicago.

Knox, R. (1681) (reprinted 1958), *An Historical Relation of Ceylon*, Tisara Prakasakayo, Colombo.

Krishnan, T.N. (1976), 'Demographic transition in Kerala: facts and factors', *Economic and Political Weekly*, 11, special number:1203-1224.

Krishnan, T.N. (1985), 'Health statistics in Kerala State, India', in Halstead *et al.*, 1985, pp.39-45.

Leach, E.R. (1971), *Pul Eliya, a Village in Ceylon: A Study of Land Tenure and Kinship*, Cambridge University Press, Cambridge.

Leslie, C. (ed.) (1976) *Asian Medical Systems: A Comparative Study*, University of California Press, Berkeley.

Lipsky, G.A. (1959), *Saudi Arabia: Its People, Its Society, Its Culture*, HRAF Press, New Delhi.

Lorimer, F. (1946), *The Population of the Soviet Union: History and Prospects*, League of Nations, Geneva.

Malalgoda, K. (1976), *Buddhism in Sinhalese Society, 1750-1900: A Study of Religious Revival and Change*, University of California Press, Berkeley.

Mateer, S. (1883), *Native Life in Travancore*, W.H. Allen, London.

McKeown, T. (1965), 'Medicine and world population', in M.C. Sheps and J.C. Ridley (eds), *Public Health and Population Change: Current Research Issues*, University of Pittsburgh Press, Pittsburgh, pp.25-40.

McKeown, T. (1967a), *The Role of Medicine: Dream, Mirage or Nemesis*, Nuffield Hospitals Trust, London.

McKeown, T. (1967b), *The Modern Rise of Population*, Edward Arnold, London.

McKeown, T. and Brown, R.G. (1955), 'Medical evidence related to English population changes in the eighteenth century', *Population Studies*, 9, 2:119-141.

McKeown, T., Brown, R.G. and Record, R.G. (1972), 'An interpretation of the modern rise of population in Europe', *Population Studies*, 26, 3:345-382.

McKeown, T. and Record, R.G. (1962), 'Reasons for the decline of mortality in England and Wales during the nineteenth century', *Population Studies*, 16, 2:94-122.

Meegama, S.A. (1967), 'Malaria eradication and its effect on mortality levels', *Population Studies*, 21, 3:207-237.

Meegama, S.A. (1979), 'Cholera epidemics and their control in Ceylon', *Population Studies*, 33, 1:143-156.

Meegama, S.A. (1980), *Socio-Economic Determinants of Infant and Child Mortality in Sri Lanka: An Analysis of Post-War Experience*, Scientific Reports No.8, World Fertility Survey, London.

Meegama, S.A. (1981), 'The decline in mortality in Sri Lanka in historical perspective', in International Union for the Scientific Study of Population, *International Population Conference, Manila 1981: Solicited Papers*, vol.2, IUSSP, Liège, pp.143-164.

Meegama, S.A. (1985), 'The mortality decline in the 'fast declining' developing countries', in IUSSP, 1985, Vol.2, pp.317-327.

Mencher, J.P. (1980), 'The lessons and non-lessons of Kerala: agricultural labourers and poverty', *Economic and Political Weekly* 14, special number:1781-1802.

Mensch, B., Lentzner, H. and Preston, S. (1985), *Socio-economic Differentials in Child Mortality in Developing Countries*, United Nations, New York.

Mohs, E. (1982), 'Infectious diseases and health in Costa Rica: the development of a new paradigm', *Pediatric Infectious Disease* 1, 3:212-216.

Moore, M. (1985), *The State and Peasant Politics in Sri Lanka*, Cambridge University Press, Cambridge.

Mosley, W.H. (1983), 'Will primary health care reduce infant and child mortality? A critique of some current strategies, with special reference to Africa and Asia', paper prepared for IUSSP seminar on Social Policy, Health Policy and Mortality Prospects, Paris, (Chapter 14 of this book).

Nadarajah, T. (1976), 'Trends and differentials in mortality', in United Nations, Economic and Social Commission for Asia and the Pacific, *Population of Sri Lanka,* ESCAP Monograph Series No.4, United Nations, Bangkok, pp.123-153.

Nag, M. (1985), 'The impact of social and economic development on mortality: comparative study of Kerala and West Bengal', in Halstead *et al.*, 1985, pp.57-77.

Obeyesekere, G. (1967), *Land Tenure in Village Ceylon,* Cambridge University Press, Cambridge.

Obeyesekere, G. (1975), 'Sinhalese-Buddhist identity in Ceylon', in G. de Vos and L. Romanucci-Ross (eds), *Ethnic Identity: Cultural Continuities and Change*, Mayfield, Palo Alto, pp.231-258.

Obeyesekere, G. (1976), 'The impact of Ayurvedic ideas on the culture and individual in Sri Lanka', in Leslie, 1976, pp.217-223.

Obeyesekere, G. (1984), *The Cult of the Goddess Pattini*, University of Chicago Press, Chicago.

Orubuloye, I.O. and Caldwell, J.D. (1975), 'The impact of public health services on mortality: a study of mortality differentials in a rural area in Nigeria', *Population Studies*, 29, 2:259-272.

Palloni, A. (1981), 'Mortality in Latin America: emerging patterns', *Population and Development Review*, 7, 4:623-649.

Palloni, A. (1985), 'An epidemio-demographic analysis of factors in the mortality decline of 'slow-decline developing countries' in IUSSP, 1985, vol.2, pp.329-351.

Panikar, P.G.K. (1975), 'Fall in mortality rates in Kerala: an explanatory hypothesis', *Economic and Political Weekly*, 10:1811-1818.

Panikar, P.G.K. (1979), 'Resources not the constraint in health improvement', *Economic and Political Weekly*, 14:1802-1809.

Panikar, P.G.K. (1981), 'Towards demystifying Kerala's fertility experience', *Working Paper* no.122, Centre for Development Studies, Trivandrum.

Panikar, P.G.K. (1985), 'Health care system in Kerala and its impact on infant mortality', in Halstead *et al.*, 1985, pp.47-55.

Panikar, P.G.K. and Soman, C.R. (1984), *Health Status of Kerala: The Paradox of Economic Backwardness and Health Development*, Centre for Development Studies, Trivandrum.

Panikkar, T.K.G. (1900) (reprinted 1983), *Malabar and its Folk*, Asian Educational Services, New Delhi.

Patai, R. (1971), *Society, Culture and Change in the Middle East*, 3rd edn., University of Pennsylvania Press, Philadelphia.

Perera, P.D.A. (1985), 'Health care system in Sri Lanka', in Halstead *et al.*, 1085, pp.93-110.

Pieris, R. (1956), *Sinhalese Social Organization: The Kandyan Period*, Ceylon University Press, Colombo.

Polo, M. (tr. R. Latham) (1958, written in 1299), *The Travels of Marco Polo*, Penguin, Harmondsworth.

Prescott, N. and Jamison, D.T. (1984), 'Health sector finance in China', *World Health Statistics Quarterly*, 37, 4.

Preston, S.H. (1975), 'The changing relation between mortality and level of economic development', *Population Studies*, 29, 2:231-248.

Preston, S.H. (1980), 'Causes and consequences of mortality decline in less developed countries during the twentieth century', in R.A. Easterlin (ed.), *Population and Economic Change in Developing Countries*, University of Chicago Press, Chicago, pp.289-341.

Preston, S.H. (1985a), 'Resources, knowledge and child mortality: a comparison of the US in the late nineteenth century and developing countries today', in IUSSP, 1985, vol.4, pp.373-386, (Chapter 3 of this book).

Preston, S.H. (1985b), 'Notes on per capita income in the case study areas', in Halstead *et al.*, 1985, pp.159-161.

Preston, S.H. and Bhat, P.N.M. (1984), 'New evidence on fertility and mortality trends in India', *Population and Development Review*, 10, 3:481-503.

Prince Peter of Greece and Denmark (1955), 'Polyandry and the kinship group', *Man*, 44:179-181.

Puthenkalam, J. (1977), *Marriage and the Family in Kerala: With Special Reference to Matrilineal Castes*, Journal of Comparative Family Studies Monograph Series, University of Calgary Press, Calgary.

Ratcliffe, J. (1978), 'Social justice and the demographic transition: lessons from India's Kerala State', *International Journal of Health Services*, 8, 1:123-144.

Ravindran, T.K. (1972), *Asan and Social Revolution in Kerala*, Kerala Historical Society, Trivandrum.

Reddy, P.H. (1978), 'Size of village settlements and educational development in India', in J.R. Rele and M.K. Jain (eds), *Population Change and Rural Development in India*, International Institute for Population Studies, Bombay, pp.149-162.

Rienks, A. and Iskandar, N. (1981), 'Primary and indigenous health care in rural Central Java: a comparison of process and contents', *Hedera Report*, no.4, Gadja Madah University, Faculty of Medicine, Yogyakarta.

Roberts, M. (1982), *Caste Conflict and Elite Formation: The Rise of the Karava Elite in Sri Lanka, 1500-1931*, Cambridge University Press, Cambridge.

Ronaghy, H.A. and Solter, S. (1974), 'Is the Chinese 'barefoot doctor' exportable to rural Iran?', *Lancet*, 1:1331-1333.

Rosenberg, M.B. (1979), 'Social security policymaking in Costa Rica: a research report', *Latin American Research Review*, 14, 1:116-133.

Rosero-Bixby, L. (1985), 'Infant mortality decline in Costa Rica', in Halstead *et al.*, 1985, pp.125-138.

Ruzicka, L.T. (1983), 'Mortality in countries of the ESCAP region', in V. Narain and C.P. Prakasam (eds), *Population Policy Perspectives in Developing Countries*, Himalaya Publishing House, Bombay, pp.237-264.

Ruzicka, L.T. (1984), 'Mortality in India: Past trends and future prospects', in Dyson and Crook 1984, pp.13-36.

Ruzicka, L.T. and Hansluwka, H. (1982), 'A review of evidence on mortality levels, trends and differentials since the 1950s', in Ruzicka and Lopez, 1982, pp.83-156.

Ruzicka, L.T. and Lopez, A. (eds) (1982), *Mortality in South and East Asia: a Review of Changing Trends and Patterns, 1950-1975*, World Health Organization, Geneva.

Saenz, L. (1985), 'Health changes during a decade: the Costa Rican case', in Halstead *et al.*, 1985, pp.139-145.

Safilios-Rothschild, C. (1982), 'Female power, autonomy and demographic change in the Third World', in R. Anker, M. Buvinic and N. Youssef (eds), *Women's Roles and Population Trends in the Third World*, Croom Helm, London, pp.117-132.

Sarkar, N.K. (1957), *The Demography of Ceylon*, Ceylon Government Press, Colombo.

Seligson, M.A. (1980), *Peasants of Costa Rica and the Development of Agrarian Capitalism*, University of Wisconsin Press, Madison.

Sigerist, H.E. (1939), *Socialized Medicine in the Soviet Union*, Norton, New York.

Sivamurthy, M. (1981), 'The deceleration of mortality decline in Asian countries', in IUSSP, 1981, vol.2, pp.51-78.

Stirling, P. (1966), *Turkish Village*, John Wiley, New York.

Stolnitz, G. (1965), 'Recent mortality trends in Latin America, Asia and Africa', *Population Studies*, 19, 2:117-138.

Stycos, J.M. (1982), 'The decline of fertility in Costa Rica: literacy, modernization and family planning', *Population Studies*, 36, 1:15-30.

Sumathipala, K.H.M. (1968), *History of Education in Ceylon, 1796-1965*, Tisara Prakasakayo, Colombo.

Sushama, P.N. (1989), 'The causes of fertility decline in Kerala', unpublished. Ph.D. thesis, Australian National University, Canberra.

Swearingen, R. (1971), 'Key figures in critical non-communist countries: S.A. Dange, E.M.S. Namboodiripad and Jyoti Basu', in R. Swearingen (ed.), *Leaders of the Communist World*, Free Press, New York.

Taeuber, I.B. (1958), *The Population of Japan*, Princeton University Press, Princeton.

Tharakan, P.K.M. (1984), 'Socio-economic factors in educational development: the case of nineteenth century Travancore', *Working Paper* no.19, Centre for Development Studies, Trivandrum.

United Nations (1982), *Levels and Trends of Mortality Since 1950*, United Nations, New York.

United Nations, Department of Economic and Social Affairs (1956), *Methods for Population Projections by Sex and Age*, Manuals on methods of estimating population, Manual 3, United Nations, New York.

United Nations, Department of Economic and Social Affairs (1975), *Poverty, Unemployment and Development Policy: A Case Study of Selected Issues with Reference to Kerala*, United Nations, New York.

United Nations, Department of International Economic and Social Affairs (1983), *Demographic Yearbook, 1981*, United Nations, New York.

United Nations, Department of International Economic and Social Affairs (1985), *Socio-economic Development and Fertility Decline in Costa Rica*, United Nations, New York.

United Nations, Economic and Social Commission for Asia and the Pacific (1976), *Population of Sri Lanka*, ESCAP Country Monograph Series No.4, United Nations, Bangkok.

Woodcock, G. (1967), *Kerala: A Portrait of the Malabar Coast*, Faber and Faber, London.

Woodward, R.L. (1976), *Central America: A Nation Divided*, Oxford University Press, New York.

World Bank (1952), *The Economic Development of Ceylon: Report of Mission Organized by the International Bank for Reconstruction and Development at the Request of the Government of Ceylon*, Ceylon Government Press, Colombo.

World Bank (1984), *World Development Report 1984*, Oxford University Press, New York.

World Fertility Survey (1978), *The Sri Lanka Fertility Survey 1975: A Summary of Findings*, Summary No.7, World Fertility Survey, London.

World Health Organization (1978), *Alma-Ata 1978. Primary Health Care. Report of the International Conference on Primary Health Care, Alma-Ata, 6-12 September 1978*, World Health Organization, Geneva.

Wrigley, E.A. and Schofield, R.S. (1981), *The Population History of England, 1541-1871: A Reconstruction*, Edward Arnold, London.

Yalman, N. (1963), 'On the purity of women in the castes of Ceylon and Malabar', *Journal of the Royal Anthropological Institute of Great Britain and Ireland*, 93:25-58.

Yalman, N. (1967), *Under the Bo Tree: Studies in Caste, Kinship and Marriage in the Interior of Ceylon*, University of California Press, Berkeley and Los Angeles.

Zachariah, M. (1969), 'Whither Kerala? Social change in twentieth century Kerala', Ph.D. dissertation, University of Minnesota.

Zagoria, D.S. (1973), 'Kerala and West Bengal', *Problems of Communism*, 22, 1:16-27.

Zschock, D.K. (1980), 'Health care financing in Central America and the Andean region', *Latin American Research Review*, 15, 3:156.

Chapter 2

HOUSEHOLD INFLUENCES ON CHILDHOOD MORTALITY: EVIDENCE FROM HISTORICAL AND RECENT MORTALITY TRENDS*

Alaka M. Basu

In recent years there has been a spate of research, mainly based on data from the developing countries, to suggest that household (especially maternal) attributes are an important determinant of childhood mortality (Caldwell, 1979; Arriaga, 1979; Ramnath, 1980; Haines and Avery, 1982; Frenzen and Hogan, 1982; Farah and Preston, 1982). The hypothesis is that the willingness and ability of the family to prevent child deaths exert an effect quite independent of the income level of the household and its external environment, including the medical services theoretically at its disposal. According to Caldwell (1979), the mother is of prime importance in this situation, and it is her knowledge, autonomy in household decision making, and ability to interact with outside agencies, that define the level of household child mortality even if the outer limits are set by the economic resources of the household and the medical facilities in its area. Education, it is alleged, is a crucial determinant of these three attributes, and hence the frequently observed link between maternal education and childhood mortality.

All the studies which have focused on this relationship have tended to use cross-sectional data to establish differentials in child mortality experience according to the educational level of the mother. In this paper a different approach is used to support the same hypothesis. Age patterns of long-term historical mortality declines are determined, and an attempt made to relate falls in child mortality to indicators of rising maternal competence.

MATERIALS AND METHODS

This analysis is conducted separately for the developed and developing countries, and from this it emerges that overall rises in life expectancies have been composed of different age patterns of mortality decline at different times and in different places. Moreover, these patterns can be quite neatly related to the known influences on the

*First published in *Social Biology*, 34(3-4)1987.

drop in crude death rates in these different times and places. More specifically, in the context of the present paper, it is seen that:

1.   Changes in childhood mortality are often dissociated from changes in overall mortality levels and tend to follow their own course, which can vary quite substantially from one area to another and at different times. That is, childhood (including infant) mortality may not begin to decline at the same time or at the same pace as mortality at the older ages.

2. The decline in childhood mortality, once initiated, may not stop even if the decline in general mortality slows down or stops at levels less than those obtained elsewhere.

3.   This variation in the course of childhood mortality trends can be related to variations in the onset of social change (particularly at the individual level, as measured by female literacy and education), as opposed to purely economic development or medical advances.

These conclusions are consistent with the hypothesis that a fall in child mortality is influenced by other factors besides those influencing general mortality. If changing attitudes and behaviour is one of these factors, it is quite plausible that these changes begin somewhat later than the economic development and public health, and public health and medical technology changes, which are believed to have initiated large-scale declines in overall mortality in the developed and developing countries respectively. But even when the latter have slowed down or become difficult to maintain, it is still very possible that the change in individual perceptions and abilities, being an accelerating process, continues and carries with it further declines in childhood mortality.

Before examining the evidence for the above conclusions, some important qualifications must be stressed. The most important of course is the problem of data availability, reliability, and comparability. The problem is especially acute for data on infant and child mortality, where information from vital statistics is generally inadequate, and indirect estimation requires several assumptions to be made. Add to this the present requirement for data at least at two points in time (preferably more often, to avoid relying on freak cases), and it is quite likely that the selection of areas with adequate data for the present analysis introduces a bias in the kind of results obtained.

Secondly, the base levels of childhood mortality are probably important while looking at the causes of declines. But the present analysis does maintain some uniformity by concentrating on the transition from fairly low levels of expectation of life at birth, which were characterized everywhere by high infant and child mortality. In fact the proposition is that wide variations in infant and childhood mortality first emerge as life expectations rise.

Thirdly, the present hypothesis does not preclude the role of other influences on the course of declining child mortality. But it is stated that these are complementary to the overriding importance of changes in maternal knowledge, attitudes, and practices. In a related context, it should be pointed out that this is not equivalent to saying that this childhood mortality is intentional (as proposed, for example, by Scrimshaw, 1978). The present hypothesis is much weaker and says that a decline in child mortality (as opposed to the maintenance of high child mortality levels) requires an element of volition at the individual or family level, in that it involves a change in values and attitudes, especially towards the child, increased knowledge (both processes in either order of occurrence), and, finally, modified behaviour to accord with these changed attitudes and new knowledge.

Finally, it would be useful to disaggregate childhood mortality (that is, between the ages of 0 and 4) wherever possible. It is likely, for example, that a fall in neonatal mortality is not as dependent on changing attitudes and behaviour as post-neonatal mortality and, even more so, mortality at the 1-4 ages. This could partly explain why mortality at ages 1-4 has been found to be high relative to the infant mortality rate in places such as India (for example, Wyon and Gordon, 1971), Bangladesh (Committee on Population and Demography, 1981) and sub-Saharan Africa (Azefor, 1981). The decline in infant mortality caused by exogenous factors like improved and widespread medical technology could still maintain high levels of child mortality because the infants saved are entering early childhood without the simultaneous changes necessary to increase their survival beyond the age of one. Unfortunately, the data available seldom permit us to distinguish between neonatal and post-neonatal, or between infant and child mortality. Instead, heavy reliance may have to be placed on summary measures of ages 0-4 mortality or even the use of infant mortality as a proxy for childhood mortality. But we hope the latter assumption will not be presumptuous, at least while looking at historical declines in the developed countries, where short durations of breastfeeding meant that infants were soon exposed to all the hazards of early childhood.

RESULTS

The Developed Countries

A slow and irregular decline in mortality in the present-day developed countries had begun as early as the late eighteenth and early nineteenth centuries. By 1850, Northern and Western Europe saw steadily increasing gains in life expectancies, with the largest gains during the first two decades of the twentieth century and in the years immediately after World War II (United Nations, 1973). McKeown (1976) estimates that the total fall in mortality in England between 1700 and 1971 can be justly distributed as follows: 1700 to 1848-54, 33 per cent; 1848-54 to 1901, 20 per cent; and 1901 to 1971, 47 per cent. But the Scandinavian countries probably achieved the fastest and greatest falls in death rates during the earlier phases of this mortality transition. Expectation of life at birth crossed 40 years as early as in the 1820s in Sweden and stood at 55.7 years by 1900 (United Nations, 1973).

In contrast, steady falls in mortality in other parts of Europe, including European Russia, began much later, toward the end of the nineteenth century, but were much more rapid (Stolnitz, 1955) so that they soon narrowed the gaps between themselves and the early starters. This more rapid decline in crude death rates continued well into the present century and by the late 1960s there was little in these rates to distinguish the pioneers from the laggards in the developed countries. CDRs all fell in the narrow range of 8-12 deaths per thousand population.

However, the different groups of countries beginning their mortality transitions at different times did not display identical age patterns of mortality declines. True, the general trend was a movement from a U-shaped curve of age-specific mortality rates to a J-shaped one. But the exact paths they followed to reach this end varied considerably, as is evident from several direct and indirect sources. Perhaps the best evidence is found in the regional model life table system generated by Coale and Demeny (1966). These tables are based on the actual mortality experience of populations from the mid-nineteenth century to the late 1950s, as represented by 192 national and subnational populations. The fact that the authors found it convenient to divide the life tables so obtained into different groups, based on distinct region-specific age patterns of mortality at similar levels of overall life expectations at birth, is strong indication that the relation between mortality changes at the younger and older ages as death rates fall is not the same for different areas at different times. Moreover, the differences in the age patterns of mortality in the four regional models also vary in character as one moves from higher to lower levels of mortality. The experience from the developed countries therefore is that the same end-level of expectation of life at birth can be reached with quite different age patterns of mortality change under different circumstances.

An examination of the timing and tempo of declines in childhood mortality for those developed countries (mainly in Western Europe) for which reliable data are available far back enough in time suggests that the hypothesis that social change at the individual or family level is an important determinant of such declines is a plausible one. Or, to put it more weakly, the evidence is at least not incompatible with such a hypothesis, which is a fair achievement given the nature of the hypothesis and the limitations of the empirical data available to support or refute it.

In England, for example, mortality between the ages of five and 45 had begun declining significantly very early in the eighteenth century (Logan, 1950; Peller, 1965), and Hollingsworth (1965) concludes from an examination of changes in line expectancy at age five that the centre of the period of rapidly falling mortality in the general population of England was in fact as early as about 1755. McKeown (1976) estimates that during the nineteenth century as well the fall in mortality was proportionately greatest at the later childhood and young adult ages.

On the other hand, major improvements in infant and early childhood mortality did not begin until the end of the nineteenth century. For example, Wrigley and Schofield (1983), using reconstitution data from five counties in England which they think are representative of the country as a whole, find little decisive fall in child mortality even until the last quarter of the eighteenth century, as shown in Table 1. Even the 1838-54 life table for England and Wales shows 26 per cent of children dying by the age of five. Moreover, this figure is not much lower, at 23 per cent, for the 1891-1900 life table (Hollingsworth, 1965).

TABLE 1: INFANT AND CHILD MORTALITY FROM POOLED DATA FOR 13 PARISHES IN ENGLAND AND WALES: RATES PER 1000

Mortality	1600-49	1650-99	1700-49	1750-99
$1q0$	161.3	166.7	169.2	133.4
	(162.3)[a]	(169.7)	(195.3)	(165.5)
$4q1$	89.3	101.5	106.5	103.5

Source: Wrigley and Schofield, 1983.

[a]The rates in parentheses include a correction designed to offset the effect of the increasing delay between birth and baptism and the attendant risk that a young infant might die before being baptized and its burial might not be recorded.

Similarly, from cause-of-death registration data for England, Wales, Sweden, France and Ireland, McKeown (1976) concludes that while mortality from air-borne infections had begun to fall by the 1950s, it was not until the end of the nineteenth century that there was an appreciable decline in deaths from water and food-borne diseases – the major infant and young child killers.

What were the major influences on the overall mortality declines during this entire period? Although the details of the role of different factors in reducing mortality continue to be a matter of some controversy, over the years a consensus has emerged on the view that the widespread application of advances in preventive and curative medicine could not have had a major impact on falling death rates until the 1930s and was certainly not responsible for initiating secular falls in mortality. Since sustained declines in mortality did take place before the 1930s in the present-day industrialized countries, in these countries the debate has centred less and less on the relative merits of the socio-economic development versus medical technology case to explain mortality decline. But this is not to state that there is no argument about the determinants of rises in life expectancies until the 1930s. For even the socio-economic factors underlying industrialization and urbanization, and plausibly reducing mortality, are several, and include developments in housing, agriculture, environmental sanitation, personal hygiene, medical services, and health consciousness among the people; and it has just not been possible to quantify their separate influences.

However, even if it is not possible to measure separately the effects of all these factors at any one time, it is at least possible to identify the calendar periods during which specific factors could have first assumed importance, an exercise which is now attempted.

It is now believed that the slow rise in population growth rates as early as the beginning of the eighteenth century was a result not so much of a fall in general death rates as a lowering of the peaks of mortality which erupted during regular epidemics and famines in earlier times (Helleiner, 1965; United Nations, 1973). These declines in 'catastrophic mortality' predated the process of industrialization and, in England and Wales at least, have been attributed to rising nutritional levels as subsistence crises in agriculture occurred less frequently and were less often followed by epidemic diseases (McKeown and Brown, 1955). Similar conclusions have been drawn to explain the early nineteenth century falls in mortality in the rest of Northern and Western Europe. Writing in 1886, the noted French statistician and doctor Leon-Clergy Vacher dismissed as negligible the role of medical advances in significant mortality reductions occurring until that time. To begin with, he felt that:

It is certain that consumption has increased significantly everywhere. It is also certain that this increased consumption of basic necessities has improved resistance to disease, increased the vitality of men and women, and diminished mortality rates in all of Europe. These results are more the work of scientific and industrial revolution than that of any political revolution (Vacher, 1979 [1886]:169).

The processes involved were essentially technological and economic and included greater productivity of land and labour with improved farming techniques, advances in transportation, better methods of food storage, and rising wages with industrialization. Social changes, especially at the individual level, were not yet an important factor in reducing mortality risks. For example, Oddy (1970), while examining nineteenth century English diets, concluded that the average low-income Englishman could have had a much more nutritious diet at a lower price if he had been prepared to change his consumption patterns and that this might be a contributory factor in the observed paradox between the rise in real wages and the low standards in nutrition and health in England at the turn of the twentieth century. Confirmed cynics will be gratified by Oddy's further conclusion that even if the people *had* understood dietary requirements, it is still not certain that better diets would have resulted, so strong is the pull of culture and habit.

After the middle of the nineteenth century, however, greater social consciousness led to sanitary reform and public health movements which began to assume increasing importance as factors influencing mortality declines. As the relationship between an unclean environment and disease became more recognized (by pioneers like Edwin Chadwick in England and Lemnel Shattuck in the United States), there was pressure for greater involvement of the state in public health issues, an event which undoubtedly led to significant falls in mortality as new public health legislation was introduced (McKeown, 1965; United Nations, 1973). Important community measures included the operation of public agencies for refuse disposal, the construction of sewerage systems, and the purification of water supplies. As a result of these improvements in public sanitation, mortality rates from the bowel diseases and from typhoid declined (McKeown, 1976). For a contemporary awareness of the role of sanitary reform in falling death rates in other parts of Europe, see Vacher, 1979 [1886].

At the same time, social reformers were able to influence the introduction of several measures to improve living and working conditions in England and other industrializing countries. These included the gradual raising of the minimum age of employment, shorter working days, safer working conditions, stricter control of housing standards, and various private and governmental social security schemes.

While all the above steps required little initial co-operation from individuals, they must have had an important effect on individual attitudes and behaviour, if by nothing else, by the increased knowledge that their publicity conferred. There is some evidence that this period, particularly the last quarter of the nineteenth century, saw a greater concern with personal hygiene. Soap gradually stopped being a luxury item, and the substitution of cotton for woollen undergarments at least increased the ease of keeping these clean. It has been pointed out, however, that it is not known with certainty that the cotton clothing was actually washed more frequently, and that the increased production of soap could have been mainly for industrial use (Krause, 1958).

However, the evidence for changed behavioural patterns does not rest purely on production statistics like the above. An important influence was surely the gradual rise in literacy and education, especially as the school curriculum began to include lessons in personal hygiene and in the application of basic health practices. Although it was as early as in the last quarter of the nineteenth century that, in England and Wales at least, the question began to be seriously considered of providing mass elementary education, the actual establishment of a national system of elementary education took much longer for various reasons, a major one being an intense suspicion of interference by the state in private affairs, the sphere of 'private affairs' being very liberally interpreted. But by the mid-nineteenth century, this doctrine of *laissez faire* was increasingly challenged as political philosophers like T.H. Green argued for greater state intervention in social matters, as the mere freedom to do as one wished included the freedom of the strong to exploit the weak and this meant that the weak enjoyed no freedom at all (Wardle, 1976).

In the nineteenth century, therefore, England and Wales saw the gradual creation of a system of universal education, although the process lagged behind developments in countries such as France and the United States. The result was that from an average attendance of about 65 per cent of the roll in the 1870s, by the 1890s attendance figures were comparable to those of the present day, and for the first time the great mass of the child population attended school regularly for six or seven years (Evans, 1975). In the context of the present paper, even female secondary education not only expanded greatly during the last quarter of the nineteenth century, influenced by the recommendations of the Taunton Commission Report in 1868, but also, the girls' schools so set up also set the trend in adopting more modern and useful curricula and teaching methods (Evans, 1975).

This period also coincided with the spread of a less formal kind of education aimed at changing beliefs and practices inimical to good health. For example, a school for mothers was opened in London in 1904 and another in 1907. The health education these schools imparted was more readily acceptable because the generation of women passing through their childbearing life at this time was also the first to benefit from the Compulsory Education Act of 1870 (Benjamin, 1965). Urban infant welfare centres also rapidly multiplied, and from 1907 an even more personal approach to education was adopted in London through health visitors who contacted new mothers to impart basic information on asepsis, nutrition, and physical development. All this was coupled of course with the more ready availability of clean cow's milk to weaned infants (Beaver, 1973).

Regarding the role of advances in medicine, there is now some consensus that, except for smallpox vaccination, these were not a major factor in mortality declines until about 1935 (McKeown, 1976). Most other gains in medical knowledge were of little practical use from the patient's point of view until the twentieth century, which saw rapid developments both in the prevention of the previously fatal diseases (including tuberculosis, typhoid, cholera, measles, yellow fever, whooping cough, and influenza) and in their cure once these diseases had occurred. The use of sulphonamides and then penicillin and other antibiotics after the 1930s, coupled with the immunizing agents mentioned above, meant that mortality from several infectious diseases declined to levels lower than had been earlier thought possible.

To recapitulate, during the late eighteenth and most of the nineteenth centuries, the major possible influences on reductions in overall mortality in the developed countries were improvements in nutrition and standards of living, and public sanitary reforms, in that order of occurrence. There is little evidence of major changes in individual attitudes and behaviour until the end of the nineteenth century. While opinions may differ about the role of such social changes in promoting falls in childhood mortality, the timing of the onset of these falls at least does not contradict the possibility of such a role.

The second characteristic of the mortality decline in the developed countries is that though significant improvements in infant and child mortality lagged behind improvements in mortality at the older ages, once they had been initiated, they tended to be greatest at these early ages (see Table 2).

TABLE 2: **PERCENTAGE DECLINE OF MORTALITY RATES BY AGE GROUP IN SELECTED EUROPEAN COUNTRIES, 1876-85 TO 1946-55**

Sex and age	France	Netherlands	Norway	England and Wales
Males				
1-4	90	94	92	95
5-14	85	85	85	85
15-24	79	80	79	76
25-34	74	82	77	80
35-44	64	77	68	78
45-54	42	64	55	56
55-64	25	51	42	34
65-74	26	43	18	24
Females				
1-4	91	94	94	96
5-14	89	91	91	89
15-24	84	88	86	81
25-34	81	83	84	82
35-44	73	82	78	79
45-54	59	65	64	65
55-64	52	53	50	56
65-74	44	43	27	43

Source: United Nations, 1973.

TABLE 3: TRENDS IN MEDIAN AGE-SPECIFIC DEATH RATES, 1950-54 TO MID-1970S, MORE DEVELOPED COUNTRIES

Age group	Percentage decline in median age-specific death rates			
	1950-54 to Mid-1970s	1950-54 to 1960-64	1960-64 to 1970	1970 to Mid-1970s
Males				
Under 1	55.6	30.6	23.1	16.9
1-4	59.9	41.1	17.2	17.8
5-9	48.2	31.3	5.3	20.4
10-14	41.2	27.9	8.2	11.1
15-19	20.6	15.8	+0.9	5.5
20-24	26.2	20.9	2.0	4.8
25-29	26.5	21.1	2.1	4.9
30-34	24.4	18.2	5.3	2.5
35-39	21.3	17.3	2.6	2.2
40-44	17.3	16.3	+1.5	2.6
45-49	13.3	13.1	+0.4	0.5
50-54	14.4	12.7	2.3	+0.2
55-59	11.2	5.7	0.7	5.2
60-64	5.8	0.4	0.6	5.3
65-69	3.1	0.2	+4.4	7.0
70-74	3.4	0.9	+3.6	5.9
75-79	2.7	2.6	+2.6	2.6
80-84	6.8	6.2	0.1	3.0
85 and over	10.5	1.9	5.8	3.0
Females				
Under 1	59.6	34.0	23.8	19.7
1-4	60.9	41.4	19.2	17.5
5-9	47.4	31.6	12.8	11.8
10-14	47.8	37.0	3.5	14.3
15-19	36.6	33.8	4.3	–
20-24	52.9	41.4	13.1	7.5
25-29	54.3	43.3	12.5	7.9
30-34	47.3	32.0	11.8	12.2
35-39	44.0	26.6	11.8	13.4
40-44	31.9	24.3	3.2	7.1
45-49	28.5	20.4	4.6	6.0
50-54	24.0	16.3	3.5	5.8
55-59	21.7	15.2	2.9	4.9
60-64	24.4	13.9	2.8	9.7
65-69	24.5	12.0	2.1	12.4
70-74	24.6	11.6	5.2	10.0
75-79	20.7	9.5	6.2	6.6
80-84	16.2	18.6	8.2	0.3
85 and over	11.4	3.8	4.5	3.6

Source: United Nations, 1982.

That is, once infant and childhood mortality have begun their way downhill, they seem to follow an independent and rapid course which may or may not coincide with the paths taken by mortality at other ages. As seen in Table 2, the first half of the twentieth century saw the largest reductions in mortality in most European countries occurring in early childhood, that is, at about age three, and the minimum mortality rate, which earlier occurred at about the fifteenth year of life, gradually moved downward (United Nations, 1973).

The quarter century since 1950 has seen a continuation of this trend in the developed countries (United Nations, 1982). In general, the greatest declines in mortality were observed in the youngest age groups and the smallest declines in the oldest age groups, with the largest relative decline taking place in the age group 1-4 years (see Table 3).

The particularly interesting aspect of Table 3 is that gains in early childhood mortality have maintained their lead while the ordering at other ages has often changed, and there has even been a deterioration in death rates in some age groups during some periods. In an analysis comparing the medians of these developed countries' age-specific male death rates for 1950-54 and the mid-1970s with the rates associated with different mortality levels in the Coale and Demeny 'West' model life table system, the United Nations (1982) found that the size of the reduction in the medians of the observed death rates at the older ages has not matched the improvements in the younger age groups when measured against the standard of the model life tables. For females, on the other hand, the match with the model life tables was closer, and at the older adult ages there was even a tendency to drift toward life tables with lower mortality.

This kind of steady and more rapid decline in childhood mortality is compatible with the suggestion that it is heavily influenced by social changes at the individual and family behavioural level. Such changes tend to generate their own momentum once they have been initiated, a momentum which soon gets divorced from changes in other economic or technological factors, as is demonstrated more vividly with evidence from the developing countries.

The Developing Countries

A few countries in this group began a sustained mortality reduction before the 1940s. The data available are limited, but among these exceptions should probably be included Argentina, Chile, Uruguay, and Costa Rica in Latin America (Palloni, 1981) Sri Lanka, Taiwan, and Singapore in Asia (United Nations, 1973); and Mauritius and possibly Egypt in Africa (United Nations, 1973).

But the real take-off for mortality decline in the developing countries as a whole occurred after World War II. The first couple of decades of this period saw remarkable gains in life expectancy in nearly every developing country, often averaging annual gains of more than one year in countries as diverse as Taiwan, Malaysia, Jamaica, Mexico, Sri Lanka, and Mauritius, the last two recording gains of two years annually in the 1940s and early 1950s (Gwatkin, 1980). In India, the crude death rate declined from about 27 per thousand in the 1940s to about 17 in the 1970s. In Africa too, expectation of life at birth seems to have risen from a low of 30 years in the 1930s to a more impressive (though still far short of potential) figure of 43 years by the 1960s (Preston, 1980).

TABLE 4: PERCENTAGE DECLINE OF MORTALITY RATES BY AGE
GROUP IN SELECTED DEVELOPING COUNTRIES, BOTH SEXES, 1940 TO 1965

Age	Ceylon 1946-63	Chile 1940-60	Taiwan 1940-65	Jamaica 1943-60	Mauritius 1940-62	Puerto Rico 1940-60	Trinidad and Tobago 1946-60
Under 1	70	38	84	49	68	78	47
1-4		69	86	47	73		
5-14	69	52	82	72	76	84	68
15-24	72	71	73	70	83	81	73
25-34	72	56	75	67	84	82	64
35-44	66	45	73	59	78	73	56
45-54	58	36	64	45	67	62	45
55-64	48	27	50	30	54	55	36
65 and over	22	24	27	25	39	38	12

Source: United Nations, 1973.

However, unlike the experience of the developed countries in the present century, where falls in childhood mortality have tended to outstrip gains at other ages, in the developing world, as Table 4 illustrates, it appears that in the immediate postwar decades which recorded the most dramatic falls in crude death rates, the gains by young adults have been at least as great as, and often higher than, those by young children. This is also in contrast to the situation in the prewar years where any falls in mortality benefited young children the most, as for example in Sri Lanka (Sarkar, 1957) and Jamaica (Roberts, 1950).

Further evidence that in the developing world the relation between childhood and adult mortality has been distorted when compared to that expected by looking at rises in life expectancies in the developed countries is available from the increasingly recognized incompatibility between age-specific death rates in the developing countries and the regional model life tables (based mainly on developed country data) prepared by Coale and Demeny (1966). Almost all this incompatibility has arisen from childhood mortality rates in the underdeveloped countries being higher than the model life table rates at similar levels of adult mortality.

For example, Palloni (1981) derived expected values of $_1q_0$ and $_4q_1$, or the probabilities of dying before age one and between the ages of one and five respectively, using modes 'West' of the Coale-Demeny system, for those Latin American countries which had reliable data on e_{15}, the life expectancy at age 15, for the 1970s. He found that with the exception of Trinidad and Tobago, the expected values of $_1q_0$ were lower than those actually observed, and with the exception of Argentina, Chile, and Trinidad and Tobago, the expected values of $_4q_1$ were lower than the observed values.

Similarly, Adlakha and Kirk (1974) found the 1968-69 Sample Registration Scheme (which has been accused of under-registration if anything) estimates of the 0-4 year death rate in India to be much higher than the rate predicted by applying the SRS life expectancies at age five to the regional model life table system. This was the case whichever family of model life tables was chosen, even the South family with its much higher level of childhood mortality for a given level of adult mortality.

It is this reduced relevance of model life table systems based on the recorded experience of the developed countries to the declines in mortality in the present-day developing countries which has prompted the United Nations Secretariat (1982) to develop a new model life table system based on the more reliable of the age- and sex-specific death data available for the less-developed areas, a system which is expected to be more applicable to demographic analysis for these areas.

The overall impression, therefore, from whatever data sources are available is that gains in mortality at the young childhood ages in the developing countries have tended to lag behind improvements at older ages (Dyson, 1977; United Nations, 1982). It is also in this age group of 1-4 years that mortality differentials between the developed and developing countries have become the most marked. For example, the United Nations model life table project gives a death rate of 36 per thousand population for Indian girls aged 1-4 (1970-72 life table) and 27 for boys, compared to average death rates of 0.83 per thousand population for boys and 0.66 for girls in the more developed countries (United Nations, 1982).

As for causes, the medical advances which became significant contributors to falling death rates in the developed countries only after about two centuries of economic and social change were of the kind which could be transferred relatively easily to areas which had reached very differing levels of social and economic development, as long as the political will existed (which it fortunately generally did) to implement these new technologies. That is, the chronological order of the influences on declining mortality was often completely reversed in these countries: first came the effect of the widespread adoption of developments in medicine and public health, followed after varying intervals of time by the economic and/or social changes needed to sustain these falls in mortality.

Several writers have stressed the initial rapidity of the gains in longevity obtained in the underdeveloped countries compared with the record of the developed countries at similar levels of mortality (see, for example, Stolnitz, 1965). But at least at the earlier stages of rises in life expectancies, this is only to be expected, as the impact of new medical technologies is more sudden and impressive in the short run than the gradual effect of changes in standards of living. So effective have been these developments in the prevention and (especially) treatment of disease that the early postwar years saw an increased weakening of the relation between economic development and mortality (Stolnitz, 1965; Arriaga and Davis, 1969; Preston, 1975), a situation in marked contrast to that obtaining in earlier decades not only in the developed countries but also in the few developing areas that saw some prewar falls in mortality. For example, Arriaga and Davis (1969) show that in Latin America in the nineteenth century and up to the 1930s, the rate of improvement in national mortality levels was closely linked to a nation's level of economic development; but after 1930 all countries in the region shared nearly equally in the gains in longevity, regardless of their level or rate of economic development. In line is Diaz-Briquets' (1981) conclusion, from an examination of cause-specific mortality in Cuba, that public health and sanitary reforms and nutritional improvements were largely responsible for the country's initial declines in mortality throughout the first half of the twentieth century, while after World War II, the relevance of economic conditions as a determinant of mortality decline diminished considerably.

In all these countries, the most important health-technology factors responsible for such dramatic falls in death rates have probably been antimalarial campaigns, immunization against tuberculosis, smallpox, and certain other diseases, and antibiotics to treat infectious and respiratory diseases (Preston, 1978). As important as the development of the scientific technology involved in these medical advances has been the fact that they could be imported by states at low levels of development and spread by a massive growth and expansion of public health and medical services.

But having identified the more important medical and public health technologies responsible for large-scale declines in mortality in the developing world, we find the debate about the determinants of mortality decline is by no means over. For it is far from accepted that these were the *sole* factors in the observed mortality decline. As discussed earlier, it is probably more accurate to attribute to them the great weakening of the link between economic and social development and rises in life expectancies.

What all these controversies do agree on, however, is that the effect of medical measures on falling death rates tends to taper off unless it is backed by more general rises in personal living standards. This is especially apparent once health interventions to reduce mortality have removed the 'soft rock' of causes of death, the 'hard rock' consisting of factors less amenable to direct medical control and more a function of poverty and underdevelopment (United Nations, 1963). Indeed, all indications are that such slowdowns in the rate of mortality decline have already occurred in several parts of the developing world at levels of mortality well above those prevailing in the developed countries (Gwatkin, 1980). Moreover, there has been a reversal of the trend toward convergence of death rates which was so typical among the developing countries during the accelerated mortality decline of the early postwar years. Both these events are discernible not only from whatever reliable mortality data are available for these countries, but also from the even more fragmentary cause-of-death statistics which show that the major causes of death are decreasingly the infectious and parasitic diseases open to medical interventions and increasingly the less easily attackable gastrointestinal and respiratory ailments. Preston and Nelson (1974) have concluded from such data that mortality from diarrhoea in the developing world is typically two to three times higher than it was in the developed countries at similar overall mortality levels.

Gwatkin (1980) has related these decelerations in the pace of overall mortality declines to the slow rate of progress in recent economic and social trends in several developing countries. In the context of the present paper, which is concerned with development leading to changes in individual attitudes and behaviours, rises in population literacy and education levels are an important factor. And the development of this factor has been rather uneven in the developing countries. Although educational levels have not generally been specifically mentioned in the literature on the causes of overall mortality declines in the underdeveloped countries, some of these inter-country variations are worth noting. For example, by the early 1970s, the Latin American countries of El Salvador, Guatemala, Nicaragua, and Peru had 38 per cent or more of their adult populations illiterate, while in Costa Rica, Argentina, Chile, and Uruguay, this figure hovered around 10 per cent (Preston, 1980). Similarly, in Asia, countries like Sri Lanka and Malaysia with their still high levels of adult illiteracy of around 20 per cent, nevertheless had fared much better than Bangladesh (80 per cent), Pakistan (80 per cent), India (40 per cent), and Jordan (62 per cent). In Africa, Mauritius with an adult illiteracy level of 20 per cent was about the single exception to the rule of well over 60 per cent of the adult population being illiterate. It should be noted that all these figures of adult illiteracy are biased downward as far as female (the more relevant group for the present hypothesis) illiteracy is concerned, as all the countries display a marked sex differential in educational attainment.

Similarly, the developing countries have had differing levels of success or failure with attempts to reduce childhood mortality. Just as the differentials in mortality between the developed and developing countries are the most marked at ages under five, so within the developing countries themselves there is a wide range of variation in the achievements in lowering child mortality. That is, the transition from a U-shaped to a J-shaped curve of age-specific mortality in the developing countries has found different areas with greatly differing lengths of the left hand side of the curve at the same point of time. Indeed, the United Nations life table project (United Nations Secretariat, 1982), based on the mortality experience of less developed countries, has identified four distinct age patterns of mortality in addition to a residual category of life tables more akin to the Coale-Demeny West system. For example, the life tables for India, the Matlab *thana* area of Bangladesh, Iran, Tunisia, Pakistan, Nepal, and Turkey all display characteristics of what has been labelled the 'South Asian' pattern – very high mortality rates under age 15 and high rates again at the older ages, with correspondingly lower mortality in the prime age groups.

That is, age patterns of mortality change in the developing world are not only distinct from those that occurred during the mortality transition in the developed countries, they also show significant variations among themselves. And where falls in childhood mortality are concerned, these variations can often be linked to the possible influence of social (especially behavioural) change on these falls. Where the mortality decline has been predominantly or even solely guided by medical factors, the tendency has been for childhood mortality to decline much less rapidly than when the rise in life expectancy has also been accompanied by developments in literacy and education, particularly of females. While such developments can generally be subsumed under general socio-economic growth, they can also occur without such growth. The cases of Jamaica and Sri Lanka, where mortality declines before the medical and public health revolutions were characterized by greater gains in early childhood than at the older ages, have already been mentioned. But even in the postwar falls in overall mortality in the developing world, there has been a distinct pattern of countries with greater social change displaying greater falls in child mortality.

Taking Latin America as an example, Palloni (1981) calculated for those countries with reliable data the expected values of $_4q_1$ given their levels of e_{15} in the early 1970s, had these countries followed the European-North American mortality experience as represented by the Coale-Demeny West model life table system. It is true that in almost all cases the expected values were lower than those actually observed, but within themselves they fell into two distinct groups. Cuba, Costa Rica, Uruguay, Barbados, Argentina, Chile, and Trinidad and Tobago formed a separate cluster of nations with distinctly lower excess childhood mortality than the rest of the countries. Interestingly, these are the very Latin American countries where, by the early 1970s, adult female literacy had reached levels of 90 per cent or more (UNESCO, 1982). On the other hand, the largest deviations were seen in those countries with the least success in combating female illiteracy – Bolivia, Dominican Republic, Ecuador, El Salvador, Guatemala, Honduras, Mexico, and Paraguay. All these countries had well over 35 per cent of their adult female populations illiterate by the early 1970s (UNESCO, 1982).

In Asia, Sri Lanka represents the special case of a country where social development has followed an independent course from economic growth, with effects on overall mortality declines which are still being analysed. To recapitulate the postulated influences on the dramatic falls in crude death rates in Sri Lanka: before 1946 the major influence was the economic and social change that the country witnessed. After World War II and to the mid-1950s, mortality benefited from a continuation of at least this social change together with the medical prophylaxis and therapy developments of the West, including an intensive malaria eradication campaign. In the 1960s and 1970s whatever mortality declines have occurred must be attributed to the limited economic growth but continuing social development that has been taking place, including the fact that between 1953 and 1971, the percentage of females aged ten and above that were literate rose from 53.6 to 70.9 per cent (Meegama, 1981).

Table 5 contains the annual rates of decline in age-specific mortality in Sri Lanka between 1920-22 and 1971. And the figures fit in quite well with the hypothesis that childhood mortality declines are greatest when the primary influence on mortality is social change. Before 1947, infants and young children were the greatest beneficiaries of declines in mortality; between 1945-47 and 1952-54 the gains were greatest among the young adult groups; and after 1952-54, children aged one to four have shown the relatively largest declines, which have been sustained even after the deceleration in the rate of overall mortality decline has set in, as in the 1960s, and some age groups even experienced a rise in death rates.

TABLE 5: ANNUAL RATES OF DECLINE IN AGE-SPECIFIC DEATH RATES DURING SELECTED PERIODS, SRI LANKA, 1920-22 TO 1971

	Annual rates of decline (percentage)							
	1920-22 to 1945-47		1945-47 to 1952-54		1952-54 to 1962-64		1962-64 to 1971	
Age	Male	Female	Male	Female	Male	Female	Male	Female
Under 1	1.4	1.3	4.9	5.9	3.3	3.2	2.1	1.9
1-4	1.9	1.8	4.5	4.5	5.2	5.2	4.8	4.9
5-9	2.9	2.7	4.0	4.7	3.1	3.8	3.1	3.3
10-14	2.2	2.0	9.5	10.4	1.4	2.1	1.0	1.1
15-19	1.9	1.5	9.6	9.5	0.0	2.7	0.8	1.6
20-24	1.9	1.6	8.6	8.4	1.5	3.0	+2.0	3.9
25-29	1.9	1.5	8.7	8.2	0.9	3.1	+1.6	2.8
30-34	1.6	1.6	9.0	8.3	1.7	3.3	+2.1	3.0
35-39	1.8	1.7	8.4	7.6	1.0	2.6	+2.1	2.5
40-44	1.7	1.7	8.5	7.9	0.8	2.1	+2.8	2.4
45-49	1.6	1.5	8.0	7.3	0.2	1.1	+1.7	2.2
50-54	1.5	1.5	7.5	6.6	0.4	1.6	+2.0	1.4
55-59	1.3	1.7	5.9	6.1	0.5	0.7	+1.3	1.7
60-64	1.1	1.7	5.3	6.0	0.9	0.9	+1.2	1.0
65-69	1.2	1.7	4.8	4.8	+0.7	+0.8	1.0	2.6
70-74	1.5	1.8	3.6	3.9	+0.4	+0.6	0.7	1.4
75-79	1.5	1.8	3.9	4.0	+1.0	+0.8	+0.2	2.0
80-84	1.2	1.1	3.1	3.6	+0.2	+0.5	+0.4	0.6

Source: ESCAP, 1976.

In India, on the other hand, the overall rise in female education and therefore, by extension, presumably the change in attitudes and behaviour, has been far less spectacular and so has been the decline in childhood mortality. The United Nations (1982) life table for India for 1970-72 estimated for ages 1-4 a male death rate of 27 and a female one of 36, in contrast to Sri Lanka's vital registration rates of five and six respectively.

However, it makes more sense to compute childhood mortality rates for a country as large and diverse as India on a more regional basis, and once this is done there is seen to be a distinct geographical pattern. Using indirect techniques to estimate $_2q_0$ values from the 1965-66 National Sample Survey, Bhat *et al.* (1984) found that all the southern states, including Maharashtra, had relatively low childhood mortality compared to their adult mortality levels, while all the central and north-western states, except Haryana, had relatively high childhood mortality compared to their adult mortality levels. This is compatible with the cultural and social differences in the two groups of states which result in much higher levels of female literacy and autonomy in the southern states (see Table 6 and Dyson and Moore, 1983).

And once more, as it does on measures of female education, so too in childhood mortality, the state of Kerala stands apart even from the other relatively low child mortality states in the south. Not only are childhood mortality estimates for this state significantly lower than in the rest of the country, urban-rural differentials are much less marked (in keeping with the low urban-rural differentials in female literacy and the more equitable distribution of health services). It is the one state which has steadily maintained declines in child mortality is spite of relative stagnation of economic growth. This last fits in with the hypothesis that declines in childhood mortality tend to have their own momentum, being influenced by the kind of social changes which are self-accelerating processes which soon become independent of growth on other fronts.

TABLE 6: **REGIONAL DIFFERENTIALS IN FEMALE LITERACY AND CHILD MORTALITY IN INDIA**

Region/State	Per cent rural females literate (1981)	Rural infant mortality rate (1978)	Rural 0-4 years death rate (1978)
South			
Kerala	64.25	42	13.1
Tamil Nadu	25.80	120	44.1
Andhra Pradesh	14.08	120	40.9
Karnataka	19.77	81	29.4
Maharashtra	24.88	84	24.9
North			
Gujarat	24.06	127	42.8
Rajasthan	5.46	139	60.8
Uttar Pradesh	9.49	127	67.9
Madhaya Pradesh	8.99	141	56.5
Punjab	27.63	111	38.7
Haryana	15.37	116	35.1

Source: (1) Registrar General of India, 1983; (2) Registrar General of India, 1981.

CONCLUSION

It has been suggested in this paper that declines in childhood mortality, as distinct from declines in general mortality, require an element of volition at the household or individual level and can therefore be analysed within a framework similar to that commonly used for examining changes in fertility. Support for this hypothesis was sought from information which suggests that declines in childhood mortality are related to changes in other indicators of individual, especially maternal, knowledge, attitudes and practices, *viz.*, social changes. Though socio-economic changes were often used as a proxy for social changes where differentiation was not possible, it should be noted that while such social development generally accompanies economic development, rapid economic growth is not always a necessary condition for the kind of social change we are concerned with, as was illustrated with a few specific examples. Here, wherever possible, changes in female education and literacy were considered as a more direct proxy for changes in maternal attributes.

It is stated that the coincidence between changes in child mortality, and the absence of a similar coincidence between developments in the known influences on overall mortality and changes in child mortality, do not refute the possibility that family (especially maternal) behaviour is an important determinant of childhood mortality.

ACKNOWLEDGEMENTS

I am grateful to Peter Xenos and Lincoln C. Chen for comments on an earlier draft.

REFERENCES

Adlakha, A. and Kirk, D. (1974), 'Vital rates for India 1961-1971 estimated from 1971 consensus data', *Population Studies*, 28:381-400.

Arriaga, E.E. (1979), 'Infant and child mortality in selected Asian countries', in *Proceedings of the Meeting on Socio-economic Determinants and Consequences of Mortality (Mexico)*, United Nations, New York.

Arriaga, E.E. and Davis, K. (1969), 'The pattern of mortality change in Latin America', *Demography*, 6:223-242.

Azefor, M.N.A. (1981), 'Counteracting forces in the continued decline of mortality in Africa', in IUSSP, 1981.

Beaver, M.W. (1973), 'Population, infant mortality and milk', *Population Studies*, 27:243-254.

Benjamin, B. (1965), *Social and Economic Factors Affecting Mortality*, Mouton and Company, The Hague.

Bhat, P.N.M., Preston, S. and Dyson, T. (1984), *Vital Rates in India 1961-1981*, National Academy Press, Washington D.C.

Caldwell, J.C. (1979), 'Education as a factor in mortality decline', *Population Studies*, 33:395-413.

Coale, A.J. and Demeny, P. (1966), *Regional Model Life Tables and Stable Populations*, Princeton University Press, Princeton.

Committee on Population and Demography (1981), *Estimation of Recent Trends in Fertility and Mortality in Bangladesh*, National Academic Press, Washington, D.C.

Diaz-Briquets, S. (1981), 'Determinants of mortality transition in developing countries before and after the Second World War: some evidence from Cuba', *Population Studies*, 35:399-411.

Dyson, T. (1977), 'Levels, trends, differentials and causes of childhood mortality – A survey', *World Health Statistics Reports*.

Dyson, T. and Moore, M. (1983), 'On kinship structure, female autonomy and demographic behavior in India', *Population and Development Review*, 9:35-60.

ESCAP (1976), *Population of Sri Lanka*, Country Monograph Series, No. 4, United Nations, ST/ESCAP/30, New York.

Evans, K. (1975), *The Development and Structure of the English Educational System*, University of London Press, London.

Farah, A.-A. and Preston, S.H. (1982), 'Child mortality differentials in Sudan', *Population and Development Review*, 8:365-384.

Frenzen, P.D. and Hogan, D.P. (1982), 'The impact of class, education and health care on infant mortality in a developing society: the case of rural Thailand', *Demography*, 19:34-51.

Glass, D.V. and Eversley, D.E.C. (eds.) (1965), *Population in History: Essays in Historical Demography*, Edward Arnold, London.

Gwatkin, D.R. (1980), 'Indications of change in developing countries' mortality trends: the end of an era?', *Population and Development Review*, 6:615-644.

Haines, M.R. and Avery, R.C. (1982), 'Differentials in infant and child mortality in Costa Rica, 1968-1973', *Population Studies*, 36:31-44.

Helleiner, K.F. (1965), 'The vital revolution reconsidered', in Glass and Eversley, 1965, pp.79-86.

Hollingsworth, T.H. (1965), 'A demographic study of the British ducal families', in Glass and Eversley, 1965, pp.354-378.

IUSSP (International Union for the Scientific Study of Population) (1981), *International Population Conference, Manila, 1981*, IUSSP, Liège.

Krause, J.T. (1958), 'Changes in English fertility and mortality, 1781-1850', *Economic History Review*, 11:52-70.

Logan, W.P.D. (1950), 'Mortality in England and Wales from 1848 to 1947: a survey of the changing causes of death during the past hundred years', *Population Studies*, 4:132-178.

McKeown, T. (1965), 'Medicine and world population', in M. Sheps and J. Ridley (eds.), *Public Health and Population Change: Current Research Issues*, University of Pittsburgh Press, Pittsburgh, pp. 25-40.

McKeown, T. (1976), *The Modern Rise of Population*, Edward Arnold, London.

McKeown, T. and Brown, G. (1955), 'Medical evidence related to English population changes in the eighteenth century', *Population Studies*, 9:119-141.

McKeown, T. and Record, R.G. (1962), 'Reasons for the decline of mortality in England and Wales during the nineteenth century', *Population Studies*, 16:94-122.

Meegama, S.A. (1981), 'The decline in mortality in Sri Lanka in historical perspective', in IUSSP, 1981.

Oddy, D.J. (1970), 'Working class diets in late nineteenth century Britain', *Economic History Review*, 23:31-44.

Palloni, A. (1981), 'Mortality in Latin America: emerging patterns', *Population and Development Review*, 7:623-650.

Peller, S. (1965), 'Births and deaths among Europe's ruling families since 1500', in Glass and Eversley, 1965.

Preston, S.H. (1975), 'The changing relation between mortality and levels of economic development', *Population Studies*, 29:231-248.

Preston, S.H. (1978), 'Mortality and development', *Population Bulletin*, U.N. Economic Commission for Western Asia.

Preston, S.H. (1980), 'Causes and consequences of mortality declines in the less developed countries during the twentieth century', in R. Easterlin (ed.), *Population and Economic Change in Developing Countries*, University of Chicago Press, Chicago.

Preston, S.H. and Nelson, V.E. (1974), 'Structure and change in causes of death: an international summary', *Population Studies*, 28:19-51.

Ramnath, T. (1980), 'The influence of maternal education on live births, child mortality and their inter-relationships', *Journal of Family Welfare*, 26:64-72.

Registrar General of India (1981), *Survey of Infant and Child Mortality 1979*, Government of India, New Delhi.

Registrar General of India (1983), *Consensus of India, 1981, Series I – India. Paper 2 of 1983, Key Population Statistics Based on 5% Sample Data*, Government of India, New Delhi.

Roberts, G.W. (1950), 'A note on mortality in Jamaica', *Population Studies*, 4:64-85.

Sarkar, N.K. (1973), *The Demography of Ceylon*, Government Press, 1957, Colombo, cited in United Nations, 1973.

Scrimshaw, S. (1978), 'Infant mortality and behavior in the regulation of family size', *Population and Development Review*, 4:383-403.

Stolnitz, G.J. (1955), 'A century of international mortality trends', *Population Studies*, 10:17-42.

Stolnitz, G.J. (1965), 'Recent mortality trends in Latin America, Asia, and Africa', *Population Studies*, 19:117-138.

United Nations (1973), *The Determinants and Consequences of Population Growth – New Summary of Findings on Interaction of Demographic, Economic and Social Factors*, ST/SOA/SER.A/50, United Nations, New York.

United Nations (1982), *Levels and Trends of Mortality since 1950*, ST/ESA/SER.A/74, United Nations, New York.

United Nations, Department of Economic and Social Affairs (1963), *Population Bulletin of the U.N.*, No. 6, United Nations, New York.

United Nations Secretariat (1982), 'Construction of the new United Nations model life table system', *Population Bulletin of the United Nations*, No. 14, United Nations, New York.

UNESCO (1982), *Statistical Yearbook*, United Nations, New York.

Vacher, L.C. (1979[1886]), 'On the decline of the mortality rate and the increase of the average life span since the end of the last century', paper presented to the Rome Congress of the International Statistical Institute in 1886, excerpted in *Population and Development Review*, 1979, 5:163-170.

Wardle, D. (1976), *English Popular Education 1880-1975*, 2nd edn, Cambridge University Press, Cambridge.

Wrigley, E.A. and Schofield, R.S. (1983), 'English population history from family reconstitution: summary results, 1600-1799', *Population Studies*, 37:157-184.

Wyon, J.B. and Gordon, J.E. (1971), *The Khanna Study – Population Problems in the Rural Punjab*, Harvard University Press, Cambridge, Mass.

Chapter 3

RESOURCES, KNOWLEDGE AND CHILD MORTALITY: A COMPARISON OF THE US IN THE LATE NINETEENTH CENTURY AND DEVELOPING COUNTRIES TODAY*

Samuel H. Preston

The great forces driving mortality levels in the past century are enhanced material resources and improved knowledge of means to avoid diseases and death. Improved knowledge of diseases can lead to better personal hygiene as well as to public preventive programmes of which most individuals are unaware. Richer countries can afford to mount more complex health programmes, just as richer people are likely to arrange to have superior medical care within any given system.

We have argued earlier (Preston, 1975, 1980) that increased availability of resources has not been the dominant force in twentieth century mortality decline. The evidence for the conclusion is simply that countries at a given level of per capita real national income enjoyed higher life expectancies as the century progressed. The curve relating life expectancy to income shifted upwards by about 8-10 years between the period around 1935-40 and the period around 1965-70. The shift was ascribed to technical advances, usually embodied in government programmes.

In this paper we attempt to clarify the importance of knowledge factors and resource factors by examining micro-level mortality differentials under an unusual range of circumstances. In particular, we compare child mortality differentials in the United States in the late nineteenth century to mortality differentials in certain developed countries today. The scheme that underlies the analysis can be illustrated as follows:

*First published in IUSSP, *International Population Conference, Florence, 5-12 June, 1985*, Vol. 4., Ordina, Liège, 1985.

Level of technical knowledge about health

		Low	High
	Low	A (Third World countries in nineteenth century)	B (Third World countries today)
Level of economic development			
	High	C (United States in late nineteenth century)	D (Developed countries today)

The choice of the US is based upon its having the only national data on children ever born and children surviving that are available for the nineteenth century. Because of its size, affluence, and ethnic heterogeneity, it may even be the preferred choice if only one country were used to represent stage C.

Obviously, both income and health knowledge are distributed along a continuum rather than dichotomously. But by choosing the two relatively discordant circumstances represented by B and C, we expect to be able to illuminate the important role of both sets of factors under varying circumstances. That the US in the late nineteenth century was a relatively rich country is shown by the following data. According to the National Bureau of Economic Research's series of GNP estimates, per capita GNP in the US in 1929 dollars rose from $415 to $497 per capita between 1890 and 1900 (US Bureau of the Census, 1966 Series AII). Converted into 1982 dollars, the range is from $2,148 to $2,572. This places the US 1890-1900 in a range with Hungary, Portugal, Romania, Argentina and Chile today (World Bank, 1984:219). But while these latter countries have a life expectancy at birth of 70-71 years (Ibid.), the US in 1895-1900 had a life expectancy of 49-50 years (Preston and Haines, 1984:275,277).

The US in 1890-1900 was also relatively well educated. Seventy-eight to 79 per cent of youths aged 5-17 were enrolled in school, although the average pupil appears to have attended school only the equivalent of about four months per year (US Census Bureau, 1966: Series B 36-39). In 1910, the median adult had attended school an average of 8.1 years (Ibid., Series B 40), and a prior absence of trend in school enrolment figures suggests that the figure was not much lower twenty years earlier. In the 1900 US Census, 87.8 per cent of ever-married women were literate, as were 89.0 per cent of their husbands. Like income, these are also very high levels relative to most developing countries today.

Why didn't these high levels of literacy and income translate into high levels of life expectancy? Our answer — tautologically correct in view of universality of goals to improve health — is that the US in this period simply did not know how to effect this conversion. The germ theory of disease had been validated only in the 1880s and still met with opposition or indifference in many circles. The following brief illustrations of the state of knowledge regarding disease may be informative. We refer mainly to the period of the 1890s; we will use cumulative child mortality data from the US Census of 1900, which refer on average to 1895.

1. Frederick Hoffman, chief actuary of the Prudential Life Insurance Company, wrote a monograph for the American Economic Association in 1896 focused on the social demography of the American black population. Hoffman attributed the slow

natural increase and the excess mortality of blacks from virtually every cause of death (even including malaria, where the sickle cell trait clearly affords many blacks protection) to inherent genetic inferiority. The following statement is typical (p. 95):

> It is clear now that we have reached the underlying cause of the excess mortality (of blacks) from consumption and the enormous waste of child life. It is not in the conditions of life but in the race traits and tendencies that we find the causes of the excessive mortality ... the effect will be to increase the mortality by hereditary transmission of weak constitutions, and to lower still further the rate of natural increase, until the births fall below the deaths, and gradual extinction result ...

The notion that unhygienic conditions could cause disease is almost completely missing from Hoffman's account, whose major message is that the white race is inexorably increasing because of its superior innate powers of vital resistance. Hoffman wrote a good deal on health during this period and was frequently cited. Irving Fischer, often described as the greatest American economist, was also a serious student of mortality, having written a census monograph on the subject in 1899. A later book on health (Fischer, 1909) is full of fascinating misinformation about fatigue poisons, eye strain, nervous prostration from prolonged sitting, and sexual irritability from meat eating (pp. 41, 75, 91, 95 among others).

2.   In 1894, a crowd of 3,000 persons armed with clubs, knives, and stones gathered in front of a home in Milwaukee, where health officials were expected to attempt to take a two-year old child to the hospital with a suspected case of smallpox. The family had previously lost a child in the hospital, which was a notorious death house. The riots spread and prevented many other potential patients from entering the hospital (Leavitt, 1979).

3.   As Vogel (1979) has shown, at the turn of the century hospitals were in the midst of changing from an institution most akin to an almshouse to a technical centre. The movement was contentious and costly. In 1908, the superintendent of New York Hospital and President of the American Hospital Association declared 'I am absolutely at a loss for an understanding of the value of a medical library in a hospital'. He shut the library and gave away its books (Vogel, 1979:113).

4.   One student of the history of American medical practice, building on the work of Charles Rosenberg, has offered the following characterization of medical knowledge in the nineteenth century (Pellegrino, 1979:246-247):

> At the beginning of the nineteenth century, therapeutics was fixed in a notion of health and illness held in common by physicians and their patients. On this view, illness was an imbalance in the economy of the whole body, expressed in a disturbance in the relationships of input or output of food, sweat, secretions, urine, phlegm, and the like. Treatment was aimed at restoring harmony and balance between environment and constitution. This was best accomplished not by specific attack on some symptoms of disease, but by inducing a physiological effect – sweating, febrilysis, diuresis, vomiting – which helped the body to recover its internal and external balance ... At the close of the nineteenth Century, physicians were understandably ambivalent about accepting the new conception of a type of therapeutics specifically tailored to particular disease entities which had slowly emerged during the course of the century ... It was difficult, as always, to give up long held theories about the nature of disease and how it should be treated. The burgeoning achievements of pharmaceutical chemistry, anesthesia, and surgery *in the early twentieth century*, however, finally compromised the older theories. (Emphasis ours.)

The holistic imbalance theories still present at the end of the nineteenth century doubtless made it much easier to ascribe the high mortality of blacks from such diseases as malaria to racial traits rather than to mosquitoes.

5. The urban public health movement was at the early stages of development. In 1890, 26 of 96 large cities reported having no sewerage system at all, and in the remaining 70 cities less than half of the dwellings were connected (Meeker, 1972). Improvements in sanitation were surely occurring, but it is likely that only a small minority of the US population lived in sanitary conditions appreciably different from those of 1800. Beyond smallpox vaccination, the only important medical advance by 1900 was the deployment of diphtheria antitoxin in the 1890s.

The foregoing paints a picture of quite considerable ignorance on the part of the intelligentsia and the medical profession at the turn of the century, and a slow implementation of the new ideas about disease causation. Of course, preposterous statements about health matters could be cited today, but it is not likely that they would have the imprimatur of the American Economic Association or the Committee of One Hundred on National Health of the federal National Conservation Commission, as did the monographs of Hoffman and Fischer. It is equally unlikely that they would gain much credibility among the intelligentsia in developing countries today.

If ignorance (by modern standards) was widespread in the US at the turn of the century, we should observe a different pattern of mortality differentials than the pattern that prevails today in the developing world. In particular, there should be much less payoff to increasing amounts of schooling. Schooling effects should reflect only the accretion of material resources that result from the increased earnings opportunities; the additional portion of the effect that would reflect closer connection to good health knowledge and practice among the well-educated should be largely inoperative in a situation where education 'buys' one little knowledge. Indeed, for similar reasons the size of *all* social class differentials in mortality should be smaller in the US in 1890-1900.

Table 1 compares the size of child mortality differentials in classes arranged by father's occupation in the US in 1900 and in certain developing countries in the 1970s. The values appearing in the table are based upon identical types of data and procedures. All countries have data on the number of children ever born and children surviving. The number of children ever born for each woman is converted into an expected number of child deaths by reference to her age or duration of marriage (an index of exposure) and to the average level of child mortality in the population as a whole as represented by an appropriate model life table. Deaths and expected deaths are then aggregated for all women in a class. For details, see Preston and Haines (1984) and Mensch *et al.* (1985).

Table 1 shows that the size of mortality differentials in the US in 1890-1900 (the period to which the mortality data refer, on average) is much smaller than that observed in developing countries today. In particular, the professional/managerial/clerical classes had a mortality level only 7 per cent lower than the national average, compared to the 35 per cent advantage that this group enjoys, on average, in developing countries today. None of the 11 contemporary countries examined shows less that a 21 per cent advantage for this group.The other large discrepancy occurs for farmers and farm labourers. This group has mortality 11 per cent below average in the US in 1890-1900, but 21 per cent above average in developing countries today. The comparison between professional and agricultural classes is therefore particularly striking. Agricultural classes have mortality 85 per cent *higher* than professional classes in our sample of LDCs, today, but 5 per cent *lower* in the US in 1890-1900.

TABLE 1: COMPARISON OF RELATIVE MORTALITY IN DIFFERENT OCCUPATIONAL CLASSES, UNITED STATES 1900 AND DEVELOPING COUNTRIES IN THE 1970s. (RATIO, DEATHS TO EXPECTED DEATHS AMONG CHILDREN EVER BORN; EXPECTED DEATHS ARE BASED UPON THE AVERAGE CHILD MORTALITY LEVEL IN A PARTICULAR COUNTRY)

Father's occupational category	US 1900	Mean of 11 developing countries in 1970s	Ghana 1971	Kenya 1978	Lesotho 1977	Southern Nigeria 1972	Indonesia 1971	Nepal 1976	S. Korea 1971	Sri Lanka 1975	Thailand 1975	Chile 1970	Peru 1978
Professional, managerial, clerical	.933 (769)	.652	.621 (2948)	.652 (425)	.743 (66)	.726 (536)	.789 (11721)	.784 (187)	.673 (101)	.556 (225)	.606 (132)	.629 (455)	.401 (491)
Sales	.831 (173)	.913	.775 (874)	.887 (388)	1.343 (35)	.933 (252)	1.033 (6850)	.844 (173)	.883 (613)	.868 (242)	.519 (108)	1.128 (196)	.828 (406)
Service	1.001 (165)	.841	.665 (1179)	.665 (1179)	.984 (85)	.910 (111)	1.002 (2402)	.760 (148)	– –	.767 (189)	1.061 (72)	.866 (135)	.732 (209)
Agriculture	.890 (3375)	1.206	1.128 (30446)	1.059 (1943)	1.197 (66)	1.195 (10481)	1.000 (43467)	.995 (3884)	.956 (1266)	1.141 (1288)	1.123 (1378)	1.213 (685)	1.304 (2197)
Production workers	1.150 (2967)	1.007	.802 (5081)	1.051 (1203)	1.006 (1705)	1.052 (421)	1.028 (3965)	1.253 (423)	1.088 (491)	.938 (771)	.881 (278)	1.059 (1444)	.921 (1242)

Source: Tabulations of public use data files performed at the University of Pennsylvania.

The explanation of the poor performance of professional classes is not to be found in a peculiar composition of the group in 1900. The sub-group that we can label the intelligentsia shared the unexpectedly high mortality of the professional classes, as shown in Table 2. It is particularly illuminating that doctor's children had mortality of only 8 per cent below the national average, and higher than that among coal miners or farmers. Likewise, teachers were clearly not moved to a position of advantage by whatever health doctrines were being conveyed in schools. Only pharmacists enjoy the same advantage as professional classes have in LDCs today, but their mortality level is based on only 14 expected deaths.

TABLE 2: RATIO OF CHILD DEATHS TO EXPECTED DEATHS IN SELECTED OCCUPATIONS IN THE UNITED STATES, 1900

Father's occupation	Child deaths / expected deaths	Number of expected deaths
Physicians, surgeons, dentists	.927	35.6
Clergymen	.805	32.3
Teachers	.999	26.0
Lawyers	.757	22.4
Pharmacists	.647	13.9
Total intelligentsia	.853	130.2
Coal miners	.902	118.6
Farmers	.863	3056.0

Taking the figures in Table 1 one step farther, we can estimate the absolute (rather than the relative) mortality of children born into the different classes in the US in 1890-1900 and in a composite of LDCs today. The composite is formed in the following way. The level of life expectancy at birth in LDCs in 1975-1980, as estimated by the United Nations (1983), is 54.8 years. This corresponds to level 15.6 in the Coale-Demeny (1983) 'West' model life tables. At that level, the probability of dying before age five [q(5)] is .137. The mean of relative mortality levels for a particular class in Table 1 for our 11 LDCs is then applied to this figure to produce the values in Table 3. This procedure assumes that the average of the 11 countries is representative of the average of LDCs. 'West' mortality levels are in fact relatively close: an average level of 14.9 for our 11 versus 15.6 for LDCs as an aggregate. The US 1900 level is estimated to 13.65 (Preston and Haines, 1984:275), and relative mortalities in Table 1 are applied to the q(5) of .176 that corresponds to that level. There is good reason to suppose that this multiplicative property of q(x)'s that is implicit in our procedure is valid to a close approximation (Trussell and Preston, 1982).

Table 3 shows that the US in 1900 had much higher child mortality than today's developing world in every occupational class except agricultural workers. Its disadvantage is particularly great among the professional/managerial classes. The US professional classes in 1900, in fact, had no better child mortality than agricultural workers in developing countries today, who are by every account a seriously disadvantaged group. The combination of high national income, high national literacy, and high relative social status in 1900 produced the same mortality level as is observed in the most disadvantaged social group in the world today. Clearly, the manner in which material resources are converted into mortality levels has changed dramatically.

TABLE 3: ESTIMATED PROBABILITY OF DYING BY AGE FIVE IN TWO POPULATIONS

Father's occupational category	US, 1900	Composite of developing countries 1975-80	Ratio
Professional, managerial, clerical	.165	.089	.539
Sales	.146	.125	.856
Services	.176	.115	.653
Agricultural	.157	.165	1.051
Production workers	.202	.138	.638
All classes	.176	.137	.778

Table 4 presents similar comparative data on literacy and urban/rural residence. The results on literacy are similar to those on social class, but less dramatic. The child mortality advantage for literate mothers in the US was 30 per cent, compared to an average of 43-47 per cent in developing countries today. Lacking direct data on literacy in most of the developing countries, we have presented two series, one assuming that literacy is achieved with four years of schooling and the other that it is achieved after seven years of schooling. In either series, the difference with the US is appreciable. Of the 11 countries examined, only Lesotho and South Korea show a lower payoff to literacy than did the US in 1900.

Multivariate results are more decisive, although the absence of identical data in the different countries means that exact comparability in specification cannot be achieved. Nevertheless, such standard factors as educational attainment (or literacy) of mother and father, occupation of father, and urban/rural residence are available in all data sets. A well-known result is that mothers' education or literacy tends to retain a powerful effect in developing countries even after all other socio-economic variables are controlled (e.g., Cochrane, 1980). Such a result is also observed in the developing countries examined here. Mensch et al. (1985) have shown that the average coefficient on mothers' years of schooling in these countries with all other variables controlled is about .035. If the illiterate have an average of one year of schooling and the literate an average of eight – reasonable figures in the US in 1900 – it implies that the literate should have about 25 per cent lower mortality. But the coefficient on mothers' literacy in the US is only .06, about one-quarter of the expected effect, and it is statistically insignificant.[1]

---

[1]This result obtains when we have controlled race, maternal grandmothers' place of birth, husbands' literacy (also having a coefficient of −.06), paternal grandfathers' place of birth, husbands' occupation in ten categories, husbands' predicted income, urban/rural residence, ownership of home, husbands' age and unemployment status, presence of boarders and servants in the house, division of current residence, predicted state income, and length of time in the US.

TABLE 4: COMPARISON OF RELATIVE MORTALITY LEVELS IN DEVELOPING COUNTRIES TODAY AND UNITED STATES, 1890-1900

	Ratio, child mortality among literate mothers to child mortality among illiterate mothers		Ratio, child mortality among urban mothers to child mortality among rural mothers
	Series 1ᵃ	Series 2ᵇ	
US, 1900	.697		1.279
Ghana, 1971	.495	.361	.732
Kenya, 1978	.666	.613	.809
Lesotho, 1977	.851	.861	1.055
Southern Nigeria, 1972	.609	.611	.816
Indonesia, 1971	.631	–	.831
Nepal, 1976	.483	.313	.519
S. Korea, 1976	–	.714	.873
Sri Lanka, 1975	.634	–	.875
Thailand, 1975	.319	–	.580
Chile, 1970	.699	.583	.782
Peru, 1978	.357	.264	.604
Mean developing countries	.574	.540	.770

ᵃAssuming women with 4+ years of education are literate.
ᵇAssuming women with 7+ years of education are literate.

Unfortunately, income data are not present in the US data set. The brilliant Woodbury study of 1911-15 in eight US cities included income data as well as literacy and many other variables. Literacy was dropped from the final report (Woodbury, 1925), perhaps because preliminary results showed it to be unimportant. But the report on the largest city studied, Baltimore, presented a cross-tabulation of infant mortality by fathers' income and mothers' literacy (Rochester, 1923). It is reproduced here as Table 5. Clearly, literacy has little if any explanatory power after income is controlled, contrary to results observed in today's developing world.

Table 4 also shows very different relations between mortality and urban/rural residence in the US, 1900 and in today's developing countries. Urban residents (defined as living in places of 5,000 + residents) had 28 per cent higher mortality in the US in 1900, compared to an average of 23 per cent *lower* mortality in developing countries today. Multivariate results are also quite different for the two populations. In most of the developing countries examined, urban/rural residence loses its significance when other variables are introduced, and often turns around in sign (Mensch et al., 1985). The lower mortality of urban residents shown in Table 4 is thus primarily ascribed to their higher social standing. But in the US in 1900, urban residence gains significance when other variables are introduced (Preston et al., 1981); the higher social status of urban residents was actually serving to mask some of the disadvantages of urban life. Indeed, size of place of residence seems to be the single most important variable in accounting for variance in child mortality in the US in 1900.

TABLE 5: INFANT MORTALITY RATE (PER 1000 BIRTHS) BY LITERACY OF MOTHER AND EARNINGS OF FATHER IN BALTIMORE, 1915

Annual earnings of father	Literate mothers		Illiterate mothers	
	Infant mortality rate	Number of births	Infant mortality rate	Number of births
Under $450	161	1193	143	349
$450-549	120	1206	108	241
$550-649	107	1314	126	174
$650	79	5660	86	233

Source: Rochester (1923:332).

Haines (1985) reaches similar conclusions regarding literacy and urbanization in his analysis of US data. Rather than explaining variance at the individual level, he first groups mortality data into occupational classes and attempts to explain why one occupational group has higher or lower mortality than another. The proportion of literate wives in a group is insignificant; the coefficient of the urban proportion in a group is about 2.4, very large and significant.

To what extent was the US typical of other new-developed countries at the end of the nineteenth century? It clearly shared with them the pattern of higher urban than rural mortality (United Nations, 1983:132-136). Much less is known about social class differences in child mortality. The only other study of children ever born/children surviving data for the nineteenth century of which the author is aware is Matthiessen's (1972) study of the Copenhagen Census of 1880. This study also shows relatively small social class differences. The ratio of q(5) among 'officials, professionals, and manufacturers' to that among the 'working class' is .747 (.231/.309), the ratio for 'teachers and clerks' to the working class is .881 and for 'master artisans and shopkeepers', it is .990. The US ratio of 'professional, managerial, and clerical' to 'production workers' from Table 1 is .811, well within the range of the Copenhagen data and much higher than in developing countries today (.647). A disproportionate concentration of the professional/managerial classes in high mortality cities like Copenhagen would probably have further reduced their advantage relative to mortality in Denmark as a whole. A later data set for England and Wales, 1911, however, shows much larger social class differences than in the US in 1900 (Haines, 1985). Professional classes and farmers had mortality very close to one another, as in the US in 1900, but blue collar classes had much higher child mortality than either group. It is likely that this difference in the pattern of differentials reflects a faster adoption by the professional classes of hygienic practices between 1900 and 1911; the much higher degree of urbanization in England in 1911 than in the US in 1900, reducing the relative disadvantage of urban living for the professional classes; and a greater inequality of income in England. The forthcoming availability of a 1910 US Census public use sample will permit the testing of the first of these explanations.

DISCUSSION

There is probably no population in the world, today or in centuries past, in which higher levels of material resources in the household are not associated with lower mortality. More and better food and clothing, more space, more leisure, and better sanitary facilities will produce lower probabilities of dying in any environment. These factors are measurable and their impact ubiquitous. As a result, they tend to be emphasized in many accounts of mortality trends and differentials (e.g., McKeown, 1976; Mosley, 1983).

It is increasingly evident that another powerful set of factors has also been at work, which we have labelled 'knowledge/technique'. First, the material factors fail to account for a majority of the rapid mortality decline between 1940 and 1970 (Preston, 1975, 1980). Second, child mortality in developing countries tends to be powerfully influenced by mother's schooling and by ethnicity even when differences in levels of resources associated with these factors are controlled (Mensch et al., 1985). Such results imply that there are unmeasured variables reflecting child care practice with which literacy and ethnicity are associated. Third, very privileged groups before the twentieth century, such as the European aristocracy, have levels of mortality that would be shockingly high by contemporary standards (see papers in Glass and Eversley, 1965). We have attempted to give further support to this position by showing that knowledgeable and highly advantaged classes in the US in 1900 – highly advantaged even by today's standards – had been unable to convert that advantage into a reasonable mortality level. Indeed, they fared no better than the poor agricultural classes in the developing world today. We have argued that this failure reflects a substantial ignorance about health matters, which we have attempted to document with several examples.

This ignorance was not necessarily confined to such matters as the germ theory of disease. A good bit of the high mortality of the advantaged classes resulted from their living disproportionately in urban areas, which were clearly unhealthy at the turn of the century. But this unhealthiness was not supernaturally imposed; it reflects the widespread failure of urban residents to activate the political institutions that were capable, then as now, of sharply reducing mortality. So the ignorance to which we refer is some combination of ignorance about personal health and ignorance about what public institutions could accomplish in the area of health. That this ignorance has largely disappeared is vividly suggested by the fact that urban residents in developing countries no longer suffer the excessive mortality that their dense living arrangements would otherwise foster.

The fact that literacy had a much smaller health payoff in the US in 1900 than it has in developing countries today, particularly in multivariate relations, helps shed light on the mechanisms through which this variable is operating today. It suggests that health knowledge itself (perhaps more of hygienic practices than of disease causality, as Lindenbaum (1983) suggests) is one of the most important routes through which education is operating. When relatively little was known about means for reducing mortality, increased schooling produced relatively little mortality reduction.

The importance of these non-material, knowledge-related, factors underscores the possibilities for continued health advance in developing countries. Material progress occurs slowly and is already the major objective of national policy in most countries. That there may be major, affordable, and unexploited means left for improving health knowledge and technique in developing countries is suggested by the sizeable mortality differences associated with ethnicity and literacy. However, the rate of shift in the curve relating life expectancy to income, literacy, and calories appeared to slow down in between 1965-69 and 1975-79. Instead of an exogenous gain of three years per decade estimated for the previous 20 years period, the gain was only about one year in the most recent decade (Preston, 1983). It is possible that the slowdown reflects diminishing returns to the knowledge/technique factors, or simply a weakened ability or will to take advantage of what possibilities remain. But whether or not these factors hold the key to the future, they appear to be critically important in understanding the past.

ACKNOWLEDGEMENTS

This paper is an outgrowth of two collaborative projects, one conducted with Michael Haines and the other with Barbara Mensch, Harold Lentzner, and students at the University of Pennsylvania. I am grateful for their assistance. I am also grateful for comments by Etienne van de Walle. The projects are supported by the Ford Foundation and the US National Institute of Child Health and Human Development.

REFERENCES

Coale, A.J. and Demeny, P. (1983), *Regional Model Life Tables and Stable Populations*, Academic Press, New York.

Cochrane, S. (1980), *The Effects of Education on Health*, World Bank Staff Working Paper No. 405, Washington, D.C.

Fischer, I. (1909), *Report on National Vitality, Its Wastes and Conservation*, Bulletin of the Committee of One Hundred on National Health, Prepared for the National Conservation Commission, Government Printing Office, Washington, D.C.

Glass, D.V. and Eversley, D.E.C. (eds.) (1965), *Population in History: Essays in Historical Demography*, Edward Arnold, London.

Haines, M.R. (1985), 'Inequality and childhood mortality: a comparison of England and Wales, 1911, and the United States, 1908', *Journal of Economic History*, 45,4:885-912.

Hoffman, F.L. (1896), *Race Traits and Tendencies of the American Negro*, Publication of the American Economic Association, Vol. 11, Nos. 1, 2, and 3, MacMillan, New York, pp. 1-329.

Leavitt, J.W. (1979), 'Politics and public health: smallpox in Milwaukee, 1894-95', in Reversby and Rossner, 1979, pp. 84-102.

Lindenbaum, S. (1983), 'The infuence of maternal education on infant and child mortality in Bangladesh', Report, International Centre for Diarrhoeal Disease Research, Bangladesh, Dhaka, (Chapter 6, of this volume).

Matthiessen, P. (1972), 'Application of the Brass-Sullivan method of historical data', *Population Index*, 38,4:403-408.

McKeown, T. (1976), *The Modern Rise of Population*, Academic Press, New York.

Meeker, E. (1972), 'The improving health of the United States, 1850-1915', *Explorations in Economic History*, 9:353-374.

Mensch, B. Lentzner, B. and Preston, S.H. (1985), *Socio-economic Differentials in Child Mortality in Developing Countries*, United Nations, Department of International Economic and Social Affairs, New York.

Mosley, W.H. (1983), 'Will primary health care reduce infant and child mortality? A critique of some current strategies, with special reference to Africa and Asia', paper presented to the IUSSP Seminar on Social Policy, Health Policy, and Mortality Prospects in Paris February 28-March 4, (Chapter 13, of this volume).

Pellegrino, E.D. (1979), 'The sociocultural impact of twentieth century therapeutics', in M.J. Vogel and C.E. Rosenberg (eds), *The Therapeutic Revolution*, University of Pennsylvania Press, Philadelphia, pp. 245-266.

Preston, S.H. (1975), 'The changing relation between mortality and level of economic development', *Population Studies*, 29,2:231-248.

Preston, S.H. (1980), 'Causes and consequences of mortality decline in less developed countries during the twentieth century', in R.E. Easterlin (ed.), *Population and Economic Change in Developing Countries*, University of Chicago Press, Chicago, pp.289-360.

Preston, S.H. (1983), 'Mortality and development revisited', background paper prepared for World Bank, 1984 (published in *Population Bulletin of the U.N.*, No. 18, 1986).

Preston, S.H. and Haines, M.R. (1984),'New estimation of child mortality in the United States at the turn of the century', *Journal of the American Statistical Association*, 79,386:272-281.

Preston, S.H., Haines, M. and Pamuk, E. (1981),'Urbanization, industrialization, and mortality in developed countries', in International Union for the Scientific Study of Population, *International Population Conference, Manila, 1981*, Vol. 2, IUSSP, Liège, pp. 233-254.

Reversby, S. and Rossner, D. (eds) (1979), *Health Care in America: Essays in Social History*, Temple University Press, Philadelphia.

Rochester, A. (1923), *Infant Mortality: Results of a Field Study in Baltimore, Md. Based on Births in One Year*, US Department of Labor, Children's Bureau, Bureau Publication No. 119, Government Printing Office, Washington, D.C.

Trussell, T.J. and Preston, S.H. (1982), 'Estimating the covariates of childhood mortality from retrospective reports of mothers', *Health Policy and Education*, 3:1-36.

United Nations Population Division (1983), 'World population prospects as assessed in 1982', printout, November.

US Bureau of the Census (1966), *Long Term Economic Growth, 1869-1965: A Statistical Compendium*, Government Printing Office, Washington, D.C.

Vogel, M.J. (1979), 'The transformation of the American hospital, 1850-1920', in Reversby and Rossner, 1979, pp. 105-116.

Woodbury, R.M. (1925), 'Causal factors in infant mortality', US Department of Labor, Children's Bureau, Bureau Publication No. 142, Government Printing Office, Washington, D.C.

World Bank (1984), *World Development Report*, Oxford University Press, New York.

EDUCATION

Chapter 4

MATERNAL EDUCATION AND CHILD SURVIVAL IN DEVELOPING COUNTRIES: THE SEARCH FOR PATHWAYS OF INFLUENCE*

John G. Cleland and Jerome K. van Ginneken

INTRODUCTION

There is nothing new about the belief that the spread of education with its impact on knowledge and outlook is a central force behind demographic transition. In 1934 Penrose wrote:

It would seem that when a community has gained the knowledge and acquired the habits necessary to reduce the death rate it will sooner or later gain the knowledge and acquire the habits necessary to reduce the birth rate. There may be a time lag between the two processes, but both of them in a large share are the outcome of education (Penrose, 1934:119).

It is thus surprising that investigation of the specific influence of parental education on the mortality of children in developing countries was neglected until recently. Education typically was regarded as an indicator of socio-economic status and thus the common finding of a strong inverse relationship between education and childhood mortality was accorded a simple economic interpretation. The turning point was an analysis of survey data from Ibadan, Nigeria which demonstrated that mother's education was a more decisive determinant of child survivorship than more economic family characteristics such as husband's occupation (Caldwell, 1979). Following this influential investigation, there has been a deluge of papers on the topic, most of which have confirmed the large impact of parental, and particularly maternal education on survival and health of children. The greater contribution to mortality decline of educational advance compared to health care provision has been argued, representing a new twist to the old development versus medical technology

*First published in Social Science and Medicine, 27(12)1988.

debate (Mosley, 1985:103). Inevitably the beginnings of a counter-reaction may be discerned. Caldwell (1986) has stressed that the influence of education should not be considered in isolation from the wider context, while Cooksey *et al.* (1986) consider that the effect of maternal education may have been exaggerated.

Little progress towards an understanding of practical or policy implications will be made until the mechanisms by which parental education influences health and survivorship are identified. Most of this paper is thus devoted to a discussion of the intervening mechanisms which could explain this impact of education. We start, however, by describing the nature of the statistical association between maternal education and mortality. This is followed in the third section of this paper by an examination of the possible influence of reproductive health variables. In the fourth section, results of research are presented on the possible confounding influence of, in particular, economic variables such as income and this is followed by a short discussion of selectivity. In the sixth section we will consider whether education exercises an influence on mortality because more educated mothers are able to make better use of existing health services both for preventive and curative purposes than less educated mothers. In the seventh section the role of domestic health care as an intervening factor is examined. Conclusions are drawn in the last section. Most of the results to be reported below are derived from sample surveys which have been conducted in many developing countries during the past 20 years. Studies conducted at the national level, which have attempted to compare the effects on mortality of literacy or education with those of income, income distribution and government health expenditures, will not be considered in detail.

THE ASSOCIATION BETWEEN MATERNAL EDUCATION AND CHILDHOOD MORTALITY

Two major comparative analyses of the association between maternal education and mortality have used indirect measures of mortality, based on proportions of children dead to mothers of specified ages or marriage durations. In the univariate part of their analysis, Cochrane *et al.* (1980) assembled data from 33 countries, of which about ten were derived from the World Fertility Survey (WFS). The United Nations (1985) analysed data of 15 countries of which seven were WFS surveys. Though the overlap in data sources between the two studies is small, the results are remarkably consistent. Both found an essentially linear relationship between maternal education and childhood mortality, with an average of 7-9 per cent declines in mortality ratios with each one-year increment in mother's education. In neither study was any strong regional divergence apparent, though there was a hint in the UN analysis that effects might be less pronounced in Africa and more pronounced in Latin America.

One of the defects of analyses of indirect mortality measures is their inability to disclose the age pattern of mortality. The great advantage of studying the effects of education at different ages is seen clearly in the compilation of Rutstein (1984) of results from all 41 WFS surveys, which made use of directly reported ages at death.

The other advantage of this study is its wide geographical representation which permits more confident disaggregation of results by major regions. The findings are summarized in Table 1 in terms of relative risks of death in infancy (first year after birth), early childhood (second year) and later childhood (third, fourth and fifth year) for the offspring of mothers with 1-3, 4-6 and 7 or more years of schooling, compared to the no schooling category. It is immediately clear that the education-mortality association is appreciably stronger in childhood than in infancy. Maternal schooling of 4-6 years duration is associated with a fall in infant mortality of about 20 per cent (except in Latin America where the fall is greater), but with falls ranging from 30 to 58 per cent in early childhood and from 43 to 72 per cent in later childhood. The overall magnitude of the association is consistent with the results of the Cochrane and UN studies. The stronger association in childhood than in infancy also is confirmed by research in Latin America (Palloni, 1985), India (Srinivasan *et al.*, 1985) and West Africa (Mbacké and van de Walle, 1987).

Table 1 shows several departures from linearity.

TABLE 1: **RELATIVE RISKS OF DEATH IN INFANCY AND CHILDHOOD BY REGION AND EDUCATION (AVERAGE OF WFS SURVEYS)**

Region	Years of schooling			
	0	1-3	4-6	7+
First year				
Sub-Saharan Africa (n = 8)	1.00	0.85	0.78	0.56
Latin America (n = 9)	1.00	0.86	0.65	0.45
Arab countries (n = 8)	1.00	1.05	0.76	0.66
Asia (n = 9)	1.00	0.88	0.80	0.59
Second year				
Sub-Saharan Africa	1.00	1.00	0.70	0.45
Latin America	1.00	0.73	0.42	0.18
Arab countries	1.00	0.69	0.60	0.20
Asia	1.00	0.95	0.63	0.15
Third-Fifth year				
Sub-Saharan Africa	1.00	0.64	0.53	0.43
Latin America	1.00	0.75	0.41	0.17
Arab countries	1.00	0.52	0.28	0.13
Asia	1.00	0.75	0.57	0.27

Source: Calculated from Rutstein (1984).

For the eight Arab states, infant mortality is slightly higher among the offspring of mothers with 1-3 years of schooling than among the uneducated; and for the African and Asian groups of countries, the risks in early childhood are no different between the no schooling and 1-3 years schooling categories. The results may reflect genuine threshold effects, but it is equally likely that they are the outcome of data defects. WFS estimates are sensitive not only to omission of deaths but also to misstatement of ages at death. While it is sometimes assumed that WFS and other surveys with detailed and painstaking interviewing procedures suffer less from omission of deaths than censuses and household surveys using much simpler methodology, there are some striking exceptions. The Sudan WFS, for instance, one of the surveys included in Table 1, clearly suffers from substantial omission of deaths; recorded infant mortality is higher in the capital, Khartoum, than elsewhere and educational differences are negligible (El Hadi, 1987; Rizgalla, 1985).

Farah and Preston (1982) obtain much more plausible results from the 1973 Sudan census; the lowest childhood mortality is recorded in Khartoum and educational differentials are strong. There are no doubt many other instances where mortality differentials have been obscured or distorted by poor data quality.

None of the three studies discussed above include India or China. To complete the geographical picture, it is worth referring briefly to national studies for these two countries. Educational differentials in infant mortality for India are available from the 1979 Survey on Infant and Child Mortality (India, 1983) and for China from the 1982 One per Thousand Fertility Survey (Yang and Dowdle, 1985). The results are summarized below as relative risks of death in infancy.

	Illiterate	Literate	Primary+	
India (1978	1.00	0.70	0.49	

	Illiterate	Elementary	Junior	Senior+above
China (1977-78)	1.00	0.77	0.48	0.42

The mortality gradients observed in these countries are very close to the WFS estimates. This is not surprising in the case of India but is more so for China, in view of the egalitarian nature of her society.

Several important generalizations can be made on the basis of these three comparative studies plus the results for India and China. The inverse education-mortality relationship is found in all major regions of the developing world; the association is very pronounced, but appreciably closer in childhood than in infancy; and even a modest exposure of the mother to formal schooling is associated with reduced risks of death in most contexts. These are remarkable results in view of the diversity of educational and health standards and of cultural and social systems existing in developing countries today. It is thus important, both for a better understanding of health determinants and for practical policy reasons, to reassess whether the education-mortality relationship is a causal one and, if so, to identify the pathways of influence.

EDUCATION AND REPRODUCTIVE HEALTH

We begin by considering sets of intervening mechanisms that merit discussion but which turn out to be of rather little importance. The relatively high risks of infant death associated with young (less than 20 years) or old (35 and over) maternal ages, with first and high order births and with short birth intervals are well documented. Equally well established is the tendency for educated women to reproduce at low risk ages because of postponement of marriage and earlier cessation of childbearing, and in some countries, to space births at wide intervals. What contribution does this favourable pattern of reproduction make to the enhanced survivorship of children born to better educated mothers?

The answer is provided by linking two analyses of WFS data (Hobcraft *et al.*, 1984, 1985). The first analysis provides unadjusted neonatal, post-neonatal and childhood mortality rates by maternal education for a large number of surveys. The second analysis produces (as an incidental by-product) estimates of the effect of maternal education, after adjustment for maternal age, birth order, sex of child and birth spacing both before and following the index child. Exponentiating the parameter estimates in this study gives adjusted risks of death for offspring of mothers with 4-6 and seven or more years of schooling, relative to the risks for children born to mothers with less than four years of schooling. For the 17 surveys where identical definitions of education were used, the averaged results for post-neonatal mortality are:

	<4 yrs schooling	4-6 yrs schooling	7+ yrs schooling
Unadjusted	1.00	0.81	0.49
Adjusted	1.00	0.81	0.56

The conclusion is clear-cut: the advantage conferred by education has little to do with shifts in reproductive behaviour.

It is not possible to adduce similar quantitative evidence to evaluate the possible importance of mother's general health status as a factor intervening between her education and the fate of her children. As Ware (1984) has pointed out, it is likely that educated mothers are better nourished, more willing to flout harmful food taboos during pregnancy and less subject to heavy manual work during pregnancy than their less educated counterparts. There is plenty of evidence that these represent serious risk factors for infant survival. There is even evidence that, in nutritionally poor settings, the superior height and weight of educated mothers may account for much of the educational effect on infant survival (Chowdhury, 1982).

Yet nutritional status cannot be the central explanation, because it only helps to explain the impact of education on neonatal and to a lesser extent, post-neonatal mortality. As shown earlier, the education-mortality relationship is stronger in childhood than in infancy.

EDUCATION AND SOCIO-ECONOMIC STATUS

The tendency is universal for better educated women to marry similarly advantaged men and to enjoy relatively high standards of living. To what extent, then, does the strong education-mortality relationship merely reflect the impact of economic advantage on health and survivorship? A precise answer to this question is made difficult by the complexities of measuring income or wealth, particularly in subsistence agricultural settings. Few demographic enquiries have made a thorough effort to collect detailed household income (or expenditure) data and thus reliance has to be placed on surrogate measures that are not fully satisfactory.

In Appendix A we summarize individual studies that have analysed the maternal education-mortality relationship, after controlling for economic characteristics of the household or the dwelling. Differences in analytic technique and in the nature of other variables included in regression models preclude simple generalizations, but usually the effect of education remains statistically significant. This is true for all six Latin American studies, but in the Arab states, evidence of the net effect of the mother's education is less emphatic. Positive evidence for Sudan (Farah and Preston, 1982) and the City of Amman (Tekce and Shorter, 1984) is balanced by negative evidence for Egypt (Cooksey et al., 1986) and rural Syria (Hanbaly and Callum, 1987).

In its 15 country comparative analysis, the UN (1985) re-examined the effect of maternal education, net of diverse economic controls. Though direct household income measures were available for only three countries, information on water supply (six countries), on toilet facilities (five countries), other dwelling characteristics (four countries) plus data on place of residence and husband's education and occupation permitted a reasonable assessment of net effects of education. The broad conclusion was that approximately half of the gross effect of mother's education could be attributed to economic advantage.

The major analysis of WFS data by Hobcraft et al. (1984) reached a very similar conclusion. The findings are summarized in Table 2 in terms of relative risks averaged for the study population, before and after adjustment for husband's occupation and education, rural-urban residence and wife's work status. The inclusion of wife's work; status is perhaps unfortunate for our purposes, because it is a personal characteristic of the mother closely related to education. However, the practical consequence is of little importance, because work status is a significant predictor of mortality in only a small minority of surveys. The results show that, for both neonatal and post-neonatal mortality, there is a severe attenuation of education effects. For only eight or nine of the 24 surveys was the educational effect statistically significant. The effects in childhood also diminish but nevertheless remain substantial. A few years of primary schooling is associated with a 20 per cent drop in the probability of dying between age one and five years; a few more years of primary schooling brings about another 10 per cent fall, while a further 20 per cent drop comes with secondary schooling.

TABLE 2: RELATIVE RISKS OF DEATH, BEFORE AND AFTER ADJUSTMENT FOR OTHER SOCIO-ECONOMIC FACTORS (AVERAGE OF WFS SURVEYS)

| Unadjusted/Adjusted | Years of schooling | | | |
	0	1-3	4.6	7+
Neonatal				
Unadjusted	1.00	0.87	0.76	0.57
Adjusted	1.00	0.98	0.90	0.86
Post-neonatal				
Unadjusted	1.00	0.82	0.73	0.45
Adjusted	1.00	0.98	0.90	0.78
Childhood				
Unadjusted	1.00	0.68	0.47	0.23
Adjusted	1.00	0.82	0.70	0.51

Source: Calculated from Hobcraft *et al*. (1984).

Do these averaged results from the UN and WFS comparative studies conceal interesting exceptions to the general finding of large net effects of maternal education on childhood survival? The three exceptions in the UN study are Nepal, Jamaica and Sudan. Nepal and Jamaica are also among the ten surveys for which no significant net effect on childhood mortality was found in the WFS study; this is reassuring because the same data set was used in both analyses. Other WFS surveys without significant effects were Lesotho, Sudan (not the same data set as used by the UN), Haiti, Guyana, Jamaica, Trinidad and Tobago, Syria and Fiji. The Nepal result is of little consequence because the number of educated mothers is very small. The Sudan result suggests that the survey used in the UN study may be as defective as the WFS survey, while the lack of a significant effect in Fiji is probably a reflection of the confounding influence of ethnicity. The indigenous Fijians are much better educated than the community of Indian descent but the difference in childhood mortality is small. The Caribbean countries, however, appear to represent a genuine and potentially interesting exception. The more detailed study of the three English-speaking Caribbean countries by Ebanks (1985) does not clarify the situation, except to reveal that substantial omission of deaths has probably occurred among non-Indian respondents with low education in Trinidad and Tobago. While Ebanks finds evidence that marital instability is a risk factor, this should not account for the weak influence of maternal education; educated women in the Caribbean are more, not less, likely to form stable relationships. Regrettably, the matter must remain unexplained.

Can we take the adjusted relative risks shown in Table 2 as a valid indication of the 'pure' effect of maternal education, after removal of the influence of economic advantages enjoyed disproportionately by families where the mother is well educated? To the extent that the socio-economic controls used in the WFS study do not adequately capture income or wealth, the residual effect of education may be overstated. However, there is a counter-reason for thinking that the effects may be understated. In deriving adjusted estimates we have assumed risks to be identical across educational categories for all surveys where the maternal education effect was not significant. As statistical significance depends not only upon magnitude of adjusted differences but on the distribution of events and exposure across categories, this assumption undoubtedly leads to a conservative estimate of net effects, because the numbers of educated mothers in some surveys are small.

The validity of adjusted results depends on the assumptions of additivity (i.e., that the effect of education on mortality is the same at all economic levels). On *a priori* grounds, an interaction between education and income and household facilities might be expected. Educated mothers may be more effective than uneducated mothers at translating financial resources and facilities into improved health and survivorship for their children. It is equally plausible, however, to argue that availability of good water and sanitation might erode the educational advantage. The general lack of evidence for such interactive effects is surprising, though there are a few exceptions. In Egypt, Cooksey *et al.* (1986) found, as they expected, that income was more closely related to the chance of infant death for offspring of educated than of uneducated mothers. In childhood, however, the interaction did not accord with expectations. In their Guatemala study, Pebley and Stupp (1987) also reported a similar income-education interaction. In Costa Rica, however, the interaction took the opposite form; economic well-being (as indicated by housing quality) was more closely related to mortality for the less educated (Haines and Avery, 1982). Against these isolated examples should be set the UN (1985) comparative study, which found that the effects of maternal education were remarkably consistent across categories formed by dwelling characteristics and income. On balance, therefore, there are insufficient grounds to challenge the additivity assumption. In turn, this allows us to reach the broad conclusion that the economic advantages associated with education (income, water and latrine facilities, clothing, housing quality etc.) probably account for about one-half of the overall education-mortality association.

EDUCATION AND SELECTIVITY

While we may be reasonably confident that the education-mortality link is not simply a reflection of differences in material living standards between educational categories, we cannot preclude the possibility that better educated mothers come from exceptional backgrounds and possess distinctive social or psychological characteristics, that, merely reinforced by formal schooling, may account for their performance as mothers. For instance, it is likely that progressive parents are more eager than conservative parents to provide an education for their daughters and that length of schooling depends partly on the child's aptitude and determination to learn about the outside world.

These considerations are particularly relevant in countries where schooling of girls has been until recently a rarity, but they lose some of their force in settings where female education has been commonplace, if not universal, in recent decades.

The persistence of the education-mortality association in societies which vary widely in access to schooling and in levels of adult female literacy suggests to us that selection biases are not of major importance.

EDUCATION AND USE OF HEALTH SERVICES

There are numerous obvious reasons why educated mothers should make more use of modern health facilities, both for preventive and curative purposes. Education is likely to impart a greater responsiveness to novel ideas and services, a greater identification with the outside world, more social confidence at handling officials and perhaps an enhanced ability and willingness to travel outside the home community in search of services. There is also ample empirical evidence to support these expectations. While participation in mass immunization campaigns may not be selective of the better educated (e.g., Friede et al., 1985; Belcher et al., 1978), most studies have shown a positive correlation between maternal education and use of modern preventive health services and, less often, of modern curative services. This tendency has been demonstrated for West Africa (Mbacké and van de Walle, 1987; Brown et al., 1982; Okediji, 1975), for Arab countries (Tekce and Shorter, 1984; Benyoussef and Wessen, 1974), and for Asia (Caldwell et al., 1983; Sullivan, 1975). The single most convincing study is a multivariate analysis of data from the WFS Surveys in Latin America (Fernandez, 1984). The key findings are summarized in Table 3. Even after adjustment for maternal age, parity, rural-urban residence and husband's occupation, differences according to maternal education in utilization of maternal and child health services remained large. (Residence and occupation also have large net effects, implying that access and income are also important determinants.)

In addition to the increased propensity of educated mothers to seek medical attention for themselves and their children, it is likely that they do so with greater timeliness, extract a higher quality of care and adhere to advice with greater persistence. Antonovsky (1980) wrote about health services in Western countries in the following terms: 'the experience of a lower class person entering the health care is one which is overwhelming and bewildering, alien and frightful'. Such hyperbole probably comes nearer to the truth in developing than developed countries, because of greater socio-economic disparities. Casual observation suggests that the poor and uneducated often receive little consideration from government officials, including those in the medical service. A study in Ibadan provides more rigorous support; literate patients received better treatment at government hospitals and health centres than illiterates, particularly by way of more specific diagnoses (Maclean, 1974). In Mexico, Levine et al. (1987) found that educated mothers were more likely to take sick children for treatment within three days of the onset of symptoms.

The shift from traditional to modern or Western medical treatment by the educated is not a complete transfer of allegiance. There is abundant anthropological evidence that belief in and practice of entirely different systems of disease classification and therapy can co-exist. But the correlation between exposure to formal schooling and propensity to resort to Western medicine is clear-cut. It is thus reasonable to expect that the advantage conferred by education may be greater in settings where modern health facilities are available. This is clearly the expectation of Orubuloye and Caldwell (1975) who found that educational differentials in childhood mortality were indeed larger in a Nigerian village with a hospital than a village without such a facility. In a subsequent re-analysis a huge interaction was found: the presence of health services improved child survivorship by 20 per cent; maternal education in the absence of services was associated with a 33 per cent improvement; but the joint effect of services and maternal education resulted in an 87 per cent improvement (Caldwell and Caldwell, 1985).

TABLE 3: **RELATIONSHIP BETWEEN MATERNAL EDUCATION AND PREVENTIVE HEALTH CARE IN LATIN AMERICA, UNADJUSTED (UA) AND ADJUSTED (AD) FOR OTHER FACTORS**

Years of schooling	Ecuador		Mexico		Paraguay		Peru		Dominican Republic	
	UA	AD	UA	AD	UA	AD	UA	AD	UA	AD
Per cent mothers receiving antenatal care from doctor or midwife										
0-2	33	41	42	48	59	63	20	32	63	65
3-5	48	53	59	60	74	76	58	40	73	73
6+	80	73	85	76	93	89	85	69	88	85
Per cent deliveries attended by doctors or midwife										
0-2	23	36	53	60	43	56	19	34	66	70
3-5	39	47	69	76	55	61	60	54	77	79
6+	78	66	95	83	87	74	90	69	91	81
Per cent infants receiving health care										
0-2	46	53	50	55	33	44	44	55	22	26
3-5	48	53	59	60	49	55	59	55	30	32
6+	71	63	83	74	84	71	85	68	57	47
Per cent children receiving any immunization										
0-2	40	49	47	52	18	31	44	52	35	36
3-5	47	53	60	67	26	33	65	62	44	45
6+	71	60	82	71	62	45	83	69	60	55

Source: Adapted from Fernandez (1984).

These are spectacular results but, to our knowledge, have never been replicated elsewhere. A contrary and more common theoretical stance is taken by Palloni (1985) and by Rosenzweig and Schultz (1982). Palloni argues that in societies where services are widely available, personal characteristics, including education, become less important determinants of health. This is analogous to the claim that strong family planning programmes can reduce socio-economic differentials in contraceptive use and fertility (Entwistle *et al.*, 1986). Rosenzweig and Schultz are more specific: they regard the public information component of health services as a partial substitute for the superior knowledge or skills of better educated mothers and, for this reason, expect educational differences to be smaller in the presence of a good health

programme. In an analysis of 1973 Colombian Census data, they adduce some
support for this view. In urban areas, access to public and private medical facilities
has a greater impact on the survivorship of children of less educated mothers than for
the educated, thus narrowing the differential.

In a multi-level analysis, Cochrane *et al.* (1980) demonstrated that educational
differentials in mortality tend to decrease as per capita health expenditure rises.
Further support for the thesis that medical services can erode the advantage to
offspring of educated mothers comes from those countries that have achieved very
high life expectancy in relation to the national income. The most notable examples –
China, Costa Rica, Cuba, Kerala and Sri Lanka – have attracted close attention in
recent years (e.g., Caldwell, 1986; Halstead *et al.*, 1985). At least two of these states,
Cuba and Sri Lanka, have rather modest educational differentials in mortality (Behm,
1980; Meegama, 1980). A more convincing illustration of the possible equalizing
influence of health services is the fact that differentials have diminished over time in
Costa Rica and China. In Costa Rica, the risk of infant death for children born to
mothers with less than four years schooling relative to those with seven or more years
changed from 3.7 in 1965-69 to 2.1 for the period 1975-79 (Rosero-Bixby, 1985).
The convergence is even more pronounced in China, as may be seen in Table 4.
Between 1964 and 1977, the infant mortality of offspring of mothers with senior
schooling and above remained static: over the same period, the rate for the illiterate
group declined by 40 per cent.

TABLE 4: TRENDS IN INFANT MORTALITY RATES (PER 1000 LIVE BIRTHS) BY EDUCATION IN CHINA

Fiscal year	Level of education			
	Illiterate	Elementary	Junior	Senior and above
1964-65	87	50	32	21
1965-66	80	54	33	21
1966-67	83	57	34	18
1967-68	81	51	30	15
1968-69	71	47	30	18
1969-70	74	51	34	15
1970-71	67	46	26	17
1971-72	68	47	27	18
1972-73	62	43	24	17
1973-74	58	40	26	17
1974-75	60	38	25	20
1975-76	58	38	30	21
1976-77	52	37	23	20

Source: Yang and Dowdle, 1985.

The ability of superior service provision to erode the advantage conferred by
education should not be exaggerated. Large differences in relative risks of infant
death across social classes and educational categories still persist in developed

countries (e.g., Bross and Shapiro, 1982; Szabady, 1963). Moreover, most cross-sectional studies in developing countries demonstrate that the sharpness of educational inequalities in childhood mortality is unaffected by controls for access to modern health services (e.g., Al-Kabir, 1984 for Bangladesh; Borja, 1985 for Ecuador; Young *et al.*, 1983 for Peru). In so far as urban areas are better endowed with health services, the similarity of maternal education effects in both urban and rural sectors suggests that educated mothers maintain their advantage, regardless of access to health services. Such a similarity of maternal education effects was found in the UN (1985) comparative study and in a detailed analysis of Colombian data (Rosenzweig and Schultz, 1982).

Regional analyses for Kenya and India provide further evidence of the independence of the maternal education effect from health care provision. Both countries have huge regional disparities in health services provision and/or utilization. In Kenya, however, the child mortality gradient by education is maintained across provinces (Mosley, 1985) and across districts (Ewbank *et al.*, 1986). For India, a state-level analysis by Jain (1985) came to the conclusion that the relationship between mother's education and infant mortality could be largely explained by differential utilization of modern health care, specifically medical attendance at delivery and vaccination of infants. Our reading of the evidence leads to a different conclusion. There is no correlation among the various states between the percentage of births that are medically attended (a reasonable proxy for use of preventive health services) and educational differences in infant mortality. Nor incidentally does there appear to be any marked divergence between northern and southern states in the relative effect of maternal education on infant death, which might perhaps be expected because of geographical differences in the autonomy of mothers (Dyson and Moore, 1983). Jain's conclusion is further undermined by evidence from several large-scale surveys that access to government health facilities is not closely related to the level of infant mortality. Mortality differences between villages in Bihar, Rajasthan and Orissa with and without a government health facility were found to be small and inconsistent in direction (Srinivasan *et al.*, 1985; Srinivasan and Kanitkar, 1982).

The persistence of a strong influence of maternal education on child survivorship, regardless of the proximity or effectiveness of government health care provision, suggests that domestic child care practices may be the major intervening mechanism. The relevant evidence is examined in the next section. However, the possible importance of differential utilization of allopathic medical advice and treatment cannot be discounted. Access to drugs and advice in many developing countries is by no means confined to the formally qualified medical sector. A wide spectrum of pharmacists, hawkers and traditional medical practitioners cater to health needs. No doubt they dispense a mixture of both modern and more traditional drugs and remedies. Mosley (1985) cited work by Taylor (1982) which reported that 75 per cent of the drugs used by traditional practitioners in India are Western medicines. Where the formal sector is weak, their combined efforts may have a large impact on health and survivorship. This is certainly the implication of a village study in rural Uttar Pradesh (Khan, 1982). Though only 2.5 km from a primary health centre, this village had no less than eight resident, unqualified private medical practitioners, who had treated 90 per cent of the 264 persons who had been sick in the previous month. Among the reasons cited by informants for their reliance upon local treatment rather than government facilities were convenience, attitude of service providers and the limited availability of drugs at the health centre. Though Khan and colleagues did not report on educational differences in health behaviour, it seems plausible that educated mothers in this village obtain better treatment for their children by judicious choice between the eight medical practitioners and greater adherence to their advice.

In conclusion, the interrelationship between maternal education, health service provision and childhood mortality is complex and variable. This reflects the complexity of the real world. There are countries whose primary health services are so weak that they have no effect on the health of mothers or children. There are no doubt other countries whose services may tend to accentuate educational disparities because of differential access. Finally, there are countries, perhaps few in number, with services of sufficient accessibility and effectiveness to offset the advantage of education and bring about greater equality in health and survivorship. As argued powerfully by Caldwell (1986), the key to low mortality at the societal level may be a synergy between mass education and egalitarian politics which leads to demands for a health service that caters to the needs of all.

EDUCATION AND DOMESTIC HEALTH CARE OF CHILDREN

The main conclusions of the preceding sections are that a substantial proportion of the maternal education effect on survivorship of children is independent of income and material resources and that the effect transcends access to modern health services. Another important factor to be discussed here is the mother's care of children within the domestic context.

Before reviewing the rather meagre evidence on the possible behavioural links, we will consider attitudinal, social and cognitive consequences of education. Such consequences may underlie changes in maternal behaviour towards children leading to improved health and lower mortality, and thus form an important part of any comprehensive explanation.

The most obvious of these is knowledge of disease causation, prevention and cure and of the nutritional requirements of infants and children. Either as a direct consequence of school curricula or as an indirect consequence of schooling on subsequent exposure to and comprehension of health messages, educated mothers may have a better knowledge of health requirements than uneducated mothers. The relationship between length of formal education and the nature of beliefs concerning disease and treatment has been studied surprisingly infrequently and the evidence is conflicting. In rural Ghana, Fosu (1981) demonstrated that adults with primary schooling were more likely than those with no schooling to attribute natural causes to diseases. Respondents were first asked to name any five diseases and then required to classify each according to its cause. For those with no schooling, diseases were classified thus: natural causes 33 per cent, supernatural causes 52 per cent, both types of cause 15 per cent. The corresponding breakdown for those with primary schooling was 53, 31 and 16 per cent. The proportion of diseases attributed to natural causes rose further among those with secondary or higher schooling, but the largest difference lay between the no schooling and primary school groups.

Another small-scale study found no such impact of primary schooling on beliefs or knowledge (McLaren, 1982). Only among Lebanese mothers with 7-9 years of schooling did knowledge of nutritional needs appreciably improve. An anthropological study in Bangladesh reveals a similar absence of any permanent effect of primary schooling on knowledge of health related matters (Lindenbaum *et al.*, 1985). Among both educated and uneducated mothers, there was general agreement that infant disorders result from spirit attacks and that illness in all age groups is associated with bodily imbalances. More specifically the cause of infant diarrhoea was believed to be spoilage of breastmilk. Similarly, the extensive discussion of the social determinants of mortality decline in South India by Caldwell *et al.* (1983) makes little mention of superior health knowledge of educated mothers. While this evidence is too sparse for sound conclusions to be drawn, we consider it rather likely that schooling below the secondary level imparts sufficient understanding of health matters to guide maternal behaviour in later life.

One striking similarity of both the Bangladesh and South India studies cited in the preceding paragraph is the profound social consequences for women of education, at least in male-dominated societies. Education provides a wider social network, new reference groups and authority models and a greater identification with the modern world. One consequence of this transformation is a greater willingness to make use of government health services, which we have already discussed. But it is equally likely that the wider social horizons of educated mothers make them more responsive to innovative remedies, even if their knowledge of the rationale is little better than that of the uneducated. Furthermore, education may inculcate a greater sense of personal responsibility for, and control over the welfare of children, replacing the more resigned and fatalistic outlook of the uneducated mother.

Caldwell has laid particular stress on the greater autonomy of educated mothers within the family, which, allegedly, carries important health benefits for children. Yet another idea attributable to Caldwell to have gained wide currency is that education brings about a profound change in the relationship between generations, whereby exploitation of children by older kin is transformed to indulgence. The practical consequence of such changes in family values may be a more equitable division of food and resources between parents and children and between sons and daughters. We are unaware of any empirical confirmation of the effect of these changes on the generational division of resources, but some confirmation that educated mothers make a greater investment of emotion and time in their children than uneducated mothers comes from the intensive study of low income families in urban Mexico (Levine et al., 1985, 1987).

Regarding Caldwell's claim that educated mothers use their greater autonomy to treat sons and daughters more equitably, however, there is a growing body of contrary evidence. A number of intensive studies in Bangladesh have failed to find any narrowing of the sex differential in childhood mortality or nutritional status among families where the mother is educated (Bairagi, 1986; Bhuiya et al., 1986; D'Souza and Bhuiya, 1986). Indeed the evidence suggests that the relative disadvantage of daughters may worsen among better educated or more wealthy families. In Punjab, Das Gupta (1987) finds disturbing evidence that educated mothers deploy their skills selectively in favour of children of the desired sex. A pronounced mortality differential in the expected direction by mother's education is apparent for sons and the first daughter, but it disappears for second or higher order daughters. Das Gupta interprets this result as a consequence of the greater ability of educated mothers to manipulate events so as to achieve the family size and sex composition that they desire.

Whether or not this interpretation of individualized discrimination is valid, the absence of any significant improvement in excess female childhood mortality among families with an educated mother is confirmed in a WFS analysis (Weinberger and Heligman, 1987). Using data from ten Asian and Arab countries characterized by a preference for sons over daughters, no support was found for the expected narrowing of sex ratios of child mortality among more educated families.

One final social consequence of schooling – and in many ways the most intriguing – is that it may inculcate new codes of behaviour which persist into adulthood and influence the health of children without any such conscious intent. In many settings, schooling introduces children to totally new ideas of personal hygiene and cleanliness. For many it may be the first experience of latrines or of hand-washing before meals. These innovations come with the powerful endorsement of the modern world, which the village primary school represents. They are therefore accepted as socially desirable, without perhaps much understanding of their huge potential importance for health (Khan, 1982).

Such social changes emerge very clearly from the Bangladesh study by Lindenbaum et al. (1985). The major differences between educated and uneducated mothers was the greater emphasis on cleanliness by the former. Their houses and children appeared to be neater and cleaner and their desire for social gentility led to a preference for washing with tank or tubewell water at home, and to spurn public bathing in canals or rivers.

The discussion so far in this section may be compressed as follows.

Compared to the uneducated, educated mothers may: attach a higher value to the welfare and health of children; have greater decision-making power on health-related and other matters; be less fatalistic about disease and death; be more knowledgeable about disease prevention and cure; be more innovative in the use of remedies; and be more likely to adopt new codes of behaviour which improve the health of children though they are not perceived as having direct consequences for health.

These social and cognitive consequences of schooling of course are not mutually exclusive, nor is there much evidence by which their relative importance can be assessed.

We now turn to a consideration of behavioural links through which maternal education could lead to improved health of children. Behavioural factors to be considered here are nutrition, in particular breastfeeding, employment of women and health care provided to children at home.

The framework of Mosley and Chen (1984) allows us to identify the following major behavioural pathways, through which maternal education may enhance the health of children: greater protection against infection, primarily by means of improved hygiene; reduced susceptibility to infection, primarily through nutrition and immunization; enhanced recovery from infection, brought about by more effective domestic and external health care; and reduced risks of accidents, through supervision.

Improved domestic health care is perhaps the pathway for which the evidence is most positive. For instance, educated mothers in Kenya are likely to treat measles and diarrhoea in an effective modern manner (Maina-Ahlberg, 1984) and less likely to use traditional remedies (Anker and Knowles, 1977). In Nigeria they are also more likely to substitute modern medicines sold by pharmacies or hawkers for traditional herbal remedies (Orubuloye and Caldwell, 1975).

The evidence regarding nutrition is fragmentary, though a Bangladesh study showed a rather small effect of maternal education on quantity of food intake or nature of diet. A greater association might be expected in cultures where women, rather than men, purchase food. More is known about breastfeeding. The much weaker effect of maternal education at post-neonatal ages than in childhood may well reflect the great importance of breastfeeding for infant health. The almost universal tendency in developing countries for less educated mothers to breastfeed for long durations and, perhaps more importantly, to postpone supplementation no doubt acts as a partial safeguard against infection and nutritional deficiency in infancy (Singh and Ferry, 1984). It is also probable that the reverse tendency among more educated mothers raises infant mortality and thus narrows the differential. Goldberg et al. (1984) demonstrated that failure to breastfeed in north-east Brazil is a risk factor in infancy across all educational groups. In urban areas, the relative risk for those not breastfed was even greater for the offspring of mothers with completed primary or higher schooling than for those born to less educated mothers. In rural areas, however, the position was different; uneducated mothers who did not breastfeed experienced a particularly high loss of infants. Two other analyses of Latin America data also show a significant effect of length of breastfeeding on infant survival for educated as well as uneducated mothers, though the impact was larger for the latter (Pebley and Stupp, 1987; Palloni and Millman, 1986). Perhaps, the stronger link between education and infant survival in Latin America than in other regions (see Table 1) reflects the fact that breastfeeding is generally shorter in Latin America than elsewhere.

The greater propensity for educated mothers to work away from home represents a further mechanism which, ceteris paribus, operates against the observed education-mortality association. Child care arrangements are unlikely to be an entirely satisfactory substitute for the mother's direct supervision, particularly if work curtails breastfeeding. There is scattered evidence that mother's employment has an adverse effect in some countries (e.g., Farah and Preston, 1982; Hobcraft et al., 1984; Schultz,

1985), but most studies have failed to find such an effect, perhaps because of the offsetting influence of the contribution of mother's earnings to household income. The employment-fertility relationship has proved to be extremely complex and it appears that the employment-mortality relation is equally so.

The evidence concerning preventive health care in the home in both meagre and inconclusive. The Lindenbaum study in Bangladesh intimated that hygiene may be a powerful discriminant between the educated and uneducated. Similarly Mbacké and van de Walle (1987) show that use of mosquito coils or nets is significantly associated with maternal education, after control for income; and, in their West African site, this precaution proved to be a strong predictor of mortality. Against these shreds of evidence must be set the finding that use of soap in the household was not associated with maternal education in Amman (Tekce and Shorter, 1984) and the more general evidence that access to piped water and good toilet facilities does not diminish, to any appreciable extent, the educational advantage. Of course access cannot be equated with effective utilization and the possibility remains that educated mothers make better use of such facilities than less educated mothers.

This section has served mainly to reveal the depth of our ignorance. While it appears probable that domestic behaviour is the key to the enhanced survivorship of children born to educated mothers, we have little grasp of the precise mechanisms.

CONCLUSION

Preston (1985) pointed out that, at the turn of the century, occupational and educational differentials in mortality in the United States were almost non-existent; the difference between the agricultural and professional sectors amounted to a mere 7 per cent. Superior resources and learning were not translated into a health advantage, implicitly because of the primitive state of medical knowledge.

With regard to childhood mortality in contemporary developing countries, we observe the extreme opposite; a truly astonishing sensitivity of survivorship to the length of formal schooling of the mother. Even after adjustment for economic factors, 1-3 years of schooling is associated with a fall of 20 per cent in childhood risks of death and further large decreases are recorded with successive increments in educational attainment. This strong relationship is found in all major regions of the developing world and persists both in countries with accessible and effective health services and those with weak primary health care systems.

We have attempted to elucidate this powerful relationship and have been able to discard some hypotheses and suggested mechanisms. Reproductive risk factors, for instance, operate in favour of children born to educated mothers but only play a very minor role in explaining the overall association. Similarly, a more equitable distribution of resources and care between sons and daughters makes no contribution to the educational differential in mortality. But these are only minor matters and the central explanation remains elusive.

The reason for our ignorance is the dearth of studies that have been designed explicitly to examine the links between education and survivorship. This is a sad commentary on research priorities. The importance of education – particularly that of the mother – has been well established and widely accepted for nearly a decade: better education for women is now a familiar health slogan. Yet our understanding of the mechanisms of influence remain no better today than ten years ago. No doubt, part of the reason lies in the complexity of the subject matter. Detailed studies of household behaviour, which would need to be a key part of any research design, are not easy to conduct. Furthermore, a union of small-scale intensive investigations and of more formal quantitative studies is required. Such a methodological marriage is easier to advocate than to implement. In an increasingly specialized world, it is difficult to assemble a research team that is familiar with both observational and large-scale survey techniques. There are some (e.g., Caldwell *et al.*, 1983) who dismiss the possible contribution of quantitative research in this area. We disagree. The rich insights provided by Caldwell's work in South India, by Lindenbaum in Bangladesh and by Levine in Mexico require quantitative verification and the measurement problems are not insuperable. A further desirable feature of research on this topic is a cross-cultural dimension. It remains uncertain whether the mechanisms are the same across different settings, a point of obvious relevance to policies. In view of these demanding requirements for a major advance in our understanding of the education-mortality relationship it becomes less surprising, but no more excusable, that so little progress has been made.

This plea for further research is a common one and usually evokes little appreciation from those who are concerned more with policies. In this instance, however, the practical policy implications will remain obscure, or at least so general as to be of little use, until the mechanisms are clarified. In the present state of knowledge, little more can be said than to assert that widespread education appears indispensable for the achievement of high survivorship, except perhaps in a country like China with a unique ability for mass mobilization. By implication, medical interventions by themselves will achieve only a modest impact. But, disclosure of the mechanisms by which education influences survivorship could have important practical and concrete implications for health and educational policies.

APPENDIX: SUMMARY OF STUDIES THAT HAVE ANALYSED THE EFFECT OF MATERNAL EDUCATION AFTER CONTROLLING ECONOMIC FACTORS

Authors	Site	Mortality measure	Key economic controls	Significant net effect of education
Anker and Knowles (1977)	Kenya	3q0	Income, latrines, water supply, dwelling	Yes
Kuné (1979)	Machakos, Kenya	5q0	Income, education of household head, hygiene	Yes
Mbacké and van de Walle (1987)	Bobo-Dioulasso, Burkino Faso	PNN	Income, housing quality	1q1 only
Farah and Preston (1982)	Khartoum	1q1		
		Mortality ratios	Income, husband's SES, dwelling, objects owned	Yes
Tekce and Shorter (1984)	Squatter area of Amman	Mortality ratios	Income, occupation of household head, dwelling	Yes
Hanbaly and Callum (1987)	Syria	0-1, 2-17, 18-59 months	Husband's SES, dwelling	Yes, at ages 2-17 and 18-59, months in urban areas only
Cooksey et al. (1986)	Egypt	1q0, 4q1	Income, and husband's SES	No
Borja (1985)	Ecuador	1q0, 4q1	Income, husband's occupation	Yes
Pebley and Stupp (1987)	Gautemala	5q0	Income	Yes
Haines and Avery (1982)	Costa Rica	2q0	Dwelling	Yes
Merrick (1985)	Brazil	Mortality ratios	Income, access to piped water	Yes
Schultz (1980)	Colombia	Mortality ratios	Income	Yes
Victoria et al. (1986)	Brazil	Mortality ratios	Income, dwelling, employment	Yes
Knowles (1979)	Low income area of Karachi	3q0	Income	No
Frenzen and Hogan (1982)	Northern Thailand	1q0	Occupation of father, district development	No
DaVanzo et al. (1983)	Malaysia	1q0	Income, dwelling	Yes, at late post-neonatal ages

REFERENCES

Al-Kabir, A. (1984), 'Effects of community factors on infant and child mortality in Bangla Desh', *WFS Scientific Report* No.56, World Fertility Survey, London.

Anker, R. and Knowles, J.C. (1977), 'An empirical analysis of mortality differentials at the macro and micro levels', *Population and Employment Working Paper* No. 60, International Labour Office, Geneva.

Antonovsky, A. (1980), 'Implications of socio-economic differentials in mortality for the health system', in *Proceedings of the Meeting on Socio-Economic Determinants and Consequences of Mortality*, United Nations/World Health Organization, New York/Geneva.

Bairagi, R. (1986), 'Food crisis, nutrition and female children in rural Bangladesh', *Population and Development Review*, 12.

Behm, H. (1980), 'Socio-economic determinants of mortality in Latin America', in UN/WHO, 1980.

Belcher, D.W., Nicolas, D.D., Ofusu-Amaah, S. and Wurupa, F.K. (1978), 'A mass immunization campaign in rural Ghana', *Public Health Reports*, 93.

Benyoussef, A. and Wessen, A.F. (1974). 'Utilization of health services in developing countries – Tunisia', *Social Science and Medicine*, 8.

Bhuiya, A., Wojtiniak, B., D'Souza, S. and Zimicki, S. (1986), 'Socio-economic determinants of child nutritional status: Boys versus girls', *Food and Nutrition Bulletin*, 8.

Borja, E.M. (1985), 'Factores determinantes de una mortalidad prematura en Ecuador', *WFS Scientific Report* No.74, World Fertility Survey, London.

Bross, D. and Shapiro, S. (1982), 'Direct and indirect associations of five factors with infant mortality', *American Journal of Epidemiology*, 115.

Brown, J., Djogdom, P., Murphy, K., Kesseng, G. and Heymann, D. (1982), 'Identifying the reasons for low immunization coverage: a case study from Yaoundé (Cameroon)', *Revue Epidémologie et Santé Publique*, 30.

Caldwell, J.C. (1979), 'Education as a factor in mortality decline: an examination of Nigerian data', *Population Studies*, 33.

Caldwell, J.C. (1986), 'Routes to low mortality in poor countries', *Population and Development Review*, 12, (also Chapter 1 of this book).

Caldwell, J.C. and Caldwell, P. (1985), 'Education and literacy as factors in health', in S.B. Halstead, J.A. Walsh and K.S. Warren (eds), *Good Health at Low Cost*, Rockefeller Foundation, New York.

Caldwell, J.C., Reddy, P.H. and Caldwell, P. (1983), 'The social component of mortality decline: an investigation in South India employing alternative methodologies', *Population Studies*, 37, (also Chapter 11 of this book).

Chowdhury, A.K. (1982), 'Education and infant survival in rural Bangladesh', *Health Policy and Education*, 2.

Cochrane, S.H., O'Hara, D.J. and Leslie, J. (1980), 'The effects of education on health', *World Bank Staff Working Paper* No.405, World Bank, Washington, D.C.

Cooksey, E.R., Casterline, J.B. and Ismael, A.F. (1986), Paper presented at Annual Meeting of Population Association of America, San Francisco.

Das Gupta, M. (1987), 'Selective discrimination against female children in rural Punjab, India', *Population and Development Review*, 13.

DaVanzo, J., Butz, W.P. and Habicht, J.P. (1983), 'How biological and behavioural influences on mortality in Malaysia vary during the first year of life', *Population Studies* , 31.

D'Souza, S. and Bhuiya, A. (1986), 'Mortality differentials in rural Bangladesh', *Population and Development Review*, 13.

Dyson, T. and Moore, M. (1983), 'On kinship structure, female autonomy and demographic behavior in India', *Population and Development Review*, 9.

Ebanks, G.E. (1985), 'Infant and child mortality and fertility: Trinidad and Tobago, Guyana and Jamaica', *WFS Scientific Report* No.75, World Fertility Survey, London.

El Hadi, M. (1987), 'Socio-economic differentials of infant and child mortality', in *Infant and Child Mortality and Socio-economic Factors in Africa*, United Nations Economic Commission for Africa, Addis Ababa.

Entwistle, B., Mason, W.M. and Hermalin, A.J. (1986), 'The multilevel dependence of contraceptive use in socio-economic development and family planning program strength', *Demography*, 23.

Ewbank, D., Henin, R. and Kekovole, J. (1986), 'An integration of demographic and epidemiological research on mortality in Kenya', in United Nations, Department of International Economic and Social Affairs, *Determinants of Mortality Changes and Differentials in Developing Countries*, Population Studies No.94, United Nations, New York.

Farah, A.A. and Preston, S. (1982), 'Child mortality differentials in Sudan', *Population and Development Review*, 8.

Fernandez, R. (1984), 'Analysis of information about mother-child care taken from fertility surveys in Latin America', World Fertility Survey, London (mimeo.).

Fosu, G.B. (1981), 'Disease classification in rural Ghana: framework and consequences for health behaviour', *Social Science and Medicine*, 15B.

Frenzen, P. and Hogan, D. (1982), 'The impact of class, education and health care on infant mortality in a developing society', *Demography*, 19.

Friede, A., Waternaux, C., Guyer, B., de Jesus, A. and Filipp, L. (1985), 'An epidemiological assessment of immunization programme participation in the Philippines', *International Journal of Epidemiology*, 14.

Goldberg, H.I., Rodrigues, W., Thome, A., Janowitz, B. and Morris, L. (1984), 'Infant mortality and breastfeeding in North-Eastern Brazil', *Population Studies*, 38.

Haines, M.R. and Avery, R.C. (1982), 'Differential infant and child mortality in Costa Rica', *Population Studies*, 36.

Halstead, S.B., Walsh, J.A. and Warren, K.S. (eds) (1985), *Good Health at Low Cost*, Rockefeller Foundation, New York.

Hanbaly, N. and Callum, C. (1987), 'Levels, trends and correlates of mortality', in S. Farid and K. Alloush (eds), *Reproductive Patterns in Syria*, World Fertility Survey, London.

Hobcraft, J.N., McDonald, R.W. and Rutstein, S.O. (1984), 'Socio-economic factors in infant and child mortality: a cross-national comparison', *Population Studies*, 38.

Hobcraft, J.N., McDonald, R.W. and Rutstein, S.O. (1985), 'Demographic determinants of infant and early child mortality: a comparative analysis', *Population Studies*, 39.

India, Ministry of Home Affairs (1983), *Survey on Infant and Child Mortality*, 1979, New Delhi.

International Union for the Scientific Study of Population (IUSSP) (1985), *International Population Conference, Florence, 1985*, IUSSP, Liège.

Jain, A.K. (1985), 'Determinants of regional variations in child mortality', *Population Studies*, 39.

Khan, M. (1982), 'Interruption of shigellosis by hand washing', *Transactions of the Royal Society of Tropical Hygiene*, 76.

Knowles, J.C. (1979), 'The determinants of mortality in a low-income area of Karachi', *Discussion Paper* No. 35, Applied Economic Research Centre, University of Karachi.

Kuné, J.B. (1979), 'Some factors influencing the mortality of under-fives in a rural area of Kenya: a multivariate analysis', *Journal of Tropical Pediatrics*, 26.

Levine, R.A., Levine, S., Richman, A. and Sunderland Correa, C. (1985), 'Maternal schooling and child health in a Mexican city: preliminary findings', paper presented at International Workshop on Child Survival, Mexico.

Levine, R.A., Levine, S., Richman, A. and Sunderland Correa, C. (1987), 'Schooling and maternal behaviour in a Mexican city: the effects on fertility and child survival', *Fertility Determinants Research Notes* No.16, Population Council, New York.

Lindenbaum, S., Chakraborty, M. and Elias, M. (1985), 'The influence of maternal education on infant and child mortality in Bangladesh', International Centre for Diarrhoeal Disease Research, Bangladesh, Dhaka (mimeo.), (also Chapter 6 of this book).

Maclean, V. (1974), *Magical Medicine, a Nigerian Case Study*, Penguin, London.

Maina-Ahlberg, B. (1984), 'Beliefs and practices related to measles and acute diarrhoea', in J.K. van Ginneken and A.S. Muller (eds), *Maternal and Child Health in Rural Kenya: an Epidemiological Study*, Croom Helm, London.

Mbacké, C. and van de Walle, E. (1987), 'Socio-economic factors and access to health services as determinants of child mortality', Paper presented at IUSSP Seminar on Mortality and Society in Sub-Saharan Africa, Yaoundé.

McLaren, D.S. (1982), 'The home environment of the malnourished-deprived child', *Health Policy and Education*, 2.

Meegama, S.A. (1980), 'Socio-economic determinants of infant and child mortality in Sri Lanka: an analysis of post-war experience', *WFS Scientific Report* No.8, World Fertility Survey, London.

Merrick, T.W. (1985), 'The effect of piped water on early childhood mortality in urban Brazil 1970 to 1976', *Demography*, 22.

Mosley, W.H. (1985), 'Will primary health care reduce infant and child mortality?', in J. Vallin and A. Lopez (eds), *Health Policy, Social Policy and Mortality Prospects*, Ordina, Liège, (also Chapter 14 of this book).

Mosley, W.H. and Chen, L. (1984), 'An analytical framework for the study of child survival in developing countries', *Population and Development Review Supplement*, 10.

Okediji, F.O. (1975), 'Socio-economic status and attitudes to public health problems in the Western State: a case study of Ibadan', in J.C. Caldwell (ed.), *Population Growth and Socio-economic Change in West Africa*, Columbia University Press, New York.

Orubuloye, I.O. and Caldwell, J.C. (1975), 'The impact of public health services on mortality: a study of mortality differentials in a rural area of Nigeria', *Population Studies*, 29.

Palloni, A. (1985), 'Health conditions in Latin America and policies for mortality change', in Vallin and Lopez, 1985.

Palloni, A. and Millman, S. (1986), 'Effects of inter-birth intervals and early childhood mortality', *Population Studies* , 40.

Pebley, A.R. and Stupp, P.W. (1987), 'Reproductive patterns and child mortality in Guatemala', *Demography*, 24.

Penrose, I. (1934), *Population Theories and their Application with Special Reference to Japan*, Food Research Institute, Stanford University, Stanford.

Preston, S.H. (1985), 'Resources, knowledge and child mortality: a comparison of the US in the late nineteenth century and developing countries today', in IUSSP, 1985, Vol. 4, (also Chapter 3 of this book).

Rizgalla, M. (1985), 'Evaluation of the Sudan Fertility Survey, 1978-9', *WFS Scientific Report* No.75, World Fertility Survey, London.

Rosenzweig, M.R. and Schultz, T.P. (1982), 'Child mortality and fertility in Colombia: individual and community effects', *Health Policy and Education*, 2.

Rosero-Bixby, L. (1985), 'The case of Costa Rica', in Vallin and Lopez, 1985.

Rutstein, S.O. (1984), 'Socio-economic differentials in infant and child mortality', *WFS Comparative Studies* No.43, World Fertility Survey, London.

Schultz, T.P. (1980), 'Interpretation of relations among mortality, economics of the household and the health environment', in UN/WHO, 1980.

Schultz, T.P. (1985), 'Household economic and community variables as determinants of mortality', in IUSSP, 1985,Vol. 2.

Singh, S. and Ferry, B. (1984), 'Biological and traditional factors that influence fertility: results from WFS surveys', WFS Comparative Studies No.40, World Fertility Survey, London.

Srinivasan, K. and Kanitkar, T. (1982), 'Demographic differentials between two less developed states, Bihar and Rajastan in India: findings from recent sample surveys', paper prepared for Conference on Indian Demography, Oxford.

Srinivasan, K., Kanitkar, T., Ahmed, V. and Saraagi, L. (1985), Report on the Baseline Survey on Fertility, Mortality and Related Factors in Orissa, International Institute for Population Science, Bombay.

Sullivan, J.M. (1975), 'The influence of demographic and socio-economic factors on infant mortality in Taiwan, 1966-1968', *Academy of Economics Papers*, 31.

Szabady, E. (1963), 'Social and biological factors affecting infant mortality in Hungary', in International Union for the Scientific Study of Population, *International Population Conference, New York, 1961*, IUSSP, London.

Taylor, C.E. (1982), 'Experiences from the worldwide primary health care movement relevant to Indonesia', paper presented at Seminar on Health for All by the Year 2000, University of Indonesia, Jakarta.

Tekce, B. and Shorter, F.C. (1984), 'Determinants of child mortality: A study of squatter settlements in Jordan', *Population and Development Review (Supplement)*, 10.

United Nations, Department of Social and Economic Affairs (1985), *Socio-Economic Differentials in Child Mortality in Developing Countries*, United Nations, New York.

United Nations/World Health Organization (1980), *Proceedings of the Meeting on Socio-economic Determinants and Consequences of Mortality*, UN/WHO, New York/Geneva.

Vallin, J. and Lopez, A. (eds) (1985), *Health Policy, Social Policy and Mortality Prospects*, Ordina, Liège.

Victoria, C.G., Smith, P.G. and Vaughan, J.P. (1986), 'Social and environmental influence on child mortality in Brazil: logistic regression analysis of data from census files', *Journal of Biosocial Science*, 18.

Ware, H. (1984), 'Effects of maternal education, women's roles and child care on child mortality', *Population and Development Review (Supplement)*, 10.

Weinberger, M.B. and Heligman, L. (1987), 'Do social and economic variables differentially affect male and female mortality?', paper presented to 1987 Annual Meeting of the Population Association of America, Chicago.

Yang, S. and Dowdle, N.B. (1985), 'Trends and levels of mortality in China', paper presented at the International Symposium on China's One-per-Thousand Population Sampling Survey, Beijing.

Young, F.W., Edmonston, B. and Andes, N. (1983), 'Community level determinants of infant and child mortality in Peru', *Social Indicators Research*, 12.

Chapter 5

MASS EDUCATION AS A DETERMINANT OF MORTALITY DECLINE*

John C. Caldwell

Demographic transition theory has always held that the twin determinants of a modern pattern of demographic behaviour were declines in both mortality and fertility from high and approximately equal levels in pre-modern society to low and approximately equal levels in modern society. Furthermore, it has been held that there is a relationship in the timing of these two declines and also in their causes.

Two caveats should be made. The first is that the demographic history of the West provides some difficulties. If we take the case of England, for which we now have estimates extending back for centuries, it is clear that mortality decline began more than two centuries before fertility decline. The orthodox answer to this is that the decline was so slow that the forces causing it did not reach the cumulated strength, and hence the necessary threshold, for fertility decline until the late nineteenth century. It is usually assumed that there are greater cultural resistances to fertility control than to the reduction of mortality and hence there is a lag in the onset of fertility decline. Evidence for the validity of this argument may be found in the fact that fertility decline followed closely on mortality decline only in France, the one country where massive political and social revolution had reduced the resistances to changed fertility behaviour.

The second caveat is the existence of a minority of demographers who claim that one has to seek only the causes of mortality transition, in that the mortality decline itself was the necessary and sufficient condition for the subsequent fertility decline. They tend to see the long gap in the West between the onset of mortality and fertility transitions as being a product of the very gradualism of the mortality decline. Given our focus in this paper on the nature of mortality decline, this debate need not worry us, although I should declare my hand by saying that the evidence appears to me to argue against this viewpoint.

There are, however, two points I would like to make at this stage. The first is that the contemporary Third World is experiencing faster mortality declines – and, in most cases, faster fertility declines – than was the historical experience of the West. This means shorter lags and probably greater interaction between the two processes. The second point is that there is almost certainly a two-way interaction between the

*First presented as CASID Distinguished Speaker Series No. 6, Michigan State University, October 1988.

mortality and fertility declines. Most of the Western decline in mortality over the last three centuries has occurred subsequent to the onset of the fertility decline a century ago, and steep falls in infant and child mortality in the first decades of the present century probably owed much to the smaller family.

There are two kinds of evidence with regard to the relationship between education and mortality. The first is the evidence at the individual level that, as parental education increases, infant and child mortality declines. Over the last decade, there have been a great number of studies of this relationship and its existence is now one of the most certain contributions to social scientific knowledge. Marked differentials in child survival by the education of parents cannot be explained on other socio-economic grounds and survive all controls for income, access to health services and similar factors. In most societies the impact of mother's education is substantially greater than that of father's education, doubtless evidencing greater maternal involvement in care. There are almost certainly other, but probably weaker, relations between education and mortality, although they are harder to prove. Education probably increases an individual's own chances of survival during both childhood and adulthood, and it may improve the chances of one's spouse.

The second is the relationship between the level of education in a whole society and mortality levels in that society. In a paper that examined correlations between both infant mortality and life expectancy on one hand and a range of characteristics of Third World countries on the other, both mortality measures were more closely correlated with education than with any other characteristic (Caldwell, 1986). The only other factor that competed at all was the practice of family planning, while measures of health inputs, nutrition and income were of much less importance. Another study, which was confined to infant mortality, concluded that every one per cent reduction in female illiteracy decreased infant mortality by almost 0.3 per cent (Flegg, 1982).

I wish to proceed by examining the evidence from some of the major studies so that we can determine the factors likely to cause the beginning of mortality decline and, above all, those factors that operate right across a range of societies.

The most substantial body of good data on Third World mortality is that which was collected from 1975 onward by the World Fertility Survey. When mortality data were available for 28 developing countries, Hobcraft et al. (1984) published an analysis of socio-economic factors in infant and child health. At that time, survey data were available for only four African countries, so most of the following discussion centres on Latin America and Asia, although it might be noted that the later African data seem to follow the same patterns.

With regard to education, the focus of Hobcraft et al. (1984) was largely on differentials in the survival of children to five years of age according to mother's education, but their findings can be used to compare child mortality levels and differentials between countries.

Their most important finding at the individual level was the extraordinary stability of the relationship between maternal education and child survival across the different continents and across enormous differences in societal levels of education and mortality. For instance, if we examine the survival of children to five years of age among four groups of mothers, those with no education and those with 1-3, 4-6 and 7 or more years of schooling, and express the mortality among the children of uneducated mothers as 100, then we get the following results. In Africa, the four groups of mothers, in rising order of education, score 100, 79, 61 and 41 (representing death rates declining from 234 to 97 per thousand births resulting in deaths in the first five years of life). In Latin America, the ratios are 100, 77, 64 and 39 (representing death rates declining from 140 to 54 per thousand), while in Asia they are 100, 84, 73 and 48 (representing death rates declining from 144 to 69 per thousand). The situation is not greatly affected by the mortality level. In Asia, where stability in the ratios is somewhat greater than in Africa or Latin America, the series by maternal education is, among the higher mortality countries, 100, 82, 72 and 48, while among the lower mortality countries, it is almost identical at 100, 89, 75 and 47.

The mortality of a country, however, is not determined solely by the mix of education among adult females. There is no stability across countries in the absolute level of child survival according to mother's level of education. In Latin America, the level of child mortality among uneducated women is about one-third as much in the lowest mortality countries as in the highest, and this ratio is maintained for the next two education groups, although it rises to around half in the most educated. In Asia, mortality of only one-third as much among low mortality countries characterizes all education groups. Thus, from every one thousand births, the number of children dying before five years of age is, among uneducated women, 226 in Haiti and 237 in Peru, compared with 82 in Jamaica and 74 in Trinidad and Tobago; among women with seven or more years of education, the rates drop to 89 and 55 in Haiti and Peru and 51 and 43 in Jamaica and Trinidad and Tobago. If we scale these countries from the highest to the lowest mortality, we find again a close correlation with increasing levels of education and a somewhat weaker correlation with increasing levels of income.

There is, thus, as close a correlation between child survival and general levels of education in a community as there is between child survival and maternal education. An uneducated woman may feel more deprived in a country where most other women are educated than one in which they are not: nevertheless, her children stand a much greater chance of survival. If we take these two factors together, the contrasts are enormous. In Latin America, the death rate among the children of uneducated Peruvian women is almost seven times greater than that among Venezuelan women with seven years of education. In Asia, the mortality among children of uneducated Nepalese women is almost 15 times greater than it is among those of Malaysian women with seven or more years of schooling.

What happens where countries attain nearly universal education? The criterion of universal education used here is the enrolment of at least 95 per cent of all children and 90 per cent of girls in elementary school in 1960, namely those who were to be the parents of the 1970s and 1980s. By this measure, near-universal schooling had been attained among the analysed World Fertility countries in Latin America by Trinidad and Tobago, Jamaica, Venezuela, Panama, Paraguay, Costa Rica and the Dominican Republic, and in Asia and Oceania by Fiji, Malaysia, Korea, Sri Lanka and the Philippines. With the exception of the Dominican Republic, these countries had the greatest proportion of children surviving to five years of age: 90-95 per cent in Latin America and 91-94 per cent in Asia. By 1982 the World Bank (1984) estimates of life expectancy for these countries ranged between 65 and 74 years in Latin America and between 64 and 70 years in Asia. There is little doubt that mortality levels close to those of the industrialized countries can be achieved within two decades if nearly all children are educated through elementary school.

The Western mortality transition was not as clear-cut as this. Mortality seems to have fallen slowly from the seventeenth century. When the countries of north-western and Central Europe and the English-speaking countries of overseas European settlement moved toward universal schooling in the 1870s and 1880s, they had life expectancies in the range 40-49 years (Keyfitz and Flieger, 1968). By 1910 the range was only 50-59 years, averaging almost 15 years below today's Third World countries that attained universal schooling a quarter of a century ago. Furthermore, as Preston (1985) has shown, socio-economic status, and, by inference, the level of education, had a much more limited impact. The 1900 United States census showed that the children of the professional, managerial and clerical classes experienced, in the first five years of life, 94 per cent of the mortality of the whole population, compared with a figure of 65 per cent for similar classes in the contemporary Third World. Preston cited Rochester (1923) to illustrate that, when income was controlled, literate mothers in Baltimore of 1915 had mortality rates not dissimilar from illiterate ones. My explanation for the relatively subdued educational impact in the earlier Western health transition is that, although education did raise the level of maternal care, it did not reach its full potential because of the relative lack of assistance that medical services could provide when approached by mothers of sick children. Thus, this evidence does suggest a symbiotic relation between parental education and the development of effective health services in bringing down child mortality.

Mortality in the West between 1850 and 1910 declined slowly; life expectancy typically increased about one year for every five elapsed years. In the last 40 years, life expectancy in the Third World has gained one year in every two years or a little more. Even in sub-Saharan Africa, the period has not fallen below three years (Hill, 1987). Doubtless, more effective public health services, insecticides, antibiotics and the like are an important part of the story, but so have been increasing education levels. One should not exaggerate the proportion of Third World population even now having access to health services of any adequacy.

The Rockefeller Foundation convened a workshop in 1985 to examine certain Third World populations with particularly impressive health achievements (Halstead et al., 1985), and the background of these achievements was subsequently investigated further by Caldwell (1986). These were societies that had virtually thrown off the Malthusian shackles of economic determinism, in that they had achieved health levels almost as high as the industrial countries, and, in the case of the first three, with incomes only one-thirtieth as great. In 1982, Sri Lanka had an annual per capita income of $320, China of $310 and Kerala of perhaps $200. Their life expectancies were 67, 69 and 66 years, respectively. Costa Rica had an income four times as great, but still only one-tenth of the United States; but had achieved mortality levels almost the same as the United States.

The second study (Caldwell, 1986) identified the 11 countries in the Third World that had done much better in terms of health than their incomes would predict and the eleven that had done worst by this measure. The first group had an annual per capita income of $500, an infant mortality rate of 64 per thousand, and a life expectancy of 61 years, while the second group had a per capita income almost ten times as great, an infant mortality rate double the first group, and a life expectancy ten years shorter. What was the explanation? The investigation showed that the two groups did not differ markedly in density of health services, although the superior health achievers had been more likely to have experienced a period of social and political enthusiasm when community health services attempted to reach the poor and those in remote rural areas. They were much more likely to have their children in school, especially their girls. In 1960, the superior health achievers had 76 per cent of boys of elementary school age in school, compared with 53 per cent among the poor health achievers, but in the case of girls, this gulf widened to 55 per cent compared with 23 per cent. Islam was a major factor in explaining this gap among the low achievers. The success of the superior health achievers was no capricious whim of policy makers. The achievement of high levels of female education, the establishment of national health services, and the willingness of women to use these services and make the staff attend to their children rested upon a substantial degree of female autonomy, a radical tradition, and a deep-seated respect for education and enlightenment.

I would like to concentrate for a short time on Sri Lanka to make some of these points clear. A high degree of female autonomy has been attested to by Western observers over the last three centuries. There has always been a Buddhist respect for education, but this was raised to new heights by the Buddhist Reform Movement of the late nineteenth century, which was a cultural reaction to colonialism. One result was that the 1921 Sri Lankan census revealed a higher proportion of the population educated than did the 1971 census of Pakistan. Nevertheless, by 1930, life expectancy was still no more than 40 years. The beginning of the real breakthrough was one of the world's great experiments in social engineering. A British constitutional team, the Donoughmore Commission, appointed by Britain's last

Liberal government and with its report accepted in 1928 by its first Labour one, recommended universal female enfranchisement from 21 years of age. The express reason for this was that only women cared sufficiently about their children's health and education to be able to force governments to budget sufficiently large sums for these areas. Surprisingly, in a democratic atmosphere where parties alternated in government every three years, this is exactly what happened. Within 20 years of all adult women casting a vote for the first time (only three years after they did so in Britain), universal schooling had been achieved, there was a nation-wide free health service, and life expectancy was nearing 60 years.

What then are the mechanisms at work?

An excellent starting point is a recent comparative analysis by Cleland and van Ginneken (1987) of the statistical and other data now available. They showed that, in addition to the information from the World Fertility surveys, similar differentials by maternal education could be shown from other sources for India and China, the latter revealing that the organized egalitarian system did not discount the impact of education. They concluded from their greater range of data that:

> The inverse education-mortality relationship is found in all major regions of the developing world; the association is very pronounced, but appreciably closer in childhood than in infancy; and even a modest exposure of the mother to formal schooling is associated with reduced risks of death in most contexts. In view of the diversity of educational and health standards and of cultural and social systems, these are remarkable results (Cleland and van Ginneken, 1987:3).

They showed that maternal education has a greater relative impact on child mortality than on infant mortality, because the near-universality of breastfeeding dampens down inequalities in treatment during the first year of life. It might be noted that, as breastfeeding everywhere tends to shorten as education increases, this influence tends to hide potentially even greater differentials in survival by educating the mother. They were able to draw on analyses by Hobcraft *et al.*, to show that differentials in child survival by maternal education are not the product of differences in reproductive patterns. They pursued the question of the relationship between women's education and other family material advantage

> to reach the broad conclusion that the economic advantages associated with education (income, water and latrine facilities, clothing, housing quality, etc.) account for about one-half of the overall education-mortality association (Cleland and van Ginneken, 1987:9).

Two points should be noted. The first is that the residual half still leaves a great deal to attribute to the purer — perhaps the care — component of education. The second is that many of the material advantages listed above flow at least partly from the mother's education and cannot be regarded as wholly external to it.

Cleland and van Ginneken showed, as we have done in our own work, that there is evidence that educated mothers are more likely to use modern health facilities and use them better. In contrast, the evidence does not seem to point to women with some schooling knowing much more about disease causation than women with no schooling. They also confirmed that in many countries maternal education was most conspicuously more important than paternal education in rural areas, while fathers' education was often just as important in towns.   This may be evidence that urbanization, as well as education, sets up modern attitudes to care, that modern health facilities are easier to access there, and that money is an important determinant of survival in towns.

How, then, does education achieve its impact?   What are the intervening mechanisms? We have spent much of the last 15 years trying to answer this question, first in Africa, then in South India and more recently in Sri Lanka.

Africa provided two lessons that our later work has sustained.   The first was the discovery that there are substantial differentials in child survival by education of mother, even in localities almost entirely cut off from modern medicine (Orubuloye and Caldwell, 1975). There is certainly a care component that goes beyond the use of modern health facilities.   The second point is that the quality of schooling seems relatively unimportant, compared with the fact of schooling having taken place and its duration.   It is not so much what you learn or understand, but how you see yourself and how others see you.

This latter point has been pursued further in Asia.   In rural Bangladesh, Lindenbaum *et al.* (1985) showed that the subsequent behaviour of school children follows a certain pattern largely because the ex-students know that this is the pattern of behaviour of those who have been to school.   They are cleaner because educated people are cleaner; not because the health and hygiene lessons taught them that soap destroyed the bacteria that were the agents of infection. We found in South India that women who had been to school thought of the school as part of the whole modern system, which included independence, five-year plans, government programmes, health centres, modern medicine and themselves (Caldwell *et al.*, 1983). They knew that they were the kind of people who took their children and themselves to health centres, and their illiterate mothers-in-law – in spite of a personal scepticism about modern medicine – knew it too.

In South India, we found the strongest relationships between education and other factors to lie in the realm of treatment.   First, there are differences in taking action with regard to sickness.   As far as we could determine, illiterate mothers are just as likely as educated ones to notice that a child is sick.   This is important, for mothers are by far the most likely to notice first that a child is sick.   But educated mothers much more frequently take action without waiting for their husbands or mothers-in-law to notice the child's condition too.   This is partly because illiterate women do feel a lack of capability when dealing with the modern world.   This has been shown well in a small-scale survey in Northern India by Khan *et al.* (1987).   Nevertheless, the difference also arises from the fact that the woman who has been to school knows that the school expects her to take action and that she should not be bound by deference to traditional decision-making patterns and excessive female modesty when children's health is at stake.   Strangely enough, this is a view usually shared by her parents-in-law.

In the subsequent treatment, the educated mother has the advantage at a whole series of points. She is more likely to get the attention of the health worker or doctor and to get it more quickly, as Okediji (1975) has shown convincingly in the case of Nigeria. She explains the symptoms and problems more clearly, understands the instructions better, and is more likely to persist in obtaining the prescribed medicines. She follows the prescribed treatment more closely, and is much more likely to persist with it. We found one major differential that is probably of widespread importance. The educated mother is much more likely to report back to the health centre if the treatment does not seem to be effecting a cure.   Educated women see the whole business as being experimental.   The illiterate tend to think in terms of fixed disorders with fixed treatments that either succeed or fail. In addition, they regard the failure as a failure of the healer and any attempt to report it back as being an attack on him or her.

This interaction with the health system is by no means all the extra care that the educated can provide. Traditional illiterate mothers do not identify all disorders as disease at all but regard many as forms of divine punishment or disfavour and as either immutable or unavoidable. Traditional Indian rural life seems to put little emphasis on the need for rest when sick, except in the case of the old. Educated mothers are much more likely to allow a sick or feverish child to rest, instead of working. Without question, the households of educated women are cleaner and the residents are cleaner. There is more attention to bacteriological pollution and less to ritual pollution.

Finally, education has its effects on each generation and has compounding multi-generational effects. Wealth flows reverse when children go to school (Caldwell, 1982). School children receive a larger share of the family resources than do illiterates in terms of health care, more general consideration and food. This appreciation of educated children and the ability of the mother to divert resources is reinforced when she too has been to school. A quarter of a century ago we investigated the situation in Ghana at a time when many households had a mix of children who had been to school and some who had not (Caldwell, 1968). Not only were the latter treated with much less consideration, but parents were surprised that we considered anything else to be logical.

We moved our research focus to Sri Lanka in 1985, partly to look at a society that was nearly wholly educated. In these circumstances, both our own work and the World Fertility Survey analyses show that the differentials in child mortality by parental education are muted. The whole society adopts new attitudes toward health and treatment. There is a heightened feeling of individual responsibility towards overcoming ill-health, both personal and in terms of close relatives. This is manifested in two ways. The first is the very brief period between identifying illness and taking first action, even if only home treatment. The second is a heightened awareness of the danger of postponing recovery, with the result that patients who do not recover transfer themselves, or are transferred by relatives, every four or five days from one treatment to another or from one doctor to another (Caldwell *et al.*, 1989). The predominant direction of these transfers is towards modern medicine and larger and more specialized institutions. There is thus a referral system that is largely operated by the patients or their families.

The Sri Lankan sensitivity to illness and the need for treatment is heightened by a governmental framework. Death registration has been effectively compulsory all this century and post-mortems are carried out in the case of any unexpected or untimely death. There is still partial enforcement of the *Sudden Death Ordinance* of 60 years ago that set up lay committees to enquire about sudden deaths.

In one sense, the real inquiry now should be into the conditions of mass education. In the south Indian state of Karnataka, we investigated the nature of the educational transition (Caldwell *et al.*, 1985). The demand to educate children is a demand for new economic opportunities, for daughters who can win superior husbands, and for a better way of life. Its strength depends on whether there is non-agricultural employment in the region. The availability of schools to meet this demand depends partly on the strength of the demand, partly on how it can be expressed through the political system, and partly on government planning policies with regard to education. The likelihood of children staying at school depends on how easily their labour at home can be forgone and on whether their success at school seems likely to make the investment profitable. Parents do not educate children so that their grandchildren will have greater chances of survival, but it is widely recognized that educated women are more likely to keep their children healthy, as well as educating them, and these factors can play some role in the choosing of a daughter-in-law.

The coincidence in timing of the mortality and fertility transitions largely depends on common changes in the economy, society and family. But there are interaction effects that are important. It is no accident that the greatest declines in Western infant and child mortality occurred in the first quarter of the present century, a generation after the achievement of universal schooling. Similarly, the level of family planning in Third World societies is an indicator of mortality levels second only to that of education. Parents are anxious that small families should survive, not only in one-child China, but far beyond. The achievement of mass schooling can accelerate both mortality and fertility declines, both by direct impact and by interaction effects.

Mass education cannot be advocated in poor countries purely because of its demographic impact. The total package of direct economic benefits, of demographic effects, and of social change, however, can be pressed both in terms of internal budgeting and for the provision of foreign donors of technical aid. Education is important socially because it fits people for a changing society and because of its impact in terms of gender equity. Demographic transition is both a product of a changing society and an important cause of further change. A small healthy family almost ensures the development of a modern economy. An educated populace may be the only way of bringing into being the community health involvement advocated by the *Alma Ata Declaration*.[1]

The remaining question is whether rapid mortality decline can be achieved by shorter and cheaper methods than universal education. There is evidence that an intensive health programme can reduce the differentials by mother's education in child mortality, but the intensity required can be economically destructive. For instance, Libya, faced in the early 1980s by the fact that only one-quarter of its young adult women had any schooling, moved to a point where it had ten times as many doctors relative to its population as did Sri Lanka and twice as many as Costa Rica; yet its infant mortality was still three times that of Sri Lanka and five times that of Costa Rica, while its life expectancy was 12 years shorter than Sri Lanka and 17 years less than Costa Rica. The situation in Saudi Arabia and Oman was similar. It should be added that Libya, like Iraq, has moved fast since, and Saudi Arabia moderately fast, to remedy the situation with regard to women's education. It may be possible to legislate, and enforce the legislation, to give young women the undisputed right to take immediate action with regard to their children's health and to make health personnel react readily to the needs of the uneducated and poor; there are some parallels to this in how the most efficient family planning programmes work. In many countries, such steps would be helpful, but are likely to be really effective only when accompanied by a major effort to get all children into school. The obvious question is whether mass adult education campaigns could not achieve the same results more cheaply and without having to wait a generation. My experience has been that such campaigns are not particularly efficient in producing lasting literacy. They are likely to be even less efficient in producing substantial declines in child mortality, largely because of the evidence that schooling affects malleable children so much because of its impact on how they see themselves, rather than what is taught them.

Let us now return to the original question. Is the attainment of mass education related to the onset of mortality decline? The answer is that the onset of mortality transition is probably as much affected by the attainment of mass education as is the onset of fertility transition. However, there may be a greater lag effect. The education of children immediately makes them more expensive and likely to force their parents to think about fertility control. Admittedly, limiting the family may also immediately change the care situation. In addition, an educated child may care for himself or herself to a greater extent than an uneducated child, and both the school and parents may add to these efforts. The total impact on mortality will not be great, however, because mortality is always low in the school-age range. The greatest impact of education on health will be achieved only in the subsequent generation

---

[1]The World Health Organization sponsored a conference at Alma Ata in the Soviet Union in 1978. Here a major programme, 'Health For All By the Year 2000', was launched. This programme is committed to meeting basic health needs through primary health care. The aim is to avoid undue concentration on major hospitals by placing emphasis on simple health services, such as those that can be rendered by paramedics.

through the medium of better parental care. Finally, the facts are quite clear. There is a symbiotic relationship between improved education and better and more comprehensive modern health services. All the budgetary eggs should not be put in one basket.

ACKNOWLEDGEMENTS

Support for the preparation of this paper was provided in part from a grant by the US Department of Education under Title VI of the Higher Education Act.

REFERENCES

Caldwell, J.C. (1968), *Population Growth and Family Change in Africa: The New Urban Elite in Ghana*, Australian National University, Canberra.

Caldwell, J.C. (1982), *Theory of Fertility Decline*, Academic Press, London.

Caldwell, J.C. (1986), 'Routes to low mortality in poor countries', *Population and Development Review*, 12, 2:171-220, (also Chapter 1 of this book).

Caldwell, J.C., Gajanayake, I., Caldwell, P., and Peiris, I.(1989), 'Sensitization to illness and the risk of death: an explanation of Sri Lanka's approach to good health for all', *Social Science and Medicine*, 28, 4:365-379, (also Chapter 12 of this book).

Caldwell, J.C., Reddy, P.H. and Caldwell, P. (1983), 'The social component of mortality decline: an investigation in South India employing alternative methodologies', *Population Studies*, 37, 2:185-205, (also Chapter 11 of this book).

Caldwell, J.C., Reddy, P.H., and Caldwell, P. (1985), 'Educational transition in rural South India', *Population and Development Review*, 11, 1:29-51.

Cleland, J. and van Ginneken, J. (1987), 'The effect of maternal schooling on childhood mortality: the search for an explanation', paper prepared for the British Society for Population Studies Meeting, Sheffield.

Flegg, A.T. (1982), 'Inequality of income, illiteracy and medical care as determinants of infant mortality in underdeveloped countries', *Population Studies*, 36, 3:441-458.

Halstead, S.B., Walsh, J.A. and Warren, K. (eds) (1985), *Good Health at Low Cost: Proceedings of a Conference held at the Bellagio Conference Center, Bellagio, Italy, 29 April-2 May, 1985*, Rockefeller Foundation, New York.

Hill, A. (1987), 'Demographic responses to food shortages in the Sahel', paper prepared for the FAO Expert Consultation on Population and Agricultural and Rural Development: Institutions and Policy, Rome, 29 June-1 July (mimeo.).

Hobcraft, J.N., McDonald, J.W. and Rutstein, S.O. (1984), 'Socio-economic factors in infant and child mortality: a cross-national comparison', *Population Studies*, 38, 2:193-223.

Keyfitz, N. and Flieger, W. (1968), *World Population: An Analysis of Vital Data*, University of Chicago Press, Chicago.

Khan, M.E., Anker, R., Ghosh Dastidar, S.K. and Bairathi, S. (1987), 'Inequalities between men and women in nutrition and family welfare services: an in-depth enquiry in an Indian village', *Population and Labour Policies, Working Paper No.158*, International Labour Office, Geneva, (also Chapter 10 of this book).

Lindenbaum, S., Chakraborty, M. and Elias, M. (1985), 'The influence of maternal education on infant and child mortality in Bangladesh', report for the International Centre for Diarrhoeal Disease Research, Bangladesh, Dhaka, (also Chapter 6 of this book).

Okediji, F.O. (1975), 'Socio-economic status and attitudes to public health problems in the Western State: a case study of Ibadan', in J.C. Caldwell (ed.), *Population Growth and Socio-economic Change in West Africa*, Columbia University Press, New York, pp. 275-297.

Orubuloye, I.O. and Caldwell, J.C. (1975), 'The impact of public health services on mortality: a study of mortality differentials in a rural area in Nigeria', *Population Studies*, 29, 2:259-272.

Preston, S.H. (1985), 'Resources, knowledge and child mortality: a comparison of the US in the late nineteenth century and developing countries today', in International Union for the Scientific Study of Population, *International Population Conference, Florence, 5-12 June 1985*, Vol. 4, IUSSP, Liège, pp.373-386, (also Chapter 3 of this book).

Rochester, A. (1923), *Infant Mortality: Results of a Field Study in Baltimore, Md. Based on Births in One Year*, US Dept. of Labor, Children's Bureau, Bureau Publication No.119, Government Printing Office, Washington DC.

World Bank (1984), *World Development Report 1984*, Oxford University Press, New York.

Chapter 6

THE INFLUENCE OF MATERNAL EDUCATION ON INFANT AND CHILD MORTALITY IN BANGLADESH*

Shirley Lindenbaum, Manisha Chakraborty and Mohammed Elias

Recent studies have directed our attention toward the effect of maternal education on infant and child mortality in Nigeria (Caldwell, 1979; Caldwell and McDonald, 1981), Kenya (Mosley, 1983) and Bangladesh (Halim and Hossain, 1981; D'Souza and Bhuiya, 1982; Chowdhury, 1982; D'Souza, 1982). It is generally agreed, as Caldwell (1979) first proposed, that maternal education acts as an independent determinant of child mortality and is normally a proxy for other social variables. Although child survival is primarily determined by the social and economic resources available in the child's family, 86 per cent of the decline in child mortality in Kenya between 1962 and 1979 may be attributed to the increase in maternal education (Mosley, 1983:16).

Most attention has been given to demonstrating the finding itself, that maternal education is inversely related to the mortality levels of infants and children. A few studies turn their attention to examining the mechanisms by which this may be brought about. LeVine (1980), for example, considers schooling as a psychological variable which affects the ways in which Third World women think about and behave toward their infants and children, Caldwell (1979) speculates on the importance of maternal education in changing structures of authority, and Mosley (1983) proposes a model of social and biological synergy which takes the level of education of women as a social determinant influencing the risk of death through several intermediate biological variables.

Since the education of the mother has been shown to be an important predictor of the mortality levels of children in Bangladesh, the present anthropological investigation was designed to examine the interacting social and biological variables that have received less attention. The study focuses in particular on the historical shift in the meaning of 'education' in Bangladesh, the psychological and social changes effected by the education of women, and the implications that these may have for the survival of infants and children, as well as for educated women themselves.

---

*First published as a report for the International Centre for Diarrhoeal Disease Research, Bangladesh, August 1983.

METHODS

Four villages were initially selected for study, two from the five villages of the Matlab SES investigation of socio-economic status, nutrition and mortality, and two villages at Shotaki Bazaar, namely Shotaki and Shugondhi in Matlab Thana some distance from Matlab, an area which until 1979 was included in the Matlab surveillance studies. The Shotaki region was selected because I carried out anthropological fieldwork there from 1963 to 1966, and for a short period in 1974. Since the first few weeks of field work indicated that the Matlab area villages did not differ significantly from the villages at Shotaki Bazaar (in socio-economic status and the educational level of women), most of the time was spent in the two villages adjacent to Shotaki Bazaar.

The study began in mid-February and came to an end at the beginning of May. Research assistance in the field was provided by Manisha Chakraborty, Health Assistant ICDDR,B, Matlab, who came to live with me at Shotaki, and Mohammed Elias, a resident of one of the villages who joined ICDDR,B as a Research Assistant for the duration of the study. Manisha Chakraborty and I took up residence in one room of my former fieldhouse, which has recently become a hospital for diarrhoeal disease, staffed by four male and one female paramedics trained by ICDDR,B. What we sacrificed in serenity and space, we gained in exposure to a constant stream of incident and information concerning the health care of mothers with children under the age of five. Most of our daytime hours, however, were spent away from the hospital. We visited every *bari* (patrilineal family compound) in the two Shotaki villages at least once, and a few *baris* almost every day.

THE IMPORTANCE OF EDUCATION FOR WOMEN

In the early days of the study, it became apparent that it would not be difficult to record the educational level of most women, young or old, in all the villages under study. In contrast to a woman's age (even the age of schoolgirls), or the specifics of the occupations of absent males (sons and brothers), information which was often vague and difficult to pin down, the educational level of females is widely and accurately known. Even boys ten to 12 years of age seem to know the educational level of most of the women in their own and adjacent *baris*, including that of their married and now departed older sisters. The only exception to this concerns non-elite elderly women, whose educational accomplishments are sometimes unknown or of little interest to others. For the most part, however, educational attainment is considered an important part of the social identity of all women.

RECENT CHANGES IN WOMEN'S EDUCATION

There are many indications that the current value attributed to the education of women is a recent phenomenon. One way to trace this shift is to look at the history of Sharifullah High School at Shotaki Bazaar, one of three high schools in the Union, and the school which most of the educated residents of the two adjacent villages have attended or currently attend. Begun as a primary school in 1939, with classes 1 to 5, it was upgraded in 1943 to admit students to Class 8, acquiring the status of a high school (up to Class 10) in 1945. In the same year, the government officially recognized the school, and the first students, who were all male, sat for the SSC (Secondary School Certificate) examination, the qualification given upon successful completion of ten years of schooling. Although a few girls from elite families attended the primary segment of the school in its early years, the first girl to enter

Class 6 was admitted in 1953. She failed the SSC examination in 1958, but another female student who entered Class 6 in 1954 passed the exam in 1959. The early 1950s thus marks a period in which there was a significant increase in female school enrolment, with more girls entering primary school and proceeding to the secondary level. The student population now consists of:

	Boys	Girls
Primary school	275	150
Secondary school	249	94

The present ratio of boys to girls in the whole school is thus 2.15:1, and in the primary grades 1.83:1. These figures seem comparable to the nation-wide trend documented by Sattar (1982:32) in which the ratio of boys to girls in primary school was 4:1 in 1950 and 1.7:1 by 1980. Although the total number of students attending primary school in Bangladesh in the last few years may have declined, since school enrolment has not kept pace with population increase (*Bangladesh Times*, 20 March 1983), the Sharifullah school data suggest that the presence of girls in the schoolroom has actually grown larger. The first woman teacher appointed to the local school began teaching primary school students in 1976. Married into an elite family of Shugondhi, she has passed the SSC and Primary Teachers Institute examinations, and her own children attend the Sharifullah school.

Islamic schools situated in the villages provide another avenue of education. The Shugondhi Islamic school (or *Maktab*) began in 1913, and at the same time taught Bengali, mathematics and Arabic. Since 1939, however, when the Sharifullah school opened, students attending *Maktab* early each morning study only Arabic, as in the other Islamic schools in the area. Not all students attend Islamic schools. About 25 boys and 25 girls attend the Shugondhi *Maktab*, and the Shotaki *Maktab* is somewhat smaller. Moreover, some children attend no school at all.

The changing educational experience of women, which began in Bangladesh in the 1950s, has many important consequences. In the first place, even though many women still do not attend school, the community of women can be divided into those over the age of 40[1] who have little or no education, and women under the age of 40 whose educational experience ranges from Primary Schooling to SSC (a graduate of Class 10), to HSC (Higher School Certificate, two years beyond SSC), or even BA (Bachelor of Arts, two years in addition). Although highly educated women (and men) tend to reside in Dhaka or some other urban area of Bangladesh, there is considerable visiting back and forth between villages and town, and the social universe of village residents may include those who work and live for a major portion of their lives in urban areas.

Information concerning educational level was obtained for every woman in the two villages. At the present time, the mean number of years of schooling for women over the age of 60 is 0.53 (n=75), and for women between the ages of 40 and 59 the mean is 1.25 years (n=199). For women between the ages of 20 and 39, however, the mean rises to 2.96 years (n=424). The dramatic increase in women's education may be better expressed in the following manner:

---

[1]Women's ages are estimated according to a consensus position based sometimes on Matlab Census registration of birth, the relative birth order of a woman among siblings, the number of a mother's pregnancies, her recollection of the Hartal of 1929 and other historic events. The ages may thus be off in either direction by several years, but since the decision as to a woman's age was in the last instance made by myself, the bias should be consistent.

TABLE 1

Age in years	Women with no education	Women with some education	Per cent with some education
60+	64	11	14
40-59	141	58	29
20-39	214	210	50
10-19	128	192	60

Although 14 per cent of women over the age of 60 report that they have some education, they did not attend schools for many years, as the following table illustrates:

TABLE 2

Age in years	Women with less than five years schooling	Women with more than five years schooling	Per cent with more than five years schooling
60+	74	1	1.3
40-59	189	10	5.0
20-39	329	95	22.4
10-19			

(school experience for this cohort is not yet complete)

Thus, the current generations of adult women have vastly different levels of educational experience. Daughters are more highly educated than their mothers. In a sample of 101 mother-daughter pairs, 66 daughters at the time of their marriage had an education that exceeded that of their mothers, 31 had the same education, and four had less than their mothers. However, of the 31 pairs with the same education, 27 had no education at all, and four had reached the same grade in Primary School. Of perhaps greater importance, daughters-in-law are now more highly educated than their mothers-in-law. A sample of 139 mother-daughter-in-law pairs shows that 72 daughters-in-law have more education, 62 the same (of which 61 have no education, and one pair studied to Class 5), and five have less education than their mothers-in-law. This generational feature of women's experience will be discussed later.

In general, women marry husbands who have more education than themselves, a situation which is not unexpected. However, a sample of 298 married couples shows that 39 wives have more education than their husbands, a finding that seems initially somewhat surprising. In most of these cases, however, the husband has a job (*chakri*) and is thus a wage-earner, or he is a farmer belonging to a family with sufficient land to produce a surplus of food. That is, the husband's economic condition is stable, or even favourable, and his family is in a position to acquire a more highly educated daughter-in-law for their son. In several cases, the more educated wife is the man's second or third partner, the earlier uneducated[2] wives having been divorced. Moreover, where the disparity between the educational level of husband and wife is highest, the contribution of the groom's family to marriage costs increases. In one family, for example, a young farmer with no education whose bride has studied to Class 5 contributed more wealth than did his brother who studied to Class 6 and married a woman with seven years of schooling. Where educational levels are equal, marriage expenses tend to be shared by the two parties. This indicates that female education has a social value at the present equivalent not to male education, but to the economic condition of the husband and his family.

The changing meaning of education for women in Bangladesh can be captured by looking at the matter from another direction. A small but educationally diverse sample of men and women 40 years of age and over were asked to give their views about the qualities they desired in marriage partners for two periods of time – the past generation and the present. They were also asked to talk about the qualities they thought desirable in members of their own gender for the same two periods of time. In general, the most frequently mentioned attributes included *bongso* (hereditary title of the lineage, such as Sarkar, Chowdhury etc.), the beauty of the bride (*sundor*, meaning in particular the lightness of her skin), the social status of the family (*bhadra lok*, upperclass, 'gentlefolk'), the economic condition of her family, and education. When rank ordered according to the number of times each attribute was mentioned, the results show an interesting shift over time:

TABLE 3: MEN'S VIEW OF QUALITIES DESIRED

In wives		In husbands	
Past	Present	Past	Present
1. *Bongso*	1. Beauty	1. *Bongso* and economic cond.	1. Employment
2. Beauty	2. Economic condition and education	2. Social status and education	2. Economic condition and education
3. Social status	3. Social status and *Bongso*	3. Employment	3. Social status
4. Economic condition and education			

TABLE 4: WOMEN'S VIEW OF QUALITIES DESIRED

In wives		In husbands	
Past	Present	Past	Present
1. *Bongso*	1. *Bongso*	1. *Bongso*	1. Employment
2. Beauty	2. Economic condition	2. Economic condition	2. Economic condition
3. Social status and economic condition	3. Beauty	3. Social	3 Education and *Bongso*
	4. Education	4. Education	

As Table 3 indicates, men have a decreased concern for the hereditary status of the bride's family, but an increased interest in her family's economic condition. They are still preoccupied with the bride's beauty, although no less so than in the past. The wife's education (unmentioned for the first period) is now of some concern. When women consider the features they desire in a husband, they show most interest at present in the husband's employment, followed by his economic condition. Hereditary status, previously a prime concern, drops to third place, which it shares with the groom's education, a feature unmentioned for the earlier period. Both men and women thus register a loss of concern for the hereditary status of the husband's family, and replace it with economic condition, which is no longer necessarily tied to *bongso*. Education has entered into the evaluation of a bride, and women's priorities are compatible with the finding that educated women are marrying men with jobs or with sufficient land to farm, even though the husbands may have less education than themselves.

Men currently view employment as the most desirable qualification of husbands, followed by education and economic condition. Hereditary status is no longer mentioned. As to the qualities of wives, women continue to regard their own family's hereditary status as important, but beauty is given less current notice by women than by men. The economic condition of a woman's family is an important feature of women's self-evaluation, as is her own education, unmentioned for the past.

Women's education is thus a rapidly moving social counter. Its current meaning differs from that of the recent past when only young women from elite families received an education. At that time, female education may have more nearly described or functioned as a proxy for social and economic status. Now, women of the four locally recognized social classes[3] may go to school, although many children from the lowest social categories still do not attend, or attend intermittently, since their contribution to household labour is of greater value. In addition, although primary school is now free, and books are distributed without cost to Classes 1 and 2, the poorest children do not have the clothing to permit them to attend school daily.

The education of women has a new value at the time of marriage, where it currently defines an important aspect of the bride's status. Whether she marries a more highly educated groom or one with no education, women marry into families

---

[3]People recognize four social classes, based at the present time on the following criteria: reputation of the bari name within the area and the Thana; the number of educated people in the bari; the amount of land and wealth; and whether family members labour for themselves or for others.

considered to be of equal or higher status than their own (isogamic or hypergamic marriages), thereby permitting family groups to continue to pursue the old strategies with new social components. Women's education has thus broken loose from an earlier cluster of socio-economic attributes, and is no longer a proxy for hereditary or social status. Women with education are now said to be less costly when their families come to arrange their marriages. Indeed, one uneducated woman said jokingly: 'I did not go to school, so I should demand 20,000 *taka* to give to my husband, since this amount was not spent on my learning'.

Education differs in one important aspect, however, from the other attributes considered desirable in a bride. Education, in a sense, belongs to the woman alone. To some degree it reflects upon her family's ability to bear the expense of schooling and suffer the loss of her youthful labour, but it is unlike the hereditary or social status of her family, in that it describes something specific to the woman herself. Like physical beauty, it contributes to her sense of identity, but unlike that physical attribute, education has a more dynamic effect on the behaviour of the educated person and of others toward her, a feature to be considered next.

HOW EDUCATION CHANGES WOMEN

Ninety people (51 men and 39 women) from all four social classes, with educational experiences ranging from no education to a Master of Commerce, were asked to discuss the ways in which education might have an effect on women. Forty-one men and 35 women thought that education was a good thing for women, but ten men and four women disagreed. Those who thought that education was not a virtue were predominantly masculine, and were all older persons with little or no education. In general, the responses were overwhelmingly in favour of women receiving an education.

The effects of female education seem to cluster around three main topics:

a. the psychological changes education brings about in the woman

b. the economic value that accrues from educating women

c. the new status given to the woman, and the implications that follow from this.

a. Psychological Effects

Men almost always mention the self-sufficiency of educated women. They 'depend upon themselves', they become 'proper persons (*manush*)', men say. They become 'brave and smart'. Even those who disapprove of educating women stress the behavioural and psychological consequences of schooling. Educated girls 'choose husbands for themselves and do not depend on their fathers and mothers', because 'their character becomes bad', and 'they do not serve their parents or nurse their husbands well'. Those who approve often point to the woman's enhanced ability to live harmoniously with her husband and his relatives. 'They become psychologists, and their dealings with their husband's family is admirable'. They also begin to behave in a 'gentle manner'.

Women agree that their relationships with their husbands' relatives improve, and stress in addition that their conjugal life is also happier. They comment that they are not too shy to discuss things in their husbands' households, they become 'frank' (*misug*), and consider that their family life is 'progressive'. Educated women feel themselves to be more intelligent, and sometimes add that the behaviour of educated women is 'more polite'.

b. Economic Value

As mentioned earlier, men and women agree that it costs less for an educated woman's family to arrange a marriage. Once married, men especially point to the fact that an educated girl who can read and write can now appreciate the income and expenditure of her new family, and has a better sense of handling financial and domestic affairs. The role of the educated mother as tutor for her children, thereby saving the family the expense of an outside tutor, is often mentioned by more educated people. Women with less education point to the skills acquired with literacy when it comes to a dispute over land. A woman who can read and write does not have to take court documents to outsiders who may not be trustworthy. An educated woman acts in an autonomous fashion, thereby protecting her own interests. Similarly, an educated woman who receives a letter from her husband does not have to risk taking it to another woman who may read the letter but convey only part of the text, thereby coming between the woman and her husband.

Women often suggest that educated girls can find employment (*chakri*), which they describe as jobs with family planning, or schoolteaching, citing instances of the few women they know who have gained these positions. They sometimes add that a woman's income will be of benefit to her mother and father, who will be supported by her earnings. Although female employment is recent and still rare for women in this region, 45 per cent of women (and 31 per cent of men) spoke about women finding paid work. Moreover, our census data on women's education show that parents, especially in non-elite families, tend to give the highest education to firstborn daughters, with subsequent daughters attending school for shorter periods of time. Thus, the firstborn daughter studies to Class 10, the second to Class 8, and the third stops at Class 5. While high education is an investment toward a marriage that will reflect upon the entire family, the parents of firstborn daughters are also actively seeking employment for them. It might be said that daughters are becoming 'sons' in many rural families. This new focus on employable daughters suggests that male and female infants might receive equal nurture, and that the greatest shift in morbidity and mortality rates of children under five should occur with the better survival of daughters, especially those of educated women.

c. New Status and its Implications

As mentioned, an educated woman is said to take upon herself the role of family tutor, helping the children learn to read and write, a task with social as well as economic implications. She is also said to become a better nurse for her husband when he becomes ill, and can also take better care of the whole family. Men add that educated wives keep the house cleaner, and entertain guests well. Women agree that their housework is good, and they say that they feel that educated women manage the family well. Uneducated women point to the fact that an educated bride acquires a good husband, and may also travel to foreign parts (*bidesh*), which sometimes means another country, but more likely refers to somewhere beyond the local community, such as Chittagong or Dhaka. She is in a good position to 'buy soap and saris and eat good food' and 'she and her children enjoy good health'. Moreover, uneducated women add, she marries at a later age than themselves and does not have to do any hard agricultural work. The latter point sometimes leads to a discussion as to how many years of schooling are necessary to provide protection from hard labour. It is generally agreed that young women with secondary schooling to Classes 5, 6 and 7 might still be found doing agricultural work, processing crops within the *bari*, but not those with matriculation and beyond. 'With education to Class 10, or a BA, you can pay maidservants to work and carry water for you'.

MOTHER'S EDUCATION AND THE HEALTH OF CHILDREN

The evidence from this last section concerning the psychological and social changes effected by educating women brings us closer to the question of the relationship of mother's education to the mortality of children. Women and men experiencing or observing the first generation of women receiving schooling (other than the small elite of earlier years) point to its liberating effect. Women themselves speak of the new tool which makes them self-propelled, of the freedom from dependency and constraint. Others comment on the way education changes the woman, gives her a kind of 'autonomous' value, and provides her with skills that at the present time are considered useful and highly respected. Education transforms the woman in the eyes of others, as well as in the estimation of the woman herself. How does this translate into better health for her children?

Some of the answers to this question have been suggested already. Educated women are said to keep themselves, their houses and their children neater and cleaner than the poor and uneducated, an observation that seems superficially to be the case. A focus on sanitation must come, in part, from the lessons learned at school. A textbook used in Class 3, for instance, has segments on sanitation and hygiene, and shows Salam and Mina washing their hands before eating. Mina also washes her plate at a tap, and covers her rice and vegetables to keep them free from contamination. The book speaks of the importance of burying rubbish and refuse, and of keeping the flies away. A Class 6 textbook likewise shows a picture of a thin, malnourished child. When a group of Class 6 children returning home from school were asked why the child seemed to be in such bad condition, they said that it was because he was dirty and did not eat good food. Class 3 children also report that the teacher talks to them about hygiene and cleanliness, confirmed by the female schoolteacher herself, who adds that she inspects children each day for tidiness, and that any child with a skin infection such as scabies is sent home until the condition improves.

When passing groups of children on a village path, it is easy to predict which of them go to school and which do not. Schoolchildren are polished clean. They have unsoiled clothes, their skin shines, and their hair is combed and glossy. Schoolgirls may be directed to focus more on cleanliness than schoolboys. Schoolbooks give more attention to Mina performing hygienic acts than Salam, and schoolgirls report that they wash their own clothing, but boys say it is their mothers who perform this task. Moreover, the one school toilet is used by the girls rather than the boys.

Schooling encourages upwardly mobile behaviour. At school, the behavioural styles of the elite are a model for others to imitate, personal cleanliness being perhaps the easiest to follow, the quality of clothing and nutrition the more difficult. The cohort of girls who travel together through secondary school keep an eye on one another. When secondary schooling is completed, they try to keep abreast of the news of higher education, marriage, and the fortunes of the first years of married life, especially of their elite companions. Schoolgirls have the freedom to move out of the *bari* every day, where they are exposed to a wider range of people and experiences than those who work at home, or even those who work as maidservants for others. For uneducated girls, given the constraints of purdah, there is no similar context in which they can join as equals with a cross-section of young people from all the surrounding villages, whose behaviour they may intimately observe and follow. An opportunity to observe the imitative behaviour of schoolgirls arose during several photo-taking sessions, where clothing, purses, reading glasses and other prestigious items were borrowed by the girl having her photo taken at each particular instant.

Schooling endows girls with prestige, and as the comments of uneducated women indicate, educated girls try hard to emulate the behaviour of 'gentlefolk'. When it is possible, educated women wash with tank or tubewell water at home, bypassing public bathing in the canals and river, thereby avoiding waters shown to be most contaminated (see Khan *et al.*, 1981).

Schooling also presents girls with new sources of authority from whom they seem willing to learn. Of the schoolgirls who visited our room in the hospital (nearly a daily event), all said they had access to a radio, even if it was not in their own house. Although Bengali songs are their passion, they also listen to broadcasts concerning health and family planning, and some girls in Class 6 knew what time of day to listen to the evening news. With the schoolbell ringing throughout the day to alert different classes to set off for school, schoolchildren become accustomed to a more structured, time-defined existence than those for whom the bells require no behavioural response.

On many occasions I was struck by the quick conversational replies of young women who had been to school, in contrast to their uneducated mothers or mothers-in-law. Young women with a Class 5 or 6 education, as well as younger schoolgirls and schoolboys, showed great interest in our work, and sometimes followed us across the borders of one or two *baris* to participate in the discussions. Educated younger people are more familiar with an interrogatory style which sometimes puzzles or fatigues their uneducated elders. Moreover, they seem to enjoy the interchange. The experience of schooling, however, goes beyond acquaintance with a new conversational style. Women speak of a newfound consciousness, a sense of mental change (*poriboton hoi*) that empowers them to act. 'If a girl studies to Class 5 she feels there is no work she cannot do', said one man who had studied to Class 5 himself. The evidence from Shotaki thus seems to support Caldwell (1979) and LeVine's (1980) suggestion that participation in the classroom is a form of assertiveness training, especially for girls who otherwise grow up in contexts that do not encourage them to express their thoughts or feelings. Caldwell notes than an educated woman is more likely to feel personal responsibility for the health and welfare of her offspring and to act in ways that redirect the intergenerational flow of family resources in favour of children, who may work less hard and live a healthier life (1979:412).

HEALTH CARE

A sample of the principal attendants accompanying patients at the Shotaki hospital[4] during three weeks in April 1983, shows that although the admission fee is 20 *Taka*, the facility serves mainly the poor and uneducated.[5] Eighty-eight people were interviewed, 77 women and 11 men. Of the 77 women, 59 had no education, while ten of the 11 men were unschooled. The percentage of uneducated women in the sample (76.8 per cent) thus substantially exceeds the percentage of uneducated women of similar age (over 20) in the population at large (53.5 per cent).

When one looks at the behaviour of the 47 mothers in the sample with children aged five years and under, the picture becomes more complicated. Thirty-one of the mothers were uneducated, and 16 had some education. Sixteen of the 31 uneducated mothers, and 11 of the 16 educated mothers had sought no treatment prior to coming to the hospital. That is, roughly half of the uneducated mothers but two-thirds of the educated women came directly to the hospital for oral rehydration solution (ORS) or intravenous saline for their children, which it might be argued is the informed choice of medical service in the case of diarrhoeal disease. From another point of view, it could be said that uneducated mothers made more vigorous attempts to find alternative medical care before coming to the hospital, and their choice of practitioners is weighted in favour of local (largely self-trained) allopaths, as Table 5 shows:

---

[4]The Union Council has named the hospital the Shaitnal Union Cholera Hospital.

[5]It could also be that the poor and uneducated encounter more illness episodes.

TABLE 5

	Mothers with no education	Educated mothers
Allopath	11	2
Homoeopath	1	2
Kobiraj	2	1
ORS from hospital worker	1	

The numbers are too small to draw any conclusions, and a more illuminating way to discover if uneducated mothers pursue different health care is to consider the following case study of Khorsheda.[6]

Khorsheda, a young widow in her late twenties, studied to Class 7. She has four children to care for. Concerned that the second eldest, a boy about eight years of age, seemed thin and slow growing, and to suffer from intermittent fevers, she sought a variety of cures during the month of March 1983. Beginning with bespelled water from a local *huzur* (an Islamic woman curer) which seemed to have no positive effect, she turned next to a local allopath and then an allopath practitioner in the distant town of Narayanganj, both of whom prescribed tonics, the latter medicine costing 50 *taka*. Toward the end of March, seeing no improvement, she made a longer trip with her son to the hospital at Munshiganj, where she had heard that MBBS trained doctors would be available. This longer trip, which was her own idea, required assistance from a variety of kin.

Khorsheda first persuaded her mother-in-law to accompany her, a considerable feat, as Khorsheda's story later illustrates. Since the journey required that she stay away from home for two days, she left the remaining three children with her mother, whose house she passed on her way to the ferry *ghat*. Her older sister's husband provided the money for the journey's expenses and the cost of the medicines. Moreover, her sister's husband had relatives who lived near the hospital, and it was with them that Khorsheda, her mother-in-law and her son stayed. After several days, she returned with the hospital laboratory reports (the child was diagnosed as having several types of worms), and with worm medicine and a tonic. As her mother commented, she carried off the venture due to the generosity of certain kin.

While it is true that the journey required a far-flung support system, it was Khorsheda who conceived of and directed the complex arrangements, against considerable odds. Since her husband's death one-and-a-half years earlier, her less educated mother-in-law has shown little sympathy for the young woman's predicament. She views her daughter-in-law instead as a girl with seven years of schooling who should find employment to support her children and herself. Immediately after her husband's death, Khorsheda began to appreciate the precariousness of her position in the household of her in-laws, and asked that a small amount of land and a house be legally allocated to help her support her children. Her parents-in-law were unsympathetic to this request, whereupon Khorsheda appealed to one of the most influential members of the community, a man who is her mother's brother (in somewhat distant kin terms). The mother's brother argued her case, and

---

[6]This is not her real name.

the deceased husband's parents reluctantly granted her half a *kani* agricultural land and a house site in the *bari*. Still, the mother-in-law repeatedly proposes that Khorsheda should leave the village to find a job that would bring in a salary.

Khorsheda, meantime, tries to devise a way in which she might earn a livelihood but continue to live at home with her four children. She wonders about a sewing machine to make and sell clothes, but does not have the money to buy the machine. She has sent a message to her mother's brother (who now resides mainly in Dhaka) that she wishes to see him when he next visits Shotaki. She continues to match wits with the mother-in-law, who she says has begun to give her children less food than they need. Fortunately, Khorsheda's mother's house is situated in an adjacent village, and the children frequently call at the mother's house for snacks and meals on their way to and from school.

This is a story of tenacity and perseverance, of the behaviour of a young woman whose educational status exceeds that of her mother and her mother-in-law. She has a sense of the social geography beyond the limits of the household compound, and she knows where good medical care is available, and how to gain access to it (cf. Nag, 1981). Further, as an educated person she is in a position to command the assistance of other elite and educated people in better circumstances than herself, who are strategically placed to help her.

Those who responded to her wishes were all her elders – her mother, sister's husband, mother's brother, even the reluctant mother-in-law who stands in the position of greatest authority over her. It is significant that the dispute between Khorsheda and her mother-in-law centres around the deployment of family resources between the generations, as Caldwell (1979) might have predicted. Khorsheda successfully orchestrates resources in favour of her children; the mother-in-law views Khorsheda instead as an educated person who should 'replace' the wage-earning son she has lost, not someone she should be obliged to support. Perhaps the most significant aspect of Khorsheda's activities concerns the fact that her behaviour is directed at 'preventive' health measures – nourishing food for the children, and an attempt to maintain a standard of healthy growth. Her children, three of whom attend school, are kept spotless and clean. Despite the recent tragic circumstance that has left her in a poor financial situation, Khorsheda has a sense of herself as an educated person of a certain social standing. She expressed embarrassment when we found her one day in a ragged sari, spreading wheat seed to dry in the *bari* courtyard.

Khorsheda's story illustrates the predicament facing a young mother who loses her husband, the mainstay in a precarious system of support. Khorsheda was able to secure help from some close and some distant kin whom she judged could assist her. Most educated women do not face widowhood so early in married life. Uneducated women, however, do suffer a similar deprivation in that they are frequently divorced during the early years of marriage. My own data on this point (not yet tabulated) show that uneducated and poor women are increasingly subject to the stress of enforced return to their parents' households, often with infants they must continue to care for. As divorced women, their social status and economic condition is unfavourable, and their ability to care for small children is greatly constrained. Any family resources they can muster will be pledged toward the expenses of another marriage, which they (and their parents) hope will provide a safer haven than the last. The number of poor, uneducated women in this situation is quite high. Shaikh's analysis (1982) based on data from Matlab between 1975 and 1979 shows also that divorce is inversely related to the education of both bride and groom. The lowest divorce rates at Matlab occur among brides and grooms with secondary education or higher. Thus, educated women tend to have access to a network of strategic support which it is acceptable to call upon, and one which is more likely to stay in place for the duration of their married lives.

Education has a substantial effect not only on the stability of marriage, but on the age at first marriage of a woman. As uneducated women at Shotaki observe, educated girls marry later than themselves, a feature of social life which may favour the future mother and her infants. Before marriage, an educated daughter does little strenuous work. This is a moment in her life when a certain amount of prestige accrues to the entire family by keeping her at home in apparently unproductive luxury, the rewards of such image management being a well-regarded marital alliance (Lindenbaum, 1975:78). Under these conditions, a young woman living at home until the age of 19 or 20 is likely to approach motherhood in a healthier and better-nourished state than an uneducated hard-working younger person. Having invested in the education of their daughters, even non-elite families give them special consideration in the few years prior to marriage. Thus, educated women may approach childbirth in a relatively well-nourished state, and give birth to babies of greater birth weight, a condition judged to be a survival advantage (Khan, 1980). They may also experience greater success in breastfeeding, especially if they return home for the birth of the first child, a custom that many women aspire to, since they eat and rest better in their own homes.

One further bio-social consequence of women's education may lie in the fact that as the present study shows, educated women tend to marry into economically 'secure' families. Moreover, in this region, women in economically well-placed families light the hearth fire twice a day for two separate food preparations (apart from breakfast, that is), in social class 1 and most of social class 2, but only once a day (in the late morning) in some of social class 3 and all of class 4. Thus, the degree of bacterial contamination of food, an important cause of diarrhoeal disease in children (Black *et al.*, 1982) may be greater in families of the poor and less educated who eat foods following longer periods of storage. School lessons concerning the reheating of cooked foods may make an important difference in families where cooking occurs once only.

One consequence of the likelihood that the children of the poor (and presumably uneducated) have higher mortality rates than their better nourished and wealthier counterparts (Chen *et al.*, 1980), concerns the fact that a mother of a breastfeeding infant with diarrhoea modifies her own dietary regime. It is universally believed that the cause of the infant's illness stems from the spoilage of the mother's milk. She thus responds by avoiding meat, fish, eggs and often salt, a regimen which if frequently repeated would further affect the nutritional status of the mother and her ability to produce breastmilk. In addition, a breastfed child on supplemental food who suffers from diarrhoea also has its diet changed. In some cases, the mother withdraws breastmilk for the duration of the illness, and in most cases eliminates rice and decreases bread, puffed rice, biscuits, banana and other supplements. These two dietary modifications would seem to have two deleterious effects. Firstly, repeated episodes of diarrhoea lead to a downward spiral in the nutritional status of both mother and child, a constitutional challenge that better-nourished better-educated women and their children may be in a position to withstand.[7] In addition, an interrupted course of suckling imposed by the mother on the child, and by an ill child on the mother, might inhibit the mother's capacity to generate a constant supply of breastmilk, leading to the infant's further nutritional deprivation. My own data are not sufficient to indicate that educated mothers follow a better course of nourishment for their infants and themselves during illness episodes. The infants admitted to the Shotaki hospital frequently cried for food, but it sometimes seemed that this was because the mothers had not prepared well for this unusual and disorienting period away from home. The matter of dietary modification during illness, and supplemental foods are topics that could be investigated more fully.

---

[7]This nutritional regime may be one cause also of the post-partum condition women call shutika, a nutritional anaemia experienced by large numbers of women at Shotaki.

HEALTH CARE BELIEFS

As the previous section indicates, the health-seeking behaviour and health status of educated women differs from the behaviour of those with no education. The question of differing health beliefs, however, is answered largely in the negative. There is no evidence in my data that education significantly changes the ideas of women about the causes of disease. Rich and poor, educated and uneducated, Muslim and Hindu women on the whole share similar beliefs about the origin of disease. It is only among the most educated women (and men), and only for certain diseases, that one finds any different notions concerning disease origins. Some fundamental cultural postulates about the workings of the human body and the universe still provide a unity from which the causes of specific diseases are deduced (see Lindenbaum, 1964, 1965 for a fuller discussion).

In conversations at Shotaki with 206 persons (155 women and 51 men) concerning the cause of disease – primarily diarrhoeal diseases, fevers and scabies – the germ theory of disease was mentioned only twice. One 40-year-old man with a Bachelor of Science degree observed that dysentery (but not diarrhoea) in a variety of age groups was caused by lack of cleanliness; diarrhoea in patients beyond breast-feeding age was said to arise from 'irregular eating'. In the second exception, a 23-year-old woman with an SSC qualification noted that her one-year-old child suffered from chickenpox, an infectious disorder caused by germs. However, dysentery in the same child, as well as in its three-year-old sibling, was said to be a hereditary disease acquired from the mother.

Apart from these two cases, there was general agreement that infant disorders result from spirit attack associated with bad winds, and that illnesses of children and older people result from various bodily imbalances caused by poor eating habits, hard work, and occasionally as punishment from God. An educated woman's understanding of the value of hygiene and sanitation sits as an epiphenomenon on these more fundamental postulates that explain the workings of the body and society, and the causes of illness. Educated women follow hygienic behaviours associated with the social standing of prestigious people. They keep their children, children's clothing and food free from dirt and contamination, and observe *bhadra lok* codes of personal behaviour; they refrain, for instance, from spitting inside houses, wipe mucus from their children's faces, and bathe in 'private' waters.

SUMMARY, SPECULATIONS AND SUGGESTIONS FOR FURTHER INVESTIGATION

The present anthropological approach treats education as an 'empty category', its meaning to be spelled out by informants' opinions and by observations of the day-to-day behaviour of educated and uneducated people in a rural setting. Compared to its meaning for women prior to the 1950s, education in the 1980s carries a different social import. Children of classes other than the elite now attend school, and a bride's education enters into an evaluation of her qualifications at the time of marriage, displacing and rearranging earlier considerations. Thus, an epidemiological approach that divides the data into educated versus uneducated, without regard to historical period, misses an important shift in meaning. Education could be said to function as a proxy for social and economic status for the earlier period only.

The search for a 'cultural definition' of education leads to the perception that education is not the same thing as literacy. Some advantages stem from the capacity to write, but as many of the Shotaki residents indicate, schooling has other transforming effects. Rural women with a few years of primary education who could not be considered 'literate', acquire a prestige that raises them above uneducated women in the village, many of whom are otherwise their seniors in age and lines of family authority. Education changes the views of other people toward the educated person as well as the view of the educated woman toward herself, as Caldwell notes. Education encourages exploratory and self-confident behaviour. Literacy adds skills that are perceived as economically and strategically useful. Moreover, 'literacy' emerges also as a culture-bound concept for Western academia (cf. Scribner and Cole, 1981), for the ability to 'read' the Koran in the absence of a further capacity to read and write in Arabic is highly respected, especially in women, and is said to be a skill that earns religious merit. In addition, the Union Council definition of literacy as an ability to write one's own name and recognize some words does not imply the degree of accomplishment conveyed by the Western use of the term.

The present study finds also that people at Shotaki are attracted to the efficacy of Western therapy, without dislodging their own theories of disease causation. Khorsheda, an educated woman, consulted indigenous spiritual practitioners before she turned to the MBBS-qualified doctors at a distant hospital. Many of the uneducated (and educated) clients who came to the Shotaki paramedic hospital had a similar therapeutic record, and their beliefs about the causes of disease showed little recognition of germ theory. The Shotaki data indicate that the differential behaviour of educated women in the pursuit of health care is carried out with little cognitive change concerning the cause of disease. Except at the highest educational levels, and in the case of one or two diseases only, educated and uneducated women (and men) share a set of common beliefs which do not stem from scientific medicine (cf. Chowdhury et al., 1981:184). Education appears to change the minds and behaviours of women in ways that influence the survival of their offspring without significantly changing their theories of disease origins.

The act of going to school in a society that restricts the movement of young women is a socially liberating experience. Each day schoolgirls now leave the confines of the household compound to make acquaintance with classmates from other villages, as well as a variety of other students from other social classes. Schooling exposes students to new information, new figures of authority, and a day structured in ways that differ from the agricultural round. Young girls exposed to the experience undergo a change that gives them a heightened sense of themselves and their own capacities, and prepares them for a style of discourse that depends on question and answer interchange. Schooling alerts them also to the delivery of information via media, such as the radio, and perhaps a willingness to accept it. The enhanced knowledge of life beyond the confines of the local community is said to provide an educated woman with the ability to handle the family budget in her husband's household, one example of the means-ends relationship that LeVine suggests follow from educating women. Some illiterate women at Shotaki, for instance, have no experience with money beyond small coinage, and they do not recognize the value of denominations of paper money such as 10- or 20- *taka* notes. The sense of personal awareness that occurs with 'literacy' may be its most important legacy. Women dwell upon the power it gives them to act independently, and in their own interest.

An educated woman gains access to a network of other educated people who may be instrumental in providing information and assistance when help is required. The social networks of the poor and uneducated are not as extensive, well-placed, or lasting. Uneducated women may ask kin and neighbours to contribute to the cost of medical emergencies, but their status in this network of support is that of an unequal supplicant. The plight of uneducated women, and their ability to nurture offspring, is further undermined by more frequent divorce and 'abandonment'. Some Shotaki men are now marrying seven or eight times, sending each wife back to her family, and keeping the small marriage dowries for their own use. Since the parents of educated women note that they are not under similar pressure to provide grooms with marriage gifts (although they are not free of the burden), education might protect some poor uneducated women from this recent strategy of wealth-acquiring males which is detrimental to the physical and emotional health of young women and their offspring.

The study of mother's education as a determinant of child survival traces a path that traverses both social and biological domains. Thus, education raises a woman's age at first marriage, protecting her from the risk of infant deaths associated with childbearing at a very young age. I would postulate further, that schooling itself safeguards young women from the performance of exacting labours during their growing years. Many children in Class 1 are eight years of age. Thus, a girl who studies only to Class 5 spends an important phase of her growth and development in the protective environment of the schoolroom. Sheltered from further excessive work before marriage, educated women presumably enter married life not only at a later age, but with physiological advantages that may protect their children, especially during illness episodes in the next few years, when the diets of mothers and their offspring are impoverished by behavioural strategies believed to safeguard them.

Uneducated women, by contrast, are frequently found as maidservants and labourers in the houses and fields of others. Between February and May at Shotaki, the most impoverished of them harvested dry crops such as coriander, millet and wheat, and then processed the produce in the owner's courtyards. The sight of women *harvesting* field crops is something new for Shotaki, and sign of increasing poverty in the region, and the migration from the village of male labour. Women speak of the arduousness of working with wheat, new crop for Bangladesh, which matures in the heat of April. Moreover, women (and many men) associate diarrhoeal disease in adults , including the mothers of breastfed infants, with 'hard work' and 'irregular eating', two hazards against which uneducated women find little protection. Poor, uneducated women perhaps have a greater chance of giving birth to low-weight infants, which they are subsequently unable to adequately nourish. While many educated women may also be poor and can be found processing field crops within the *bari*, the female field labourers at Shotaki are all women who are poor and uneducated. Educated women are not found labouring in the fields.

Observations at Shotaki indicate that education is also a form of upward mobility for women, who tend to marry husbands who are economically 'secure', and it is likely that their own nutritional status is thus relatively stable. In addition, educated women take upon themselves bathing habits, standards of cleanliness, and other forms of upper-class hygienic behaviour. Lessons learned at school concerning the contamination of food are also relatively easy to follow, even in poor households, and they distinguish educated women from others in the *bari*.

It is possible that one overriding factor will be found to be the determinant of the relationship between education and child mortality in Bangladesh, but there may be a multitude of contributing and interacting factors, as Mosley's (1983) model suggests. This pilot study indicates that the lives of educated women differ from those of uneducated women in a number of ways that may affect the chances of survival of their infants and small children. It is suggested, therefore, that the following questions be investigated in further detail:

1.   Does schooling 'protect' women? Are schoolgirls taller and heavier than their uneducated counterparts?

2.   Do educated women enter marriage and begin their reproductive careers in a state of better nutrition than uneducated women?

3.   Do educated women give birth in environments that provide better care for the new mother and infant? Do they have access to birth attendants, older family members, whose sanitary habits differ from those of uneducated birth attendants? Do they go home for first births, where they have lighter chores, and better nourishment for themselves?

4.   Do educated women have greater initial breastfeeding success than uneducated mothers, thereby avoiding the early introduction of contaminated weaning foods, as well as providing the protective advantages of breastmilk?

5.   Do educated and uneducated mothers differ in the ways they prepare and store supplemental foods? The Shotaki data suggest that water sources may be one important difference in supplemental food preparations. Uneducated women appear to use the same water that they bring in for general household use, rather than tubewell or boiled water.

6.   Does the 'illness diet' of the uneducated mother and child differ significantly from that of educated mothers and their children? Do educated and uneducated women avoid the same foods? Do educated women resort to more nourishing alternatives?

7.   Do educated mothers in poor households give greater attention to reheating foods cooked earlier in the day?

8.   Do the bathing habits of educated and uneducated mothers and their infants differ significantly? Do educated women not only bathe in 'private' waters, but where necessary, have others carry bath water to the *bari* for them? Do they also use this water for bathing their infants?

9.   What is the incidence of diarrhoeal disease or other illness in educated versus uneducated women? Is there a greater incidence of illness, especially diarrhoeal disease in women who work in the fields, as the Shotaki theories of disease causation would suggest?

10.   Is there a greater prevalence of anaemia in uneducated women?

11.   Will the new focus on employable daughters as if they were sons be reflected in the morbidity and mortality rates for females?

        (a)   are female infants showing better rates of survival than in the past?

        (b)   especially the daughters of educated women?

12.   Do educated women tend to follow preventive health measures more often than uneducated women? Do they make greater use of family planning?

13.   Do educated women have access to better information about quality medical care than uneducated women? Do they have better networks of assistance in gaining access to this care, and are their support networks more enduring?

   The first 12 of these questions should be quantifiable, and lend themselves to epidemiological investigation. Number 13 could also be quantified, but would require more extensive preliminary enquiry. The answers will contribute to a better understanding of the relationship between maternal education and the survival of small children, and thus provide policies that may contribute to reducing infant mortality. As the residents of Shotaki are aware, educating women is good social policy and an investment in health.

ACKNOWLEDGEMENTS

I am grateful to Dr William B. Greenough, Director ICDDR,B for his invitation to carry out this study, and for providing the facilities to enable me to do so. I would also like to thank Dr Stan D'Souza, Head, Community Studies Research Working Group for strategic support and encouragement, and Susan Zimicki for her insightful comments and discussion of the issues as the study proceeded. Dr Dil Mohammed, Shotaki Union Council Chairman, took an interest in the study and contributed in many ways to the ease of our living and working conditions.

REFERENCES

Black, R.E., Brown, K.H., Becker, S., Abdul Alim, A.R.M., and Merson, M.H. (1982), 'Contamination of weaning foods and transmission of enterotoxigenic *Escherichia coli* diarrhoea in children in rural Bangladesh', *Transactions of the Royal Society oif Tropical Medicine and Hygiene*, 76:259-264.

Caldwell, J.C. (1979), 'Education as a factor in mortality decline: An examination of Nigerian data', *Population Studies*, 33, 3:395-413.

Caldwell, J.C. and McDonald, P.F. (1981), 'Influence of maternal education on infant and child mortality: Levels and causes', in International Union for the Scientific Study of Population, *International Population Conference, Manila 1981*, Vol.2, IUSSP, Ordina, Liège, pp.79-96.

Chen, L.C., Rahman, M. and Sarder, A.M. (1980), 'Epidemiology and causes of death among children in a rural area of Bangladesh', *International Journal of Epidemiology*, 9, 1:25-33.

Chowdhury, A.K.M.A. (1982), 'Education and infant survival in rural Bangladesh', *Health Policy and Education*, 2:369-374.

Chowdhury, S.A., Ashraf, A., Khan, A.H., Nabi, N., Jamnat-e-Quanine, Delmonte, S. and Streefland, P. (1981), 'Health, disease, care and cure in rural Bangladesh: a study of three villages in Tangail district'.

D'Souza, S. (1982), 'Mortality case study Matlab, Bangladesh', UN/WHO Third Project Collaboration Meeting on Case Studies of Determinants of Mortality Change and Differentials, Geneva, December 14-17.

D'Souza, S. and Bhuiya, A. (1982), 'Socio-economic mortality differentials in a rural area of Bangladesh', *Population and Development Review*, 8,4:753-769.

Glass, R.I., Svennerholm, A-M., Stoll, B.J., Khan, M.R., Hossain, K.M.B., Huq, M.I. and Holmgren, J. (1983), 'Protection against cholera in breast-fed children by antibodies in breast milk', *New England Journal of Medicine*, 308, 23:1389-1392.

Halim, A. and Hossain, A. (1981), 'Women, time allocation and adoption of family planning practices in farm family', Publication No. 23, Graduate Training Institute Bangladesh Agricultural University, Mymensingh.

Khan, M. (1980), 'Infant feeding practices in rural Meheran, Comilla, Bangladesh', *American Journal of Clinical Nutrition*, 33:2356-2364.

Khan, M.Y., Mosley, W.H., Chakraborty, J., Sarder, A.M. and Khan, M.R. (1981), 'The relationship of cholera to water sources and use in rural Bangladesh', *International Journal of Epidemiology*, 10,1:23-25.

LeVine, R.A. (1980), 'Influences of women's schooling on maternal behavior in the Third World', *Comparative Education Review*, 24,2 (part 2):S78-S105.

Lindenbaum, S. (1964), 'Attitudes to health and disease in East Pakistan', Technical Committee Report, Cholera Research Laboratory, Dacca. Republished, Cholera Research Laboratory Working Papers, 1977.

Lindenbaum, S. (1965), 'Infant care in rural East Pakistan', Technical Committee Report, Cholera Research Laboratory, Dacca. Republished Cholera Research Laboratory Working Papers, 1977.

Lindenbaum, S. (1975), 'The value of women in Bengal in the 19th and 20th Centuries', in J.R. McLane (ed.) *Occasional Paper No. 25*, Michigan State University, South Asia Series, pp. 75-85,.

Mosley, W. (1983), 'Will primary health care reduce infant and child mortality? A critique of some current strategies with special reference to Africa and Asia', paper delivered for IUSSP Seminar on Social Policy, Health Policy and Mortality Prospects, Paris, 28 Feb-4 March, (also Chapter 14 of this book).

Nag, M. (1981), 'Impact of social development and economic development on mortality: A comparative study of Kerala and West Bengal', Center for Policy Studies, *Working Paper No. 78*.

Sattar, E. (1982), *Universal Primary Education in Bangladesh*, University Press Limited, Bangladesh.

Scribner, S. and Cole, M. (1981), *The Psychology of Literacy*, Harvard University Press, Cambridge.

Shaikh, K. (1982), 'Marriage and marriage dissolution in a rural area of Bangladesh', unpublished M.A. thesis, Development Studies Centre, Australian National University, Canberra.

Chapter 7

CULTURAL DIMENSIONS OF THE MOTHER'S CONTRIBUTION TO CHILD SURVIVAL*

John Simons

This paper starts with a description of the essential characteristics of a caring and skilful mother, the type familiar as a role model among educated people everywhere. The characteristics of this type are then contrasted with those of alternative types, to identify dimensions of cultural and subcultural variation. These are then used to produce a series of linked propositions about relationships between child survival and mother's values and beliefs. The series ends up with some propositions involving the role of mother's education. Succeeding sections of the paper review methods of obtaining evidence relevant to the propositions. Finally, ways of obtaining further evidence are proposed.

CONCEPTUAL FRAMEWORK

References to mother's education and child survival summon an image familiar to educated people everywhere. It is an image of a prudent, knowledgeable and caring woman, carefully protecting her offspring from injury and infection, ensuring that they are properly clothed and nourished, teaching them from early childhood to have a prudent regard for their own health and welfare. While the level of education and material resources implied make this image irrelevant to the circumstances of most mothers in developing countries, it does have some features likely to be distinctive of prudent mothers everywhere, even those who function in the most hostile of environments.

First, there is the characteristic of placing a high value on the survival of children. Accompanying this characteristic is the general belief that, by her own actions, a mother can do much to enhance the health of her child and/or diminish the prospect of illness and accident. Thirdly, there is a repertoire of specific beliefs about risks to health and ways of reducing them. Fourth, there is the practical skill to act on these beliefs: to recognize the circumstances in which they apply, and to act accordingly.

---

*First presented at the Ford Foundation's Interdisciplinary Workshop on Mother's Education and Child Survival, Ahmedabad, India, 16-18 January 1989.

These characteristics of the individual mother are normally representative of the culture, world view, of the status group within which she functions or aspires to function. Possession of such characteristics is among the criteria used by the mother herself and other members of the group to evaluate her performance as a member or prospective member. Thus the rewards of successful performance include avoidance of the negative sanctions imposed by other members of the status group. These include its fathers, who can be expected to be as committed as their wives to the survival of children, and to share their belief in the efficacy of parental intervention, though they may not share their wives' knowledge and skills.

Given this cultural model of a prudent mother, how do cultures vary with respect to the model? Clearly, one possibility is variation in commitment to the survival of children. In contrast to the cultural specification just described, it is possible to envisage an extreme form of an alternative in which children have no intrinsic value but where their value depends on the family's material circumstances. In the former case, the commitment is absolute, in the latter case relative.

Another possible dimension of variation lies in attitudes towards the efficacy of mother's intervention in child survival. At the extreme, people may believe that the survival of children depends on God or Fate or Luck, and is therefore not subject to control by actions of the mother. In the terminology of attribution theory,[1] those who hold this belief are described as having an external locus of control. Those who believe mothers can influence outcomes themselves are described as having an internal locus of control; these concepts are further explained below.

FIGURE 1: CULTURAL DIMENSIONS OF VARIATION IN COMMITMENT TO CHILD SURVIVAL

	Internal locus of control	External locus of control
Absolute commitment to child survival	Active commitment to child survival	Passive commitment to child survival
Relative commitment to child survival	Active but conditional commitment to child survival	Passive and conditional commitment to child survival

The third dimension of variation lies in the area of specific knowledge and skills. However, this is unlike the first two dimensions in an important respect. They are in principle independent of each other, though in practice they may be correlated. Knowledge and skill, however, are likely to be functions of one or the other of these variables, for logical rather than contingent reasons. People who are not committed to the survival of children, or who are sceptical about the efficacy of a mother's efforts to enhance survival chances, are not likely to be motivated to acquire the knowledge and skills necessary to successful intervention.

---

[1]Attribution theory is a sphere of social psychology concerned with the way people attribute causation.

The dimensions of commitment and locus of control are shown as axes of a classification schema in Figure 1. Within each of the four cells, different hypothesized orientations to child survival are shown.

PROPOSITIONS

The following series of propositions starts with those embodied in Figure 1 and ends with propositions involving the putative role of mother's education.

1. Important cultural (ideational) determinants of child survivorship are the extent of absolutism in the value placed on child survival by the mother, and the extent to which the mother's locus of control of child health is internal rather than external.

2. The mother is likely to be most active in preserving a child's health where an absolute commitment is combined with an internal locus of control.

3. The mother is likely to be least active in preserving a child's health where a relative commitment is combined with an external locus of control.

4. Where an absolute commitment is combined with an external locus of control, mothers will readily accept developments, such as immunization, that seem likely to improve the survival chances of their offspring, but will be slow to improve their own knowledge and skills.

5. Where a relative commitment is combined with an internal locus of control, mothers will be keen to intervene but may do so selectively, for example to favour the proportion of sons in the family.

6. Educated mothers are more likely than others to belong to sectors of society typified by an internal locus of control, because members of such groups are more likely to have seen education as a means of enabling their children to acquire, directly and indirectly, more control over the environment. It is this that accounts for most of the observed relationship between mother's education (net of income) and child survivorship, though it may be that education acts to reinforce an internal locus of control or the effects on health care of either an internal locus of control or high commitment to child survival.

7. The impact on survivorship of an internal locus of control and commitment to child survival and of any reinforcement due to mother's education, is the result, not of an effect on any one specific item of behaviour but of a pervasive effect on health-related behaviour in general. For example, a mother with an active commitment will be concerned to prevent accidents as well as to take advantage of any relevant health services, within the limits of her knowledge.

VARIATION IN COMMITMENT TO CHILD SURVIVAL

There is abundant evidence of variation in commitment to child survival in the history of developed countries and in data from developing countries.

Reviewing studies of the historical fertility decline in the West, Knodel and van de Walle (1979) proposed that negligent child-rearing practices and the resulting infant and child deaths had served to limit family size in the absence of birth control. From this perspective, they suggested, the high infant and child mortality rates found in much of Europe prior to the fertility decline could be considered as much an accommodation to high fertility as the opposite.

If, in the absence of birth control, dissatisfaction with excessive fertility led to significant numbers of infant deaths through neglect or abusive child care, this suggests that high infant and child mortality rates are not necessarily contra-indications to readiness for family planning programs, as has been generally assumed. Indeed, just the opposite may be true (Knodel and van de Walle, 1979:232).

In developing countries, the most striking evidence of variation in commitment to child survival is the data on sex differentials in mortality. According to Ware (1981) in the early 1970s there were at least five countries in Asia where discrimination against females was sufficiently strong to ensure that expectation of life at birth was shorter for females than for males: Bangladesh, Iraq, India, Pakistan and Sabah (East Malaysia). In addition, the data of three Asian populations showed that infant mortality was greater for female babies: Jordan, Pakistan and Sabah. However, there were nine populations where female mortality exceeded male mortality at ages 1-4: Bangladesh, Burma, India, Jordan, Pakistan, Sabah, Sarawak, Sri Lanka and Thailand.

That sex differentials in mortality are the result of differential care has been confirmed in a number of specific studies. For example, a study of the causes of death in Punjab (Wyon and Gordon, 1971) found that death rates from each cause were higher among females than males. During the first five years of life, the female death rate was 74 while the male rate was 50. Male babies received higher quality medical care and more supplementary food than girls. A more recent study in the same area of Punjab (Das Gupta, 1987) found that sex differentials in mortality had persisted, despite a rapid decline in overall child mortality rates, great improvements in income levels, nutritional levels, and health care delivery, and a variety of modernizing forces such as rapid increases in female education. During early childhood (1-59 months) female mortality was almost twice that of males. The excess was concentrated among females born to families that already had a surviving daughter. Expenditure on medical care for sons was 2.34 times higher than that on the daughters, and differentials in the effective utilization of medical care seemed to be the major mechanism responsible for sex differentials in mortality. Further, the findings contradict the common assumption that increasing female education necessarily improves the quality of care given to children, regardless of their sex. Among young educated women, younger sisters of surviving daughters experienced 2.36 times higher child mortality than their siblings. Das Gupta suggests this is because educated mothers have retained a preference for one or two sons while their preferred family size has dropped below three children. They are therefore under increased pressure to have fewer surviving daughters. 'Through a better ability to manipulate both their fertility and their children's mortality, educated women are better equipped than others to achieve the family size and sex composition that they desire' (Das Gupta, 1987:95). Apparently, these women belong to the bottom left cell of Figure 1.

In a review of evidence on under-investment in children in developing countries, Scrimshaw (1978) suggests other reasons, in addition to son preference, why an avoidable death may occur when a child is relatively unwanted: its high birth order, inadequate spacing between its birth and the previous birth, and the number of children already in the family. However, in her view, under-investment in child care is usually not due to the conscious behaviour of parents but is part of an unconscious set of behaviours that reflect a family's or a culture's 'population policy'. In many societies, a woman grows up in the certain knowledge that she will lose one child, so that 'of necessity' there is an acceptance of high rates of infant mortality and an accompanying lack of felt need to take desperate measures to save a child's life. Further, the death of a child is interpreted in a way that helps to resolve grief. In some Latin American countries, the death of very young children is seen as a cause for celebration because the child will become 'one of God's little angels'. Such attitudes appear to correspond with the syndrome identified in the bottom right cell of Figure 1. Finally, Scrimshaw refers to various specific ways in which under-investment in child care may occur, including poor definition of illness, inadequate breastfeeding or none at all, withdrawal of nearly all food when an infant becomes ill, withholding of physical and affective care from some (less valued) infants, inequalities in the distribution of food in the household, and similar discrimination in care during illness.

There has been much discussion in the literature of the proposition that there is a positive association between women's social position relative to that of men (especially in decision-making autonomy and economic independence) and the improvement of infant and child survival. The evidence has been recently summarized by Mason (1988) who concludes that, overall, evidence in support of the proposition seems fairly strong. However, she points to a number of weaknesses in the existing evidence. To these could be added the tendency of researchers to ignore the possible correlations between differences in women's social position and differences in much else in society. In particular, differences in men's attitudes seem to be as neglected in this field as they are in fertility research.

The next section of the paper reviews experience with modern concepts and methods employed in the investigation of values and beliefs related to commitment to child survival.

COMPONENTS OF VARIATION IN COMMITMENT

Behind what is actually observed as variation in commitment to child survival lies variation in health-related beliefs and values. This section of the paper describes a popular social-psychological model of these beliefs and values known as the Health Belief Model (Becker *et al.*, 1977a). The model has been used to predict a wide range of health-related behaviour, from accepting immunizations to adopting birth control, and including compliance with short-term and long-term treatments. The basic components of the Health Belief Model (HBM) are based on the concept of 'value-expectancy' which is derived from a well-established body of psychological and behavioural theory. Behaviour is predicted from both the individual's evaluation of an outcome and the expectation that a specific action will result in that outcome. According to the HBM, health behaviour is predicted by beliefs and values in three categories: motivation to avoid illness or get well; perceived vulnerability to, and seriousness of, specified illnesses; and perceived probability that compliant behaviour will reduce vulnerability or seriousness.

Applying the model to parental care, 'motivation' becomes equivalent to 'commitment' in the sense in which the term is used above. Presumably the greater a mother's motivation or commitment to child survival, the more likely she is to want to acquire and act on information about vulnerability to survival risks, the seriousness of particular illnesses, and available remedies. If education has an independent effect on survivorship, perhaps it is through its effect on perceptions of vulnerability, seriousness and choice of remedial action. Demographic, structural and enabling factors are included in the model, which is set out in Figure 2.

Fortunately for the purposes of this paper, Becker *et al.* have applied the model to a child-care issue: the prediction and explanation of mothers' adherence to diets prescribed for their obese children (Becker *et al.*, 1977b). The character of the model will be illustrated with a summary of this study.

FIGURE 2: THE HEALTH BELIEF MODEL

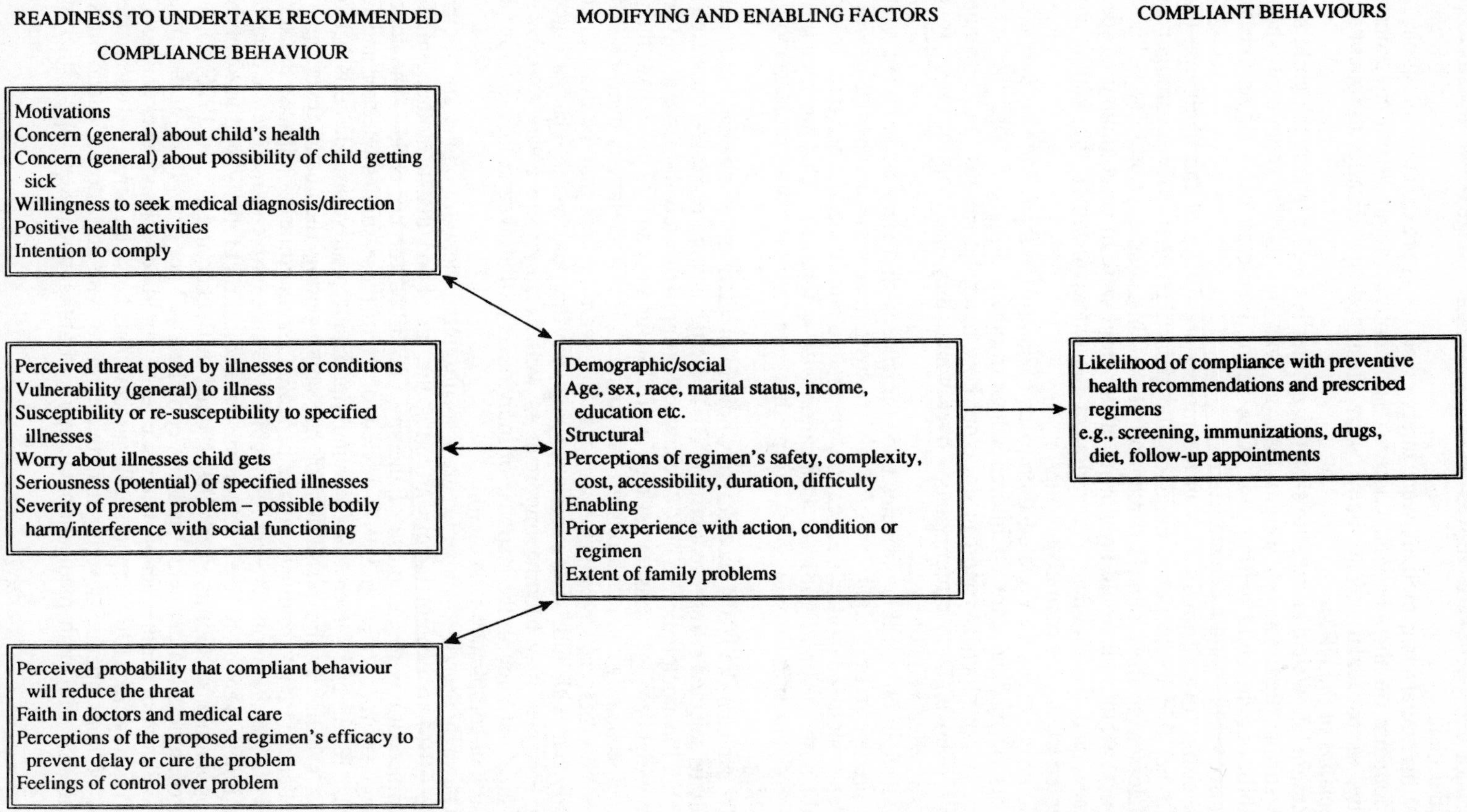

READINESS TO UNDERTAKE RECOMMENDED
COMPLIANCE BEHAVIOUR

MODIFYING AND ENABLING FACTORS

COMPLIANT BEHAVIOURS

Motivations
Concern (general) about child's health
Concern (general) about possibility of child getting
   sick
Willingness to seek medical diagnosis/direction
Positive health activities
Intention to comply

Perceived threat posed by illnesses or conditions
Vulnerability (general) to illness
Susceptibility or re-susceptibility to specified
   illnesses
Worry about illnesses child gets
Seriousness (potential) of specified illnesses
Severity of present problem – possible bodily
   harm/interference with social functioning

Perceived probability that compliant behaviour
   will reduce the threat
Faith in doctors and medical care
Perceptions of the proposed regimen's efficacy to
   prevent delay or cure the problem
Feelings of control over problem

Demographic/social
Age, sex, race, marital status, income,
   education etc.
Structural
Perceptions of regimen's safety, complexity,
   cost, accessibility, duration, difficulty
Enabling
Prior experience with action, condition or
   regimen
Extent of family problems

Likelihood of compliance with preventive
health recommendations and prescribed
regimens
e.g., screening, immunizations, drugs,
   diet, follow-up appointments

Source: Becker *et al.*, 1977b.

The study was conducted in a large paediatric clinic. The clinic served a predominantly low-income population, a fact reflected in the socio-economic status of the sample. Data on children's weight change were obtained by a dietitian at four follow-up visits to the clinic occurring at two-weekly intervals after the initial visit. The major dependent variable was the ratio of weight change between visits to weight at initial visit.

At the initial visit, mothers were interviewed for approximately one hour, with a questionnaire on their beliefs, concerns and motives about health in general and obesity in particular. The items were designed specifically to operationalize dimensions of the HBM.

Results showed that measures of the mother's concern about the child's health were strong predictors of weight loss, as was the mother's concern about the possibility of the child getting sick. One strong predictor was a single question on concern over the child's general health.

A strong overall predictor was the mother's estimate of the likelihood that she would be able to keep her child on the prescribed diet. Even stronger overall predictors were the mother's perception of the child's susceptibility to sickness, the degree to which she would be worried if the child were to get a number of specified illnesses, and the mother's perception of the extent to which the weight problem disrupted the child's normal activities.

Some questions were included on locus of control, in the section on the perceived benefits of medical care. Children whose mothers disagreed with the statement 'There is not much anyone can do about how much he weighs' and attributed the child's overweight to circumstances over which they had control, were found to achieve better weight loss.

Questions on possible obstacles to compliance with dietary advice were relatively poor predictors of weight loss, though stronger than socio-demographic variables. The latter included mother's education which, like family income and most other such variables, showed no significant association with weight loss. This has been the usual result of attempts in the West to predict compliance using socio-demographic variables.

To evaluate the HBM model as a whole in predicting compliance, belief indexes and items selected to represent critical HBM elements were regressed on weight loss. Together the nine predictors used accounted for approximately 49 per cent of variance in the weight change measured at the first follow-up visit and 22 per cent at the fourth visit. Speculating about reasons for the attenuation of correlations over the series of follow-up visits, the investigators suggest that health beliefs may be most important initially but with time and experience with the diet and weight-change outcomes, other variables may become important as well. (They were aware that, owing to biological variation in the response of individuals to diet, weight loss is an imperfect measure of compliance with diet.)

The study described above is part of a substantial literature on the use of elements of the HBM to explain factors affecting the likelihood that a mother will follow recommendations for a course of therapy prescribed for her child. The following findings are mentioned in a 1975 review of 36 of these studies (Becker and Green, 1975). Elling and Green (1960) found significant positive associations between a mother's belief in the possibility of her child getting rheumatic fever again and compliance in both administering the penicillin and in clinic attendance. Becker et al. (1974) found that mothers who felt a child was susceptible to recurrence of a current acute illness were more likely to administer medication properly, and to keep follow-up appointments. Gordis et al. (1969, cited in Becker and Green, 1975) found that more compliers (44 per cent) than non-compliers (22 per cent) thought the impact on their children of another act of rheumatic fever would be serious. Becker et al. (1974) and Francis et al. (1969) report similar associations between perceived seriousness (in terms of both organic severity and interference with the mother's activities) and compliance with both medication therapy and appointment-keeping. Other studies mentioned showed that mothers differ in the extent of their motivation to ensure their child's health, with consequences for compliance. For example, Becker *et al.* (1974) demonstrated that compliant mothers were more likely to own a fever thermometer, to give a child special food and vitamins, to have high social mobility aspirations for the child, and to worry about being a 'good mother'.

The fact that a mother acquires and acts (or declines to act) on beliefs likely to enhance the survival chances of her children implies that she has an internal locus of control: that she believes that her own efforts or their suspension can make a difference. This view is implicit in HBM models generally, and is made explicit in some studies. The subject has received much attention in its own right, and is treated as a separate topic in the next section.

'LOCUS OF CONTROL' RESEARCH

Most contemporary research on locus of control was initiated by a monograph on the subject published in 1966 (Rotter, 1966). Its two essential propositions are as follows. First, if someone perceives a desired state of affairs as contingent on his or her own behaviour, the potential for that behaviour to recur in similar circumstances will depend on whether or not the actual result of the behaviour reinforces expectations about its outcome. Those who have a general expectation that desired developments are contingent on their own behaviour are said to have an internal locus of control. Secondly, conversely, if someone sees a desired state of affairs as being outside his or her own control but dependent on '... chance, fate, powerful others, or unpredictables ...', behaviour is much likely to be affected by outcomes. Those who have a general inclination to see developments as outside their own control are said to have an external locus of control.

In a wide-ranging review of research on locus of control published since 1967, Hui (1982) reports a number of findings that are relevant to some of the propositions listed earlier. Comparative studies of ethnic groups in the Americas showed that subjects representing the ethnic minorities were more likely to have an external locus of control, in contrast to the internal locus of the dominant American value pattern. However, studies restricted to students showed either no difference by ethnic origin, or more externality among the Anglo-Americans. This could be due to the effect of education on minority-group children, or it could be that minority-group children who had an internal locus of control were more likely than their peers to reach high school or college.

Other studies reviewed by Hui dealt with the effects on locus of control of age, sex, socio-economic status and education. Studies of children and college students in India and Israel supported the idea that belief in internal control was a function of age and education level, the one confounded with the other. Other studies showed that Asian females were more likely to hold relatively more external beliefs than males ('probably due to childhood socialisation'), a finding consistent with findings among American subjects. A positive correlation between externality of locus and ideal family size was found among Chinese adults. A preference for sons was found among externals. Similar results have been reported for India. A study in Hungary found that internality was related to academic achievement as measured by grade point average and specific grade; the latter result suggesting the influence of schooling itself on locus of control, though another possibility is that it was an age effect.

Over half the 70 or so studies reviewed by Hui used Rotter's Internal-External Locus of Control scale. In a number of cases, the findings showed problems of using in other cultures a scale developed for use in the USA. Some components of the scale had cross-cultural equivalents, others had not. Presumably much depends on the relevance or salience within a particular culture of the items used in the scale. Some researchers have developed their own measure of locus of control suited to the population of interest. One example was Khan and Hassan's (1977) scale for Hindus and Moslems. A related development has been the design of scales specific to a particular domain, including health locus of control scales.

A review of research with health-specific scales (Wallston and Wallston, 1978) found evidence that they could predict both preventive behaviour and behaviour during illness. 'Internals' generally showed more positive behaviour in taking medication, making and keeping appointments with physicians, maintaining a diet, and giving up smoking. However, by no means all studies confirmed such relationships, and some found that it sometimes seemed more functional to hold external beliefs. For example, Du Cette (reported in Wallston and Wallston, 1978) found, contrary to his prediction, that long-term diabetics who were 'internals' missed an increasing number of appointments with their physicians and began to ignore their diets. He hypothesized that 'internals' found their normal response inadequate for the uncontrollable, unpredictable aspects of diabetes and reacted by relinquishing even the degree of control they might have gained. The reviewers point out that inconsistent findings may be a product of differences in, or problems with, the measurement of locus of control, or failure to consider other variables that modify its influence. They stress that, even when a health-specific scale is used, it has to be recognized that locus of control is only one of a variety of factors that affect health-related behaviour. Other important factors include the value of health, motivation, social supports, previous behaviour, and perceived costs and benefits of remedial or preventive action. It will be recalled that most of these factors are included in the HBM model, and the general implication of the research findings is that it would be wise to use both HBM and locus of control.

A SYNTHESIS: LOCUS OF CONTROL AND HBM

A synthesis of locus of control − or more generally, attribution theory − and the HBM is the subject of a paper by King (1983). She proposes that the way a person explains or interprets the cause of a particular illness can influence beliefs about the illness, which in turn will affect behaviour. King's own research on patients' ideas about their own heart disease illustrates the importance of her view. In this research, 83 patients were given questionnaires examining their individual health beliefs using HBM variables. In addition patients were asked to give their own causal explanations of their conditions. The most commonly cited causes were those related to stress, worry and tension or to rheumatic fever in childhood. Other medically accepted causes of heart disease such as smoking, overeating and lack of exercise were cited considerably less frequently. In other words, patients tended to attribute their conditions to an external and uncontrollable factor. When these explanations were entered into a multiple regression equation and regressed on perceived risk of further heart trouble, the explanations accounted for most of the variance. HBM variables (e.g., perceived severity) had no significant effect on the degree of perceived risk. Other HBM variables were also influenced by causal explanations, though generally in combination with other HBM variables. For example, patients were more likely to perceive their heart condition as serious if they found greater difficulties in following the treatment, *and* if they attributed their illness to specified causes.

Similar results were obtained from another study reported by King, of health beliefs and causal attributions that predisposed patients to attend a screening for high blood pressure in response to a request from their doctors. Six of the explanations given by patients discriminated between subsequent attenders and non-attenders in 73 per cent of cases. However, improved discrimination was achieved when explanations and HBM variables were used in the analysis together with perceived commonness of the condition and other measures. The best discriminators were perceived risk of high blood pressure, lack of control over health, attribution of high blood pressure to a situational cause, commonness of the condition and perceived benefits of the screening.

King stresses that patients' explanations can be very relevant to the way they cope with their illnesses, to their decision to comply with medical advice or to take preventive health measures. She argues that health educators need to educate people about the causes of illness as well as about their vulnerability and the benefits of preventive behaviour. On the other hand, she points out (and it is a point that modern attribution theorists are keen to stress) that explanations can be 'self-serving' in various ways. For example, the attribution of heart disease to an external and uncontrollable factor may have the effect of absolving the patient from personal responsibility. Perhaps some explanations of child death have a similar function.

RECOMMENDED RESEARCH

This section of the paper proposes ways of applying types of research reviewed in previous sections, together with other types, to the investigation of variation in commitment to child survival, and locus of control. The objective is to suggest means of testing the propositions listed earlier. The questions suggested below are, of course, for purposes of illustration only. It is assumed that the measures would be developed and their usefulness tested in the exploratory phase of the research. Successful performers could then be used in the subsequent surveys.

1. Dependent Variable

Obviously the best dependent variable would be survivorship, if the research design and sample size permitted this. Alternatives would be measures of health-related practice, which would otherwise be used as measures of intermediate or proximate determinants. That it is possible to produce a reliable and valid scale of 'under-investment' in children is suggested by a report of the development and use of such a scale in the Philippines (Ballweg and Pagtolun-An, 1986). This 13-item scale included indicators of frequency and source of premedical care; parents' investment in nutritional care; source of medical care and number of days that elapsed after onset of illness before treatment was sought; time spent on nurturance and stimulation; provision of playthings; and whether parents helped with schoolwork. The results of the study of care given to 3,486 children showed highly significant negative correlations between scale score and infant and child mortality.

2. Commitment to Child Survival

One possibility would be to assume that maximum commitment to child survival would be indicated by a preference for a moderate family size combined with an equal preference for sons and daughters. Variation could then be measured by the widely-used Coombs scales of underlying family-size preference and sex-composition preference (Coombs, 1976; Coombs and Sun, 1978). Preference for a moderate rather than a low family size would indicate that children were important, while preference for a moderate rather than a large family size would suggest a prudent concern for the welfare of the family. A balance between son preference and daughter preference would indicate the absence of a known cause of under-investment in children. Scores on these two seven-point scales could first be reordered, in a way that would give the maximum scores to moderate family-size preference and a balance between son preference and daughter preference. The scores on each scale could then be added or combined in some more sophisticated way.

Other measures of commitment could include strength of anxiety about the prospects of children experiencing a life-threatening illness or injury, and a measure of the importance attached to being regarded as a good mother. It might also be worth attempting to measure the extent to which mothers believe sacrifices should be made for children's benefit. (The following question has proved very useful in Western studies of attitudes to childbearing: do you think it is parents' duty to do their best for their children even at the expense of their own well-being?)

Mothers who are committed to their children's survival are likely to have a greater consciousness of children's vulnerability and a better understanding of the merits of Western medicine. Questions on perception of vulnerability to life-threatening illnesses and injuries could seek strength of agreement-disagreement (on five-point scales from 'completely agree' to 'completely disagree') with such statements as: 'Young children around here often fall in the river', 'Nowadays it is unusual for a child to get cholera'; it is common to order questions in such a way that the meaning of agreement is reversed in alternate questions – to avoid a response bias. Perception of the potential seriousness of specified illnesses and injuries could be measured by strength of agreement-disagreement with such statements as: 'A child who frequently has diarrhoea will probably die as a result'; 'Few children die from drinking bad water'.

Statements seeking attitudes to Western medicine might include: 'The best way of dealing with a child's diarrhoea is to follow the advice of the health centre'; 'It is usually better to get advice about medical treatment from a wise mother than from the health service'. Other statements might refer to perception of obstacles to the use of health services, such as time to reach the health centre, attitudes of husband, mother or mother-in-law.

It would be very useful to administer some questions to at least a subsample of fathers as well as mothers, to test the hypothesis that mothers and fathers usually have an equal commitment to child survival.

3. Locus of Control

Common lay explanations of child deaths can be obtained from focus group interviews and other exploratory research. In the formal questionnaire, respondents could be asked to choose among these explanations, to reveal the existence of an internal or an external locus of control. For example: 'If a young child dies from drowning is this usually because: it is God's will/the child was unlucky/the child was naughty/the mother was careless/the mother was too busy to look after the child properly?'. Similar questions could be used to seek explanations of death from various illnesses.

4. Reference Group

Presumably the sample design will allow analyses of the effects of mother's education, family income and wealth. It will also be important to test for the effects of an external reference group: the effects of a world view that is distinctive not of the respondent's own status group but of another. Probably the best way of doing this would be to ask questions (separately for each sex) about aspirations for children: how many years they will be kept at school, expectations about their likely occupations and lifestyles. It would be important to measure the respondent's estimate of the likelihood that aspirations will be attained.

A related matter to explore is the extent to which the respondent's health-related views and values were transmitted to her by parents. According to William Brass (personal communication, 1988) an analysis of some Korean data suggests that improved survival experience is distinctive of the parents as well as the children of educated mothers. If the research in India and Bangladesh were to produce similar findings, they would further support the proposition that the observed relationship between mother's education and child survivorship occurs primarily because the readiness both to have women educated and to give higher standards of care to children are distinctive of particular cultures or subcultures.

REFERENCES

Ballweg, J.A. and Pagtolun-An, I. (1986), *International Journal of Sociology of the Family*, 16:291-306.

Becker, M.H., Drachman, R.H. and Kirscht, J.P. (1974), 'A new approach to explaining sick-role behaviour in low-income populations', *American Journal of Public Health*, 64:206-216.

Becker, H.M. and Green, L.W. (1975), 'A family approach to compliance with medical treatment', *International Journal of Health Education*, 18:173-182.

Becker, M.H., Haefner, D.P., Kasl, S.V., Kirscht, J.P., Maiman, L.A., and Rosenstock, I.M. (1977a), 'Selected psychosocial models and correlates of individual health-related behaviour', *Medical Care*, 15 (Suppl.):27-46.

Becker, M.H., Maiman, L.A., Kirscht, J.P., Haefner, D.P. and Drachman, R.H. (1977b), 'The health belief model and prediction of dietary compliance: a field experiment', *Journal of Health and Social Behavior*, 18:348-366.

Coombs, L.C. (1976), *Are Cross-cultural Preference Comparisons Possible? A Measurement-Theoretic Approach*, IUSSP Paper No 5, IUSSP, Liège.

Coombs, L.C. and Sun, T.-H. (1978), 'Family composition preferences in a developing culture: the case of Taiwan, 1973', *Population Studies*, 32,1:43-64.

Das Gupta, M. (1987), 'Selective discrimination against female children in rural Punjab, India', *Population and Development Review*, 13,1:77-100.

Elling, R.R.W. and Green, M. (1960), 'Patient participation in a paediatric program', *Journal of Health and Human Behavior*, 1:183-191.

Francis, V., Korsch, B.M., and Morris, M.J. (1969), 'Gaps in doctor-patient communication: patients' response to medical advice', *New England Journal of Medicine*, 280:535-540.

Hui, C.-C.H. (1982), 'Locus of control: a review of cross-cultural research', *International Journal of Intercultural Relations*, 6:301-323.

Khan, S.R. and Hassan (1977), 'Locus of control among Hindus and Muslims', *Indian Psychological Review*, 15:19-24.

King, J. (1983), 'Attribution theory and the health belief model', in M. Hewstone (ed.), *Attribution Theory: Social and Functional Extensions*, Blackwell, Oxford.

Knodel, J. and van de Walle, E. (1979), 'Lessons from the past: policy implications of historical fertility studies', *Population and Development Review*, 5,2:217-245.

Mason, K.O. (1988), 'The impact of women's position on demographic change during the course of development: what do we know?', *Research Reports* No. 88-123, Population Studies Center, University of Michigan, Ann Arbor.

Rotter, J. (1966), 'Generalised expectancies for internal versus external control of reinforcement', *Psychological Monographs*, 80.

Scrimshaw, S.C.M. (1978), 'Infant mortality and behavior in the regulation of family size', *Population and Development Review*, 4,3:383-403.

Wallston, B.S. and Wallston, K.A. (1978), 'Locus of control and health: a review of the literature', *Health Education Monographs*, 6,2:107-117.

Ware, H. (1981), *Women, Demography and Development*, Development Studies Centre, Australian National University, Canberra.

Wyon, J. and Gordon, J. (1971), *The Khanna Study: Population Problems in the Rural Punjab*, Harvard University Press, Cambridge, Mass.

FAMILY BEHAVIOUR

Chapter 8

SEX BIAS IN THE FAMILY ALLOCATION OF FOOD AND HEALTH CARE IN RURAL BANGLADESH*

Lincoln C. Chen, Emdadul Huq and Stan D'Souza

Conclusive evidence was provided in an earlier study by the authors of higher female than male mortality from shortly after birth through the childbearing ages in a rural area of Bangladesh (D'Souza and Chen, 1980).[1]   Male mortality exceeded female mortality in the neonatal period, but this differential was reversed in the post-neonatal period. Higher female than male mortality continued through childhood into adolescence and extended through the reproductive ages.   The most marked differences were observed in the 1-4 year age group, where female mortality exceeded male mortality by as much as 50 per cent.

The higher male mortality rate during the neonatal period is consistent with evidence from many societies that the biological risk of death is higher among male children than among female children.[2]   The reversal of the sex differential of mortality, markedly so during childhood and persisting through adolescence, was postulated to be reflective of sex-biased health- and nutrition-related behaviour favouring male children.   Son preference in parental care, intrafamily food distribution, feeding practices, and utilization of health services are some of the behavioural mechanisms by which sex-biased attitudes may have led to the observed mortality pattern.

The purpose of this study is to examine the validity of this hypothesis. To do so, a framework is presented in which the mechanisms through which sex-biased attitudes and practices might operate to affect health, nutrition, and mortality are postulated. In-depth empirical data are presented from rural Bangladesh to examine the validity of the hypothesis that sex-biased health and nutrition behaviour discriminates against

---

*First published in *Population and Development Review*, 7(1)1981.

[1]According to a recent World Bank review, the Bangladesh pattern of briefer female life expectancy is typical of South Asia, including India. In other regions, however, this gender-biased relationship may not exist, for example in Indonesia and most of Latin America and North Africa. There is, regrettably a vacuum of reliable data from Sub-Saharan Africa. See World Bank, 1980:91.

[2]Male infant mortality exceeds female infant mortality in virtually all industrialized countries. The presumed biological factors responsible for such a pattern are not clearly delineated. See Van Poppel, 1978.

female children, thereby causing an aberrant female predominance in the childhood mortality rate.   The paper concludes by discussing policy and programme implications associated with these findings.

DATA SOURCES AND METHODS

The data employed in this study were obtained in Matlab Thana, Bangladesh, at the rural field research station of the International Centre for Diarrhoeal Disease Research, Bangladesh (ICDDR,B, formerly Cholera Research Laboratory).   Since 1963 the ICDDR,B has operated a demographic surveillance system and has provided diarrhoeal treatment services to a 1974 study population of 263,000.   Details of the study population's demographic and socio-economic characteristics, field data collection procedures, and diarrhoeal treatment services have been reported in several previous publications (Mosley et al., 1970; Chen et al., 1974).   For this study, Matlab birth and death registration data for 1974-77 and diarrhoeal treatment records for 1977 were tabulated and analysed.

Morbidity and nutritional data were obtained from the Matlab Food and Nutrition Study, which aimed to elucidate and quantify the effects on the growth of children under five years of household socio-economic variables, incidence of infections, food availability, and dietary practices, including food distribution, within the family.[3]   In February-March 1978, to obtain baseline information and a sampling frame for the in-depth longitudinal second phase, all 882 children under five years of age residing in six study villages were surveyed.   Information obtained included household socio-economic status, characteristics of the study children, child health history, and maternal and child anthropometric measurements.

For the second longitudinal phase, 130 Muslim families residing in four of the six villages were purposively selected using the following criteria: all households had one or more children under five years and were easily accessible from the field research station.   This latter criterion was set because dietary teams needed to reach study households at sunrise and to return home after dark.   Households were crudely grouped into thirds: poor (owns less that 0.2 hectares of land); better off (0.2 to 0.8 hectares) and well-to-do (more than 0.8 hectares).   The following measurements were obtained from each study household over a one-year period beginning in June 1978: baseline asset survey; income-expenditure survey, bi-monthly; 24-hour measurement of household and individual food intake, bi-monthly; anthropometry (weight, height, mid-upper left arm circumference, and left triceps skinfold thickness) of mothers and children monthly and all other household members, tri-monthly; and morbidity surveillance, weekly.   Minor illnesses among study family members were treated by a trained paramedic, while severe illnesses were referred to physicians at the Matlab central health facility.

For the purpose of this study, the anthropometric data obtained from the 882 children surveyed in the first phase were analysed.   Longitudinal morbidity data over the study year of some 207 study children of the second phase were also analysed. Finally, household and individual nutrient intake data obtained from dietary surveys in June-August 1978 (first round) were examined.

---

[3]The Matlab Food and Nutrition Study is a complex in-depth longitudinal study with the aim of examining the role of intrafamily factors in determining family health and welfare.   This paper represents one of the first products of the multidisciplinary data collection.   Another product is Chen, Huq and Huffman, 1980.

The methodology of the dietary survey is noteworthy because new field procedures were introduced to measure household and individual food intake simultaneously.[4] The new methodology involved first the standard 24-hour weighment method in which all foods consumed by the household in a 24-hour period are weighed before cooking (Taskar *et al.*, 1967). To ascertain intrafamily food distribution and also individual food intake, post-cooked foods were converted into volume units. Dietary workers, using standard Teflon volumetric cylinders, measured the volume of post-cooked food in cooking pots before and after serving. During meal serving, local resident female workers observed food distribution patterns by counting the number of spoonfuls distributed to each individual. Since utensil sizes had been measured in the preliminary round, the accuracy of the observation could be double-checked by comparing the volume distributed from the cooking pot with the volume computed by summing the number of spoonfuls of food distributed to individuals. Individual food intake was converted into nutrient intake by applying standard Indian and Bangladesh food conversion tables (Gopalan, 1971). Field workers were instructed strictly not to comment upon or interfere in the food distribution process. Study families were not informed of the study's interest in food distribution patterns. Rather, they were informed at the outset of the study that socio-economic, dietary, anthropometric, and morbidity information were to be obtained to assess the factors that influence child health in this community.

RESULTS

Framework of Health and Nutritional Determinants of Mortality

Table 1 presents the age-specific death rates of men and women in Matlab for 1974-1977. In the neonatal period, male mortality exceeds female mortality, a sex differential consistent with the established higher biological risk of male children. During the post-neonatal period and childhood (1-4 years), the pattern is reversed with female death rates exceeding male rates. The excess female mortality persists but declines in magnitude during adolescence (5-14 years) and the reproductive years (15-44 years). By ages 45-64 years, male mortality predominates. Among the very elderly (65 and over), however, female mortality again exceeds that of males. The sex differential in mortality is most marked in the 1-4 year age group, in which female rates exceed male rates by 45 per cent.

---

[4]Dietary methodologies employed to estimate food intake at the individual level in developing countries are fraught with difficulties. In developed countries, 24-hour recall is commonly employed. But under circumstances where literacy and numeracy may be limited in the study population, where *ad hoc* intake at bazaars or in the fields as payment for work may be common, and where containers and weights may not be standardized, established methodologies may be inadequate. The new methodology described in this paper and developed in response to these problems requires more than one person-day field worker time per 24-hour measurement of household and individual food intake. The validity and reliability of this method is examined in Chen, Huq *et al.*, 1980.

TABLE 1: MORTALITY RATE (PER 1000 POPULATION) BY AGE AND SEX IN MATLAB, BANGLADESH, 1974-1977

Age group	Both sexes	Female	Male	Ratio F/M
0[a]	131.2	131.5	130.9	1.00
neonatal (<1mo[a])	73.0	67.6	78.2	0.86
post-neonatal (1-11 mo[a])	58.2	63.9	52.6	1.21
1-4[b]	28.4	33.9	23.3	1.45
5-14	3.2	3.7	2.7	1.37
15-44	3.7	3.8	3.6	1.06
45-64	20.2	18.0	22.1	0.81
65 +	88.5	92.1	85.7	1.07
All ages	16.4	16.7	16.1	1.04

[a]per 1000 live births.
[b]Because of lack of comparability of definitions and tabulation procedures, 1974 data are not included.

A framework conceptualizing hypothetical mechanisms by which sex-biased health and nutrition behaviour might produce the observed mortality differentials in children is shown in Figure 1. The major forms of illness among children in developing countries are protein-calorie malnutrition and the common childhood infections, such as diarrhoea, measles, respiratory diseases, and infections of the skin, eyes, and ears. These two forms of morbidity are also the major causes of child deaths. A comprehensive study of infant mortality in the Americas, for example, showed that malnutrition was associated with over half of all deaths (Puffer and Serrano, 1973), and epidemiologic studies have documented that severe malnutrition is associated with as much as tenfold higher risk of child mortality (Chen, Chowdhury and Huffman, 1980). With the exception of trauma, various infectious diseases are by far the most common direct cause of child death. Diarrhoea, for example, accounts for over one-third of all deaths in the Americas, and this pattern has been noted in virtually all low-income countries (Chen, 1978; Puffer and Serrano, 1973).

Protein-calorie malnutrition is basically determined by two factors: food intake (including breastfeeding) and infections. Food consumption is obviously fundamental to nutritional well-being, but infections too are critically important in determining nutritional status because, through a series of biological mechanisms, infections cause loss of appetite, gastrointestinal malabsorption of ingested nutrients, and metabolic wastage of available nutrients in the body (Scrimshaw, 1970). Infections, in turn, are basically determined by two factors: host susceptibility and exposure to disease transmission. The capacity of the host to defend himself against infection is known to be at least in part determined by nutritional status. Exposure to disease transmission is believed to be affected by the quality of the physical (water, sanitation, housing) and personal (child care, hygiene) environment.

FIGURE 1: FRAMEWORK OF HEALTH AND NUTRITIONAL DETERMINANTS OF CHILD MORTALITY

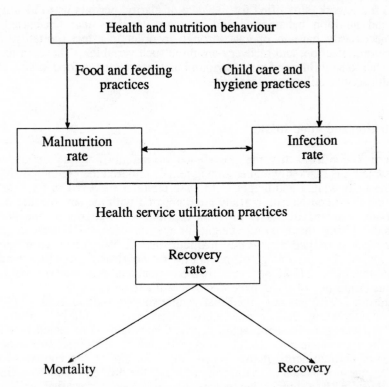

There are, thus, both separate and mutually reinforcing determinants of nutritional status and infection. Malnutrition and infections have been postulated to be 'synergistic'. A bi-directional causal relationship is postulated in which malnutrition and infection each predisposes and exacerbates the other, resulting in a combined effect that is more deleterious than either alone (Scrimshaw *et al.*, 1968). In addition, nutritional status is fundamentally determined by the quantity and quality of food intake. Infection rates are determined by exposure to disease, which is a function of the quality of the physical and personal environment, both of which are highly dependent upon child care practices.

In addition to nutritional status and infections, child mortality would also be expected to be influenced by health care practices in response to illness. The burden of morbidity is known to be many times that of mortality.[5] Thus, it may be assumed that the recovery rate from individual episodes of illness may be high. Given the power of available modern medical technologies (antibiotics) against many of the common childhood diseases and malnutrition (oral rehydration, feeding

---

[5]Although mortality rates among children in developing countries are high, the burden of morbidity is many times higher. The ratio between morbidity and mortality due to diarrhoeal diseases provides an illustration. Children under age five average three to seven episodes of diarrhoea annually, implying an average of 25 episodes from birth to age five per child. Mortality from diarrhoea, though high, only approaches about 10 per cent of all live births to age five. These crude estimates suggest a ratio of 250 diarrhoea episodes per death. The dynamics of this process are discussed in Chen, 1978. See also Chen, Rahman and Sarder, 1980.

rehabilitation), however, much higher recovery rates are possible. Improved recovery would be dependent in part upon the nutritional status of the host and the utilization of available, appropriate, and effective curative health services.

This framework, simplified for the sake of clarity, permits us to identify several health and nutrition behavioural and outcome variables that sex-biased attitudes would necessarily have to operate through in order to affect mortality. Rates of malnutrition, infection, and recovery are three such variables. These, in turn, would be expected to be influenced by behavioural patterns related to food intake, child care, and health service utilization, respectively.

Malnutrition and Food Intake

Figure 2 confirms that the prevalence of malnutrition, as defined by child anthropometry, is markedly higher among female children than among male children. When the body weight and height of the 882 children surveyed in the first phase of the Matlab Food and Nutrition Study are compared with the sex-specific medians of the Harvard standard, distinctly different distributional patterns of nutritional status are noted. Using the Harvard weight-for-age standard, 14.4 per cent of female children were classified as severely malnourished in comparison with only 5.1 per cent of males. The percentage of moderately malnourished girls (59.6 per cent) also exceeded that of boys (54.8 per cent). In the normal and mild categories of nutritional status, the proportion of males exceeded that of the females.

Waterlow (1972) has suggested that weight-for-age reflects both acute (wasting) and chronic (stunting) malnutrition: chronic deprivation would be expected to affect primarily linear growth, while acute deprivation would be expected to affect body weight for a given height. Height-for-age (stunting), therefore, might be a better indicator of chronic deprivation. When height-for-age of the Harvard standard is employed, the prevalence of malnutrition among the 882 girls and boys displayed a similar bias, with a higher percentage of girls being classified as severely or moderately malnourished than of boys.

Table 2 shows that at least some of the disparity in nutritional status between sexes may be attributed to sex discrimination against females in intrafamily allocation of food. Dietary surveys among 130 study families in June-August 1978 showed that per capita male food intake consistently exceeded that of females in all age groups. Overall, males averaged 1,927 calories per capita in comparison to 1,599 calories for females. Male caloric consumption exceeded female consumption by an average of 16 per cent among children under five years. This excess was somewhat over 11 per cent among adolescents 5-14 years, and 29 per cent for the adult childbearing age group, 15-44 years. The higher male than female caloric consumption was most marked among those aged 45 years and older, where male intake exceeded female intake by 61 per cent.

Similar sex differentials were noted in protein consumption. Because nearly 85 per cent of dietary protein in Bangladesh comes from cereals, which also contribute the overwhelming proportion of calories, the ratio of male to female protein intake follows closely that of calories (Institute of Nutrition, 1978). The possibility that the observed sex differentials in food consumption would be more marked for prestigious, high-quality foods, high in protein, is not confirmed by the data in Table 2, although the sample size and analytical techniques are probably not sufficiently large or discriminating to detect a difference, if present.

FIGURE 2: DISTRIBUTION OF 882 CHILDREN BY SEX ACCORDING TO NUTRITIONAL STATUS AS DEFINED BY WEIGHT-FOR-AGE AND HEIGHT-FOR-AGE ANTHROPOMETRY, MATLAB, BANGLADESH

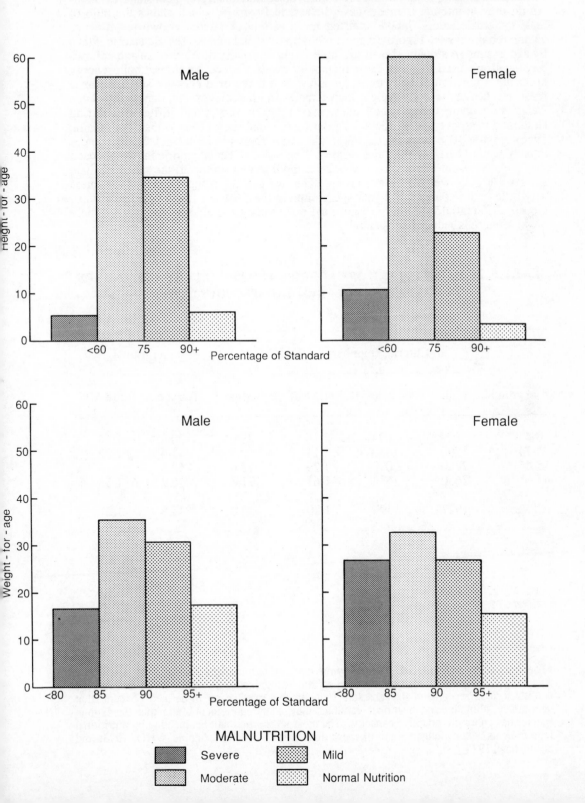

Analysis of sex differentials in actual nutrient intake may offer additional insights if nutrient intakes are compared to biological requirements. The problem in comparing intake with requirements by age and sex is the uncertainty of requirement computations; such computations are controversial and undergoing constant revision.[6] An illustrative attempt is made, nevertheless, in Figure 3, which shows the ratio of male to female caloric intake adjusted for a variety of factors known to influence caloric requirements. Figure 3A plots the ratio of actual male to female caloric intake by age groups as already shown in Table 2. In any individual, most of the calories consumed are used to meet basal metabolic needs. Since basal metabolic energy needs are a function of body mass, an adjustment is required between sexes, because males are heavier in body weight than females in all societies. In Bangladesh, men weigh more than women at all ages, varying from very small differences during childhood to an average of about 5 kg during the adult years (see Ministry of Health, 1966). Figure 3B adjusts the caloric intake ratios shown in Figure 3A by differences in body weight between men and women. The ratios of actual caloric intake between men and women at various ages have been modified according to the ratios of male and female body weights by age group. The 'weight' adjustment changes the ratios very little in the youngest 0-4 year age group. In the 5-14 and 15-44 year age groups, the sex differential essentially disappears, and, among the elderly, the marked male predominance is reduced substantially.

TABLE 2: DAILY INTAKE OF CALORIES AND PROTEIN BY AGE AND SEX IN MATLAB, BANGLADESH, JUNE-AUGUST 1978

Age group	Calories (number)			Protein (grams)		
	Male	Female	Ratio M/F	Male	Female	Ratio M/F
0-4	809	694	1.16	23.0	20.2	1.14
5-14	1590	1430	1.11	50.9	41.6	1.22
15-44	2700	2099	1.29	73.6	58.8	1.25
45 +	2630	1634	1.61	71.8	46.9	1.53
All ages	1927	1599	1.20	55.0	45.5	1.21

---

[6]The intricacies and fallacies of employing nutrient requirement standards to assess the adequacy and equity of distribution of diets are recognized. Increasingly, as controversy continues, it is recognized that absolute requirements may be an ill-defined concept, that geographic, climatic, and historical variables may alter requirements, and that the human species has enormous adaptive capacity. The most recent international meeting on nutritional requirements acknowledged some of these difficulties. See for example WHO, 1973; and Scrimshaw, 1977.

FIGURE 3: **DEVIATION FROM UNITY OF RATIO OF MALE/FEMALE CALORIC INTAKE IN RELATION TO REQUIREMENTS BY AGE GROUPS: (A) ACTUAL; (B) ADJUSTED FOR BODY WEIGHT; (C) ADJUSTED FOR BODY WEIGHT, PREGNANCY, AND LACTATION; AND (D) ADJUSTED FOR BODY WEIGHT, PREGNANCY, LACTATION, AND ACTIVITY**

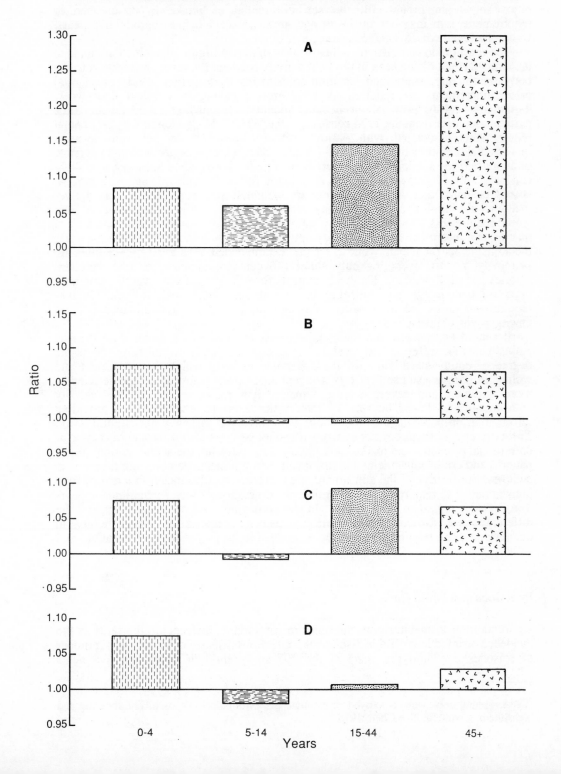

Figure 3C attempts to adjust the ratios, in addition to body weight, to the well-documented extra caloric demands of pregnancy and lactation among women in the reproductive ages. Using crude assumptions about the fertility schedule of rural Bangladeshi women, foetal wastage rates, and caloric needs and duration of breastfeeding, an average of 288 incremental calories are estimated to meet childbearing and breastfeeding requirements.[7] When this factor is combined with the ratios shown in Figure 3B, the sex differential of intake in comparison to requirements remains constant in all age groups, except in the reproductive years, where the female disadvantage is worsened.

The most crude and difficult adjustment is shown in Figure 3D, which attempts to take into account differences in physical activity between the sexes, in addition to the body weight, pregnancy, and lactation adjustments made earlier. Very substantial caloric increments are required by adult men engaging in physical field work, particularly during peak labour demand months. Employing crude labour force participation data from the 1974 census and the WHO/FAO guideline for incremental requirements associated with various activity levels, a 26 per cent average incremental requirement is calculated for adult men, which is equivalent to an average of about 500 extra calories. The increment for adolescents aged 5-14 years is slight and only a modest upward adjustment is made for adult men over age 45 years. It should be noted that these increments are weighted averages. Some 'very active' males would require several times the average increase, while more sedentary men would require less. Because of faulty national statistics on women's work and lack of quantitative information on the energy demands of household and home-based work, the adjustments for female work using the recommended WHO/FAO procedures are extremely modest, averaging only about a 6 per cent increase, or less than 100 calories per adult woman. These adjustments for physical activity overall again alter male-to-female intake-requirement ratios. For all age groups, male-to-female intake-requirement ratios are near parity, although marked male predominance persists among young children.

It should be stressed that these adjustments are illustrative rather than precise. Adjustments for differing body weights, for example, clearly do not fully reflect the degree of equity since much of the difference in body weight between men and women in Bangladesh itself reflects stringent adaptation to chronic caloric deficiency, more common and severe among females than males. The various activity adjustments are flawed because of their reliance on national statistics providing information on percentage of the labour force involved in heavy agricultural work. The extra energy requirements of women cannot be estimated accurately because of definitional problems and inadequacies in the data. Overall, the actual nutrient intake patterns and crude adjustments for sex-specific requirements demonstrate that female children, irrespective of the adjustment, are markedly disadvantaged in terms of food intake relative to requirements. A similar discrimination of lower magnitude appears to exist with regard to the elderly. In the adolescent and childbearing years, the differences are difficult to confirm conclusively because of the difficulty in quantifying extra requirements related to body weight, pregnancy and lactation, and activity.

Infections and Child Care

In addition to malnutrition, the other major variable influencing mortality is the incidence of infections. Table 3 shows the infectious disease incidence rates (number of episodes per child per year) of the 207 study children under age five years

---

[7]Crude assumptions were employed to estimate the extra caloric needs of childbearing and breastfeeding women. See Chen, 1975.

according to sex. Rates of infection among female children were consistently lower than among males, although the differences are small and statistically insignificant. Diarrhoeal attack rates for boys were 4.2 episodes per child per year in comparison to 3.8 for girls (a 10 per cent difference). The male and female respiratory disease rates were 7.4 and 7.0 per child per year, respectively; skin disease rates 1.3 and 1.2; and eye and ear infection rates 1.2 and 1.1. The lack of strong sex differentials in infection rates is consistent with the interpretation that disease exposure is similar between sexes. It would not be surprising if differences in the physical environment by sex were not significant. Preferential child care according to gender, if present, was apparently not sufficiently influential in determining disease incidence to be reflected in the infection rates.

Health Service Utilization

The last variable of interest is the recovery rate from illness. No direct measurement of this variable has been made. Since treatment can affect this rate, an indirect measure is available in Matlab because free treatment for the diarrhoeal diseases has been offered to the entire study population as an integral part of the research-service programme. Table 4 shows that age- and sex-specific utilization levels of these facilities varied markedly. Despite nearly comparable incidence levels of field diarrhoeas (Table 3), male children under age five years were brought to the Matlab treatment facility by their guardians far more frequently than female children. Diarrhoeal treatment rates averaged 135.6 per 1,000 among male children in comparison to 81.0 among female children, the former being 66 per cent higher than the latter. A similar sex differential of treatment facility utilization was observed among 5-14 year old children. Interestingly, the utilization pattern becomes reversed during the adult ages, 15-44 years. Because field data on disease incidence are not available for ages above five years, we do not know whether these sex differences in the utilization of health facilities among the older age groups are due to differences in field attack rates or to biases in health service utilization. It has been postulated, however, that mothers have significantly higher field attack rates of diarrhoea because of higher risk due to constant personal contact (breastfeeding, feeding, child care, cleaning) with children, the age group that is at highest risk of diarrhoeal diseases (Merson et al., 1978).

The juxtaposition of Tables 3 and 4 appears to provide evidence of sex-biased parental responses to illness. Field diarrhoea attack rates among children are similar (male rates 10 per cent higher than female rates) between the sexes, but hospitalization is 66 per cent more frequent for male children than for female children. The ICDDR,B diarrhoeal treatment services are free, and travel to and from the facility is provided without charge in jeeps and speedboat ambulances. Thus, the incremental financial cost in the utilization of the services is marginal. Of course, the social, time and indirect costs may be considerable. Nevertheless, despite free transport and services, male children were brought to the treatment facility more frequently than female children by their guardians.

TABLE 3: MORBIDITY (NUMBER OF EPISODES) OF SELECTED INFECTIONS AMONG 207 CHILDREN UNDER AGE FIVE BY SEX IN MATLAB, BANGLADESH, JULY 1978-JUNE 1979

Age (years)	Diarrhoea		Respiratory		Skin		Eye/Ear	
	M	F	M	F	M	F	M	F
0	4.9	4.5	10.0	9.0	1.3	1.5	1.5	1.8
1	6.3	3.6	10.3	8.5	1.7	1.3	1.8	1.4
2	3.2	4.8	5.0	6.2	1.0	2.1	0.7	0.7
3	4.2	3.6	6.2	6.3	1.3	0.8	0.8	0.8
4	3.0	2.8	6.0	5.2	1.3	0.7	1.0	0.8
0-4	4.2	3.8	7.4	7.0	1.3	1.2	1.2	1.1

TABLE 4: DIARRHOEA TREATMENT (NO. AND RATE PER 1000 POPULATION) BY AGE AND SEX AT THE MATLAB TREATMENT UNIT, BANGLADESH, FEBRUARY 1977-JANUARY 1978

Age	Number of treatment facility visits				Rate of treatment facility visits			
	Both sexes	M	F	Ratio F/M	Both sexes	M	F	Ratio F/M
0-4	4620	2945	1675	0.57	109.6	135.6	81.9	0.60
5-14	1102	703	399	0.57	13.9	17.3	10.3	0.60
15-44	1742	755	987	1.31	16.1	14.2	17.9	1.26
45 +	673	380	293	0.77	17.2	18.1	16.3	0.90
All ages	8137	4783	3354	0.70	30.3	35.0	25.4	0.72

DISCUSSION

There are several reasons why this study confirming sex-biased health- and nutrition-related behaviour in rural Bangladesh may be significant.   First, documentation of sexual differences in several major variables affecting mortality (rates of malnutrition, disease, and recovery from illness) and the processes (feeding practices and health service utilization) influencing these variables constitutes an impressive array of in-depth, empirical field data consistent with demographic findings of higher female than male mortality rates among children. The usual practice is to estimate the level, pattern, and trend of demographic variables employing strictly cross-sectional or retrospective data (United Nations, 1967). While useful, such indirect estimation techniques depend upon assumptions often not valid under real-world situations. For example, indirect estimation of mortality often assumes a stable, unchanging mortality level over time, a condition not fulfilled in Matlab.[8] More often, sex-biased attitudes and behaviour may be inherent in and may affect the outcomes of indirect estimation techniques. Differential accuracy of recall of female child mortality in comparison to male mortality, for example, could obscure a genuine higher difference between female and male mortality.[9] Documentation of consistent sex differences in levels of malnutrition, infection, and recovery from illness adds enormous reassurance to purely quantitative estimates of mortality differentials.

Second, our attempt to separate out the health- and nutrition-related variables influencing child mortality may have generated a potentially useful conceptual approach to the study of mortality and the various biological, environmental, and behavioural processes that influence mortality. For example, evidence has been provided in several studies suggesting the crucial importance of female education in lower child mortality, even when family income is controlled (Caldwell, 1979; D'Souza et al., 1980; Scrimshaw, 1978). Other than the demonstration of a strong association between two variables (female education and child mortality), these studies often do not elucidate the mechanisms or intermediate variables through which improved female education must operate to reduce child mortality. Were such a conceptual framework as the one postulated here available and were empirical evidence collected on these intermediate variables, the mechanisms by which this association may be operating could be elucidated, adding immeasurably to the confidence in the results obtained and to their potential usefulness for policy and programme utilization.

Third, the study's findings show that where behaviour can be sufficiently powerful to influence outcome, there is consistent discrimination against female children in comparison to male children. The level of malnutrition among girls is substantially higher than among boys. This may be attributed at least in part to marked differences in the intrafamily allocation of food between children of differing sexes. Infection rates, interestingly, were comparable between children of both sexes, suggesting that even if preferential child care were operating, it was of insufficient force to influence the important role of the contaminated physical environment in causing diarrhoeal, respiratory, skin, and eye and ear diseases. The recovery rate from illness may be presumed to be different between sexes. This is suggested by marked sex differences in the utilization rate of the Matlab diarrhoeal treatment facility. Overall, the observed pattern is consistent with the conclusion that in cases of family investment and consumption decisions, there is consistent and systematic discrimination against females in all age groups. The bias seems most pronounced among children and the very elderly.

The key questions, of course, concern the factors responsible for such sex-biased behaviour and the policy and programme implications of the study's findings. Clearly, one possible explanation of sex-biased health and nutrition behaviour is related to the inferior status, role, and work opportunities of women in Bangladesh. Intrafamily resource allocation and behaviour reflect such sex biases. Grown sons

---

[8]In-depth longitudinal registration in Matlab for the past 17 years has noted fluctuations, sometimes major, in response to acute crises, such as the 1971 Independence War and the 1974 famine. See Curlin et al., 1976.

[9]Sex differentials contrary to those reported from Matlab (D'Souza and Chen, 1980) were reported in a national cross-sectional survey undertaken in conjunction with the 1974 census. See Census Commission, 1977.

have better prospects than grown daughters for income-earning work and, thus, may become net contributors to family income. Old-age security of parents may also play an important role in this regard. Investment in young girls, moreover, may be perceived as investing in a human resource that will shift outside of the immediate family after marriage. Investments in girls, therefore, do not contribute in the same manner as investments in boys to long-term family well-being and security.

Informal probing and observation among study families generated some insights into these socio-economic determinants of gender-biased health and nutrition behaviour. It should be noted first that in all study families, it was women, not men, and often the mother herself, who distributed food within the family. Contrary to customary descriptions, men rarely made explicit demands for food beyond the share allocated by women. Also, although in many households the tradition of sequential feeding (first adult men, followed by male children, adult women, and female children) was practised, the family typically ate evening meals together and simultaneously, consuming shares allocated by adult women. When asked directly regarding distributional biases between children of different sexes, women tended to deny unequal treatment. Invariably, however, if the inquiry presented a situation of marked overall family shortages, male child preference was expressed by a majority of women. Interestingly, in all cases, marked sex differentials were reported with regard to food quality, with the adult male commanding choice foods. These distributional characteristics, however, related more to social perceptions of food quality (males commanding certain portions of fish and poultry, for example) than to nutritional quality (protein quantity and quality, for example), which may or may not coincide with social quality.

If biased distribution were more common during times of overall shortage, one would anticipate more marked sex-biased intrafamily food distribution in poor families and during times of seasonal shortages. Unfortunately, such analysis will require more analytical work with the longitudinal data set. It is, however, also possible that the sex differentials in food distribution would be more marked among rich families, as the social role of women may be more inferior to the status of men in rich families than in poor families, where women's economic contribution in the homes, and often beyond the household, may be crucial for family survival.

In terms of policy, the available data do not permit us to conclude whether improvements in the health and nutritional status of female children can be achieved by increasing the efficiency in the mobilization and application of available household resources or would require substantial increments in overall household resources. Nor, for that matter, are we certain regarding the relative share of incremental household resources that would be directed eventually toward the welfare consumption of disadvantaged female children. It seems likely, however, that simplistic policy prescriptions, such as increased female education, are not likely to remedy this fundamental problem, reinforced as it is by both perceived economic reality and strong cultural tradition. Rather, it seems likely that fundamental structural changes in the role, status, and economic value of women in the society will be required, in addition to alleviation of the economic poverty confronted by most of these families. The findings of a recent study of mortality in Matlab confirm the tentative nature of these conclusions (D'Souza et al., 1980). In 1974-1977, excess female-to-male mortality in the 1-4 year age group was noted even among wealthy landowning families, suggesting that competition for scarce, insufficient resources does not explain all of the disparity. Excess female mortality was higher among poor than among rich households during 1974, but rich families had higher excess female child deaths in 1977. Thus, we remain uncertain about the role of pressure of household economic resources as a contributor to sex-biased health-related behaviour.

Several specific policy and programme implications may also be derived from the findings. It is important to recognize first that sex-biased patterns of ill-health, malnutrition, and mortality are often neglected dimensions of these human problems.[10]   Studies that examine the level and patterns of ill-health often fail to take sex differentials into account explicitly.   The focus traditionally has been on differentials by age, region, class, and socio-economic groups – not sex.   Moreover, the data suggest that health and nutrition programmes aimed at delivering modern medical technologies to underserved and underprivileged populations need to take into account explicitly the disadvantaged position of females in comparison to males. As the Matlab health service utilization pattern amply demonstrates, even free services may not reach the disadvantaged, in this case female children, because of sex-biased utilization of services.   An explicit goal of such programmes, therefore, should be to ensure equitable access to services and service utilization.   Finally, implicit in the inclusion of sex considerations in programme goals is the potential usefulness of measures of sex differentials in health, nutrition, and mortality as pragmatic 'social' indicators of programme performance.   It is possible, for example, for programmes to reduce disease, malnutrition, and mortality without affecting either absolutely or relatively the welfare of the disadvantaged female population.   One 'social' indicator of policy and programme performance, therefore, should be the reduction of sex differentials.

---

[10]It should be noted that shorter female than male life expectancy is characteristic of South Asia and may not be operating in other parts of the developing world (see note 1).   More commonly, female life expectancy exceeds that of males.   However, even in such cases the roles, status, and work of women may be considered inferior.   In these cases, the inequality between sexes exists but is not reflected in survival rates.

REFERENCES

Caldwell, J.C. (1979), 'Education as a factor in mortality decline: an examination of Nigerian data', *Population Studies*, 33,3:395-413.

Census Commission, Statistics Division (1977), *Report on the 1974 Bangladesh Retrospective Survey of Fertility and Mortality*, Ministry of Planning, Dacca.

Chen, L.C. (1975), 'An analysis of per capita foodgrain availability, consumption, and requirements in Bangladesh: a systematic approach to food planning', *Bangladesh Development Review*, 3,2:93-126.

Chen, L.C. (1978), 'Control of diarrheal disease morbidity and mortality: some strategic issues', *American Journal of Clinical Nutrition*, 31:2284-2291.

Chen, L.C., Ahmed, S., Gesche, M.C. and Mosley, W.H. (1974), 'A prospective study of birth interval dynamics in rural Bangladesh', *Population Studies*, 28:277-297.

Chen, L.C., Chowdhury, A.K.M.A. and Huffman, S.L. (1980), 'Anthropometric assessment of energy − protein malnutrition and subsequent risk of mortality among preschool aged children', *American Journal of Clinical Nutrition*, 33:1836-1845.

Chen, L.C., Huq, E., Chowdhury, M. and D'Souza, S. (1980), 'A combined weightment and volumetric dietary method for estimating 24-hour household and individual food intake'.

Chen, L.C., Huq, E and Huffman, S.L. (1980), 'A prospective study of the risk of diarrhoeal diseases according to nutritional status of children', paper presented at Malnutrition Panel Meeting, US-Japan Cooperative Medical Science Program, Morioka, Japan, 28-31 July.

Chen, L.C., Rahman, M. and Sarder, A.M. (1980), 'Epidemiology and causes of death among children in a rural area of Bangladesh', *International Journal of Epidemiology*, 9:25-33.

Curlin, G.T., Hossain, B. and Chen, L.C. (1976), 'Demographic crisis: the impact of the Bangladesh independence war (1971) on births and deaths in a rural area of Bangladesh', *Population Studies*, 30,1:87-105.

D'Souza, S., Bhuiya, A. and Rahman, M. (1980), 'Socio-economic differentials in mortality in a rural area of Bangladesh', paper presented at WHO/ESCAP Meeting on Mortality in Asia: A Review of Changing Trends and Patterns 1950-75, Manila, 1-5 December.

D'Souza, S. and Chen, L.C. (1980), 'Sex differentials in mortality in rural Bangladesh', *Population and Development Review*, 6,2:257-270.

Gopalan, C. (1971), 'Nutrient conversion tables for India', *National Institute of Nutrition*, Indian Council of Medical Research, Hyderabad.

Institute of Nutrition and Food Sciences (1978), 'Nutrition survey of rural Bangladesh', University of Dacca, Dacca.

Merson, M.H., Black, R.E. and Khan, M.U. (1978), 'Epidemiology of cholera and enterotoxic *E. Coli* diarrhoea', proceedings of the Nobel Symposium, Stockholm.

Ministry of Health, Government of Pakistan (1966), *Nutrition Survey of East Pakistan, March 1962 − January 1964*, report in collaboration with University of Dacca and Nutrition Section, Office of International Research, National Institute of Health, Bethesda, Maryland.

Mosley, W.H., Chowdhury, A.K.M.A. and Aziz, K.M.A. (1970), 'Demographic characteristics of a population laboratory in rural East Pakistan', *Population Research*, September, Centre for Population Research, National Institute of Child Health and Human Development.

Puffer, R.R. and Serrano, C.V. (1973), 'Patterns of mortality in childhood', *Scientific Publication* 262, Pan American Health Organization, Washington, D.C.

Scrimshaw, N.S. (1970), 'Synergism of malnutrition and infection', *Journal of the American Medical Association*, 212:1685.

Scrimshaw, N.S. (1977), 'Effect of infection on nutrient requirements', *American Journal of Clinical Nutrition*, 30:1536-1544.

Scrimshaw, N.S., Taylor, C.E. and Gordon, J.E. (1968), *Interactions of Nutrition and Infection*, Monograph No. 57, World Health Organization, Geneva.

Scrimshaw, S.C.M. (1978), 'Infant mortality and the regulation of family size', *Population and Development Review*, 4,3:383-403.

Taskar, A.D., Swaminathan, M.C. and Madhavan, S. (1967), 'Diet surveys by weighment method – a comparison of random-day, three-day, and seven-day period', *Indian Journal of Medical Research*, 55:90-96.

United Nations (1967), *Manual IV, Methods of Estimating Basic Demographic Measures for Incomplete Data*, ST/SOA, Series A.42, United Nations, New York.

Van Poppel, F.W.A. (1978), 'Regional differences in mortality in Western and Northern Europe: a review of the situation in the seventies', *Working Report* No. 13, Netherlands Interuniversity Demographic Institute, Voorburg.

Waterlow, J.C. (1972), 'Classification and definition of protein-calorie malnutrition', *British Medical Journal*, 3:566-569.

World Bank (1980), *World Development Report, 1980*, World Bank, Washington, D.C.

World Health Organization (1973), 'Energy and protein requirements', Report of Joint FAO/WHO *ad hoc* Expert Committee, *Technical Report Series* No. 522, WHO, Geneva.

Chapter 9

KNOWLEDGE, ATTITUDES AND PRACTICES RELATED TO CHILD HEALTH AND MORTALITY IN SINE-SALOUM, SENEGAL*

Michel Garenne and Francine van de Walle

OBJECTIVES AND METHOD

This paper is a first attempt to investigate knowledge, attitudes and practices related to child health and mortality in a group of villages located in the region formerly known as Sine-Saloum, now called Kaolak, in Senegal, West Africa. This region is an area populated mostly by Wolof, Sereer and Toucouleur, but also by sizeable groups of other ethnic origins from neighbouring regions. The population of 31 villages has been followed up continuously for the last 20 years through a vital registration system by ORSTOM, a French research institute. The first survey started in December 1962. The follow-up surveys have shown a very high infant and child mortality, yielding some of the highest mortality rates ever measured in Africa (Cantrelle and Leridon, 1971; Cantrelle et al., 1980; Garenne, 1982).

The level and pattern of infant and child mortality may be affected by local knowledge of disease transmission, as well as influenced by local customs, religious beliefs, childbearing practices and parental behaviour. Maternal knowledge, attitudes and practices have been posited as critical variables. The data necessary to assess these variables are difficult to gather and to quantify, and they are susceptible to rapid changes. Furthermore the interpretation of the data is often subjective. Still, these variables may be as important as conventional socio-economic data such as income, education or access to health facilities in explaining mortality levels and patterns (Caldwell, 1984; van de Walle, 1984).

To get a preliminary basis for evaluating these cultural variables, a series of interviews conducted by Francine van de Walle in January 1983 were directed towards 21 married women with children. Mothers have been chosen rather than fathers because African women are closer to their children and more aware of their health problems than are African men. The mother lives in very close contact with

---

*First published in *International Population Conference, Florence 1985*, Vol. 4, Ordina, Liège, 1985.

her youngest child until she is pregnant again or until weaning time, feeding it day and night on demand, carrying it on her back during the day and sleeping with it during the night. A small child is never left alone. On the other hand, the father is the one who decides when to wean the child and he is usually the one who makes the decision when to take it to the doctor or when to buy medicine.

The interviews consisted mostly of a conversation between the women and the interviewer following the lines of a loosely structured questionnaire. If the husband was present and wanted to participate, he was welcome to do so. The interviews took place at the woman's home in her native language, Sereer or Wolof and they were tape-recorded. Later, they were transcribed and then translated into French. The interviewer was a Sereer man who was an enumerator in the follow-up surveys.

The study sought to examine the local views and knowledge of health and disease in comparison to modern views and knowledge. It was an attempt to evaluate the people's knowledge of the importance and frequency of various diseases and their understanding of the mechanisms of disease transmission. Attention was also devoted to attitudes and practices in a particular case of a child's sickness, usually the most recent case the mother had to deal with, and especially to circumstances leading to the choice of traditional versus modern medicine. This study was feasible because of the great attention that mothers devote to the health of their children. The same type of study would have been impossible if directed towards adult health, especially the health of older people.

KNOWLEDGE OF DISEASE

Mothers pay a great deal of attention to what happens to their children and carefully analyse all the symptoms that the child manifests. It is often possible to figure out the history of the sickness from reports of mothers:

Q: The child who has had whooping cough, how did he get it?

R: It started by a diarrhoea. Then he had a cough and so started his whooping cough. Later on he vomited. This is why his body got thinner (B5.3).

Q: Has he had pimples?

R: He has had measles pimples only.

Q: These measles pimples, have they lasted one month?

R: No, they lasted almost one week.

Q: Did he have pimples all over the body?

R: Yes.

Q: The pimples were small or large?

R: Very small.

Q: Did the pimples contain water?

R: Measles pimples do not contain water (B13.3).

Many of the common diseases which kill children are identified by people and have a name in the local language. This is the case for diarrhoea, measles and whooping cough. In many instances, however, respondents refer to a symptom rather than to a well-defined disease: fever stands for malaria, diseases of the chest for pneumonia and bronchitis, 'crisis' can be due to malaria, meningitis or any other convulsive disease. Other diseases do not relate simply to modern concepts of medicine: this is the case, for instance, of a disease of the breast of the mother that is supposed to give the child diarrhoea. Sometimes people admit that they are unable to identify the disease:

R: In some cases one cannot recognize the child's disease nor get it to the dispensary (B5.1).

PREVALENCE OF DISEASE AND MORTALITY

Mothers were asked which were the most common diseases in their villages. Usually they named two or three diseases (or their symptoms), always among the ten most frequent killers of children. Less hazardous diseases such as eye or skin diseases, that are more prevalent, were never mentioned. Diarrhoea was quoted first by many of the women. Following closely were malaria and fever, common cold and coughing. Whooping-cough and measles were also frequently cited as well as meningitis. The question never led the women to cite tetanus neonatorum although it is a well-known disease and may be described by the women on other occasions. Tetanus neonatorum is not considered an infectious disease but rather a magic disease.

Other diseases common in the villages were also mentioned during the interviews:

- Geophagy (eating earth: 'it forms a crust in the stomach, and one dies').

- Worms (very common and usually not treated until very bad symptoms appear).

- Breast diseases (the milk of the mother contains worms; the milk becomes like water).

- General tiredness (disease of the dry season primarily among adults: exhaustion due to hard work during the rain season).

If people seem familiar with most of the common ailments affecting children they have confused notions of their prevalence in the study area. First of all, isolated villages experience most of these diseases only during epidemics. Measles or meningitis may occur once in ten years in remote villages. Furthermore, diseases such as malaria are rather seasonal, and different answers would have been given if the interviews had been conducted after the dry season rather than after the rainy season. Last, due to strong migration flows in this area people may refer to diseases they have experienced in other parts of the country and they may not have been in the village for a long enough time to have seen all the prevalent diseases.

Q: Are measles common?

R: No, no, since measles have not come here yet (B2.3).

Q: In the village, what are the diseases that families fear?

R: They have not come here, really.

Q: Don't you have diseases here?

R: Maybe headaches and colds (B10.3).

Q: In the villages, are there other diseases that you worry about?

R: Besides malaria, I am not aware of any (B19.3).

If people do not have a clear idea of disease prevalence and seem to refer mostly to recent experience, their knowledge of the role played by these diseases in mortality is even further from reality. Malaria, diarrhoea and pneumonia are by far the main killers of young children in the study area, but often people refer to measles, whooping cough or meningitis as the main health hazards for young children. In fact these diseases are quite lethal and what matters to the people seems to be the total number of deaths that a disease can cause in a short period rather than an average pattern over a long period of time.

Q: What is the worst disease among these you just mentioned?

R: We are especially afraid of crisis (meningitis) (B3.4).

Q: What are the diseases you worry about in the village that assail the children?

R: Measles and whooping cough are the ones we are most afraid of (B4.2).

TRANSMISSION OF DISEASE

Most of these diseases are communicable, and people have a clear consciousness of contamination. They often isolate their children to protect them.

Q: When a child is sick in the house and when you are afraid that he will contaminate another child, do you isolate it with his mother?

R: One cannot isolate children within the compound, but if the child is in another compound one keeps the children isolated from each other (B7.5).

Q: When a communicable disease is in the village, for instance whooping cough, do you forbid your children to go and play?

R: I tell them not to go where there is whooping cough (B10.5).

Q: Do you let your healthy children play with sick children?

R: I forbid my kids every house where there is a disease; but, you know, a disease it is like the wind, it enters everywhere (B1.8).

In particular, people are acutely aware that measles and whooping cough are very contagious. 'It is enough for a child to walk on the spit of a whooping cough victim to get infected' (B6.5). Diseases may be brought by a foreigner carrying germs, from other children, or carried by the wind (B6.4).

There have been many campaigns to explain how diseases are transmitted. But the result of radio broadcasts or of explanation by physicians or nurses is confusion rather than understanding. For instance much effort has been devoted to malaria and the use of chloroquine. Although some people have received the message properly, many do not understand it and others doubt its validity:

Q: Mosquitoes, can they bring a disease?

R: I have heard doctors say so.

Q: What disease can they bring?

R: I am not sure I know the disease (B14.3).

Q: Do you know what chloroquine is useful for?

R: We buy it, but we do not know what it is useful for.

Q: Do you listen to the broadcast that doctors do on Tuesdays that deals with health of the body?

R: Yes, we listen to it.

Q: During this broadcast, what did you hear?

R: You know, we cannot remember all that the radio says; but we remember some things.

Another woman: I have heard that one should give chloroquine to children because it is good (B15.5).

Q: Do mosquitoes make people sick?

R: The radio says they give malaria (B19.6).

Some people have ideas about the germ theory of diseases:

Q: How can it (the sand) bring a disease to them (children)?

R: There are microbes. You know, a disease is microbes that are very small and that are in the soil. The eye cannot see them. You sit and they enter you without your noticing it. And children are always in the sand (B12.4).

Q: How do flies give disease?

R: They rest on dirt and they land on you or on your food where they deposit microbes (B19.6).

Other people rely more on their own experience or their preconception of disease transmission:

Q: Your child, when he has a cold, can he contaminate another of your children?

R: The cold is not contagious (B4.3).

Q: If you drink water that comes out of the well without filtering it, can it give a disease? What disease does it give?

R: When you drink it there are often small pieces of rope which are in it; they can give you stomach aches (B4.4).

Q: Water from the well, can it give diseases?

R: Water from the well?

Q: Yes

R: No, no. If water from the well were making people sick, by now we would all be finished since all the village drinks it (B5.5).

Q: What disease do they give (the flies)?

R: I do not know, but flies are bad.

Another woman: Flies can give measles (B15.6).

Q: Can a stranger give a disease?

R: A stranger who is coming with a disease can give it to us, but a relative would not do that (B10.5).

Some other people are more careful and say they do not know:

Q: And (water in the pot) can it give a disease?

R: If it can give a disease it is the doctor who knows but not us, we do not know (B19.5).

R: We listen to the radio broadcast of Doctor Ndiaye on health, but I don't remember anything he said (B16.4).

R: The doctors on the radio say that mosquitoes given diseases; I have forgotten which ones but they tell us to use mosquito screens (B8.5).

Occasional reference is made to the specific notion that mosquitoes transmit disease, but for most people mosquitoes are just a nuisance. 'They prevent children from sleeping and the lack of sleep makes them sick' (B7.5).

In contrast it is widely believed that flies transmit disease: 'Even though we are very ignorant, we know that flies give diseases' (B11.4) and women carefully cover food and water, because 'flies carry germs everywhere and deposit them on food' (B9.3). A Wolof man explains that 'flies rest on the spit of sick persons and then on you and on your food' (B8.5).

Campaigns to improve the cleanliness of water seems to have had a positive impact on people's practices. Many women seem to expend effort to keep the drinking water clean. They wash the *canari* or earthen jar regularly and filter the water they pour in it through a cloth: 'It has to be filtered, because there are worms in it and if you don't filter it, it may give you some disease' (B2.6).

Food preparation is seen as important and people are observing simple rules of hygiene to keep their children safe.

Q: Can the food that one eats cause disease?

R: When it is not covered a fly may light on it and if a child eats it, it may get diarrhoea. Used and soured food gives diarrhoea to the child. Nothing can happen with food that has been prepared and eaten immediately (B1.5).

Mothers also pay great attention to body cleanliness of their children. Children are washed several times a day, although rarely with soap, even when it is available in the village and used for laundry.

In sum, if the idea of contamination is clearly known to people their understanding of disease transmission is rather limited. And ultimately, 'It is God who makes that some get contaminated by a disease and that others don't' (Man in B1.7). The lack of knowledge in the population precludes efficiency in preventing infection in this area.

TREATMENT OF DISEASE

Most of the people who have been interviewed in this survey show an overwhelmingly favourable attitude towards modern medicine. This is not to say that they do not use traditional medicine as often as modern medicine, but they seem to rely on modern medicine to solve most of the health problems of their children:

Q: For you, do you prefer treatments from traditional healers or those of the doctor?

R: Those of the doctor, because it is where we go for everything that happens to us (B9.4).

Q: Which children's diseases lead you to Wolof healers?

R: When a child has a disease of a 'djinn' or a disease which scares us we go to see Wolof marabouts. But if the child is not cured we go to the dispensary (B20.4).

Q: Among the treatments, do you feel that traditional treatments are to be preferred to those of the doctor? Why?

R: For many diseases that bring us to the marabouts, they claim a lot of money for an uncertain treatment. After going back and forth and seeing that our child has a risk of dying in our hands we go to see the doctor who often succeeds in curing it (B20.7).

Even when asked about traditional medicine they often refer to modern drugs:

Q: Do you cure the children with traditional medicine?

R: When one does not go to the dispensary?

Q: Yes

R: It depends on the disease. Each disease has its treatment. When one has a cold, a beverage is prepared from *darkasu* leaves. For fevers, lemonade and chloroquine are prepared and given. *Darkasu* leaves cure two things: *tangat* [i.e., fever, fast respiration and coughing] and cold (B7.6).

Generally favourable attitudes towards preventive medicine are also very common in the study area. Most children are taken to vaccination centres and are given chloroquine preventively when it is distributed. This occurs even when people do not really understand what preventive medicine is:

Q: Vaccinations, what disease do they fight?

R: It is the doctor who knows against which disease he is vaccinating.

Q: Are there diseases that cannot attack you after a vaccination?

R: Doctors say so. They say that certain vaccinations protect you for seven years from the onslaught of certain diseases.

Q: Did they tell you which diseases?

R: Yes, they said some of them. They said: malaria, chest pains, jaundice, meningitis and I forgot the others. They were vaccinating children between three months and three years of age (B7.6).

This shows total confusion with the national programme of vaccination which includes seven diseases: diphtheria, tetanus, poliomyelitis, pertussis, measles, tuberculosis and yellow fever.

The favourable attitude towards modern medicine persists despite the lack of efficiency of currently available health care.

Q: Did you go to buy drugs at the village pharmacy?

R: I went there but the person who is there now is difficult. When you go to see him he says that he has too much work or that you should go back home and that he will help you later (B12.2).

Traditional medicine in the villages covers a variety of different practices, ranging from herbs and potions to prayers and talismans. It is beyond the scope of this paper to analyse traditional remedies or to relate symptoms to these treatments. Furthermore the choice of a traditional healer, as opposed to a modern practitioner, depends not only on the type of disease, but also on ethnic group and religious affiliation. Even within the same village and the same family, there may be disagreement. One of the most striking and unexpected traditional practices that was cited by these interviews is the isolation of children during epidemics of measles or whooping cough.

In the choice between traditional and modern medical practices, people seem to have a rather pragmatic attitude, trying everything that is expected to work.

Q: What kind of disease can you cure with a Wolof treatment?

R: A treatment can be efficient for one person but negative for another. This is why we proceed tentatively in our treatments. When you have tried a treatment that is not efficient for your disease, you go to another specialist who knows more. For any kind of disease we proceed this way (B7.6).

R: At one time we used to go to the village's dispensary to get pills that the children would swallow every Saturday ... We are Sereer, when we have a child who is sick we take it to the healers; we only take it to a doctor if the choice is between a cured child and a dead child (B1).

When the interviewer asked her if she thought 'black knowledge' was more solid than 'white knowledge', the same woman answered:

For us every knowledge is solid. Sometimes doctors treat patients but it is in vain. There, we go to the healers who touch us, they give us potions to drink and talismans to attach to the children until they are cured.

B12 said she would try everything when her child was sick:

R: ... a Wolof treatment plus aspro, plus asprin, yes ... and nivaquine. And I took him to the Sisters (Nuns) ... they gave him pills to drink and also a shot (B12.2).

Sometimes people give up after having tried anything they could:

R: Since he is like that, what have we done for him?

Q: I mean, as far as care is concerned.

R: We brought him to the dispensary, but nothing. We went to see tradional healers, but nothing still. Then we gave up (B17.2).

In sum, the way people treat disease seems to be a syncretic as the ideas they have on disease origin and transmission. Their symptoms are mysterious and their course unpredictable. How is one to know what specific cure will work in a specific case? 'We stumble in the dark with respect to the treatment of diseases' (B7.6).

The cost of medicine either modern or traditional is sometimes mentioned as a problem and may be a factor in the choice between modern and traditional medicine. There is little evidence that traditional medicine is always cheaper, except when it is home made, i.e., when somebody in the family is a specialist in traditional medicine. On the other hand the price of modern drugs changes and people occasionally complain about it.

R: Nivaquine used to be free, but since the creation of the village huts (village pharmacies for primary health care) you have to pay. It is expensive. It is 5 francs a pill.

R: Before 1974, pills were free, nurses would give them away (B7.7).

The messages of modern medicine are reaching the population. People seem to be willing to try any new drug or treatment. Vaccinations are extremely popular as well as chloroquine. Notions about cleanliness and sanitation are spreading. The importance of clean water, covering the food and the water jar, washing the children and their clothes may be part of traditional behaviour, but it is reinforced by modern influences.

DISCUSSION

These interviews have been conducted with a small sample of 21 women, chosen arbitrarily from a file containing some 800 women in their reproductive years. There is no reason to think that information received from these interviews can be considered as totally valid for all the population. We have relied on consistency between answers to argue about a more general pattern and even more freequently on differences between answers to show the variety of situations within the same context. Our interpretation of the interviews is by its very nature subjective. Furthermore, results depend to a large extent on questions that have been asked and the way they have been asked.

As it is a preliminary study, we do not think that final conclusions can be drawn at this stage. However, we would like to pinpoint some aspects that came out from the interviews and that may be relevant for future work.

The people of the Sine-Saloum conscientiously attend to the health of their children and strive to preserve their life as effectively as possible. They carefully follow all symptoms and have identified several diseases that match modern concepts: diarrhoea, measles, whooping-cough and epilepsy, for instance. Other symptoms common to children also have names but may correspond to various diseases. People seem to have a clear knowledge of contagion among children, but overall have a poor understanding of disease transmission despite many explanatory campaigns by doctors, paramedics and radio broadcasts. They sometimes mix traditional and modern explanations of disease transmission.

In the interviews they express a generally favourable attitude towards modern medicine and although some people clearly rely more on traditional medicine, they have never expressed distrust of modern health care. As far as practices are concerned, people appear to try any cure that they have access to. They shift from modern to traditional treatment depending on availability, personal preferences and cost. The cost of treatment is sometimes mentioned as an obstacle to get health care.

Although they are living in remote villages people from the Sine-Saloum seem to have a strong desire for modern and efficient health care, as they understand it.

REFERENCES

Note: the references to the literal quotations are extracted from a manuscript kept at ORSTOM, Dakar.

Caldwell, J.C. (1984), 'The micro-approach in demographic investigation: toward a methodology', paper presented at the IUSSP conference on Micro-Approaches, Canberra, 3-7 September.

Cantrelle, P. (1969), Etude démographique dans la Région du Sine-Saloum. Etat civil et observation démographique, *Travaux et Document de l'ORSTOM*, No. 1, ORSTOM, Paris.

Cantrelle, P. and Leridon, H. (1971), 'Breastfeeding, mortality in childhood and fertility in a rural zone of Senegal', *Population Studies*, 25,3:505-533.

Cantrelle, P, Leridon, H. and Livenais, P. (1980), 'Fécondité, allaitement et mortalité infantile. Différences inter-ethniques dans une même région: Saloum (Sénégal), *Population*, 3:623-648.

Garenne, M. (1982), 'Variations in the age pattern of infant and child mortality with special reference to a case study in Ngayokheme (rural Senegal)', Ph.D. Dissertation, University of Pennsylvania.

van de Walle, F. (1984), 'Births expectations in Bobo Dioulasso', paper presented at the IUSSP Conference on Micro-Approaches, Canberra, 3-7 September.

MECHANISMS –
ANTHROPOLOGICAL
INVESTIGATIONS

Chapter 10

INEQUALITIES BETWEEN MEN AND WOMEN IN NUTRITION AND FAMILY WELFARE SERVICES: AN IN-DEPTH ENQUIRY IN AN INDIAN VILLAGE*

M.E. Khan, Richard Anker, S.K. Ghosh Dastidar and Shashi Bairathi

INTRODUCTION

The last few years have witnessed a growing realization among planners and social scientists that in many spheres of life women are discriminated against and that as compared to men they have far less access to, for example, education, health care and employment (Anker *et al.*, 1982; Government of India, 1974; Hammer, 1982; Khan and Ghosh Dastidar, 1984; Ware, 1981:35-75). One of the factors which is especially worrying in India is the continuing decline in the sex ratio (Table 1), indicating that morbidity and mortality are higher among females than among males and that this situation has deteriorated over time.[1]   After independence the health infrastructure facilities in India expanded and the country also succeeded to a reasonable extent in bringing down mortality rates. Life expectancy at birth rose from about 34 in 1947 to about 55 in 1985, yet life expectancy for females (52) remains less than that of males (55) (Government of India, Seventh Five-Year Plan; Ministry of Health and Family Welfare, 1984). This seems to indicate that males have benefited more than females from modern health facilities.

It is now widely recognized that, not only in India, but in many other South Asian developing countries, women's access to health and family welfare services is less than that of men and this leads to a higher risk of morbidity and mortality (El Badry, 1969). In Bangladesh, D'Souza and Chen (1980) observed that male children under five years are more likely to be admitted to hospital than female children. Chen *et al.*

---

*First published as Working Paper No. 158, Population and Labour Policies Programme, World Employment Programme Research, International Labour Office, Geneva, June 1987.

[1]Excluding South Asian countries, women are known to have higher survival rates than men (El Badry, 1969).

(1981) also showed how gender bias affects the health, nutrition and mortality of women in Bangladesh. Similarly, Dyson and Moore (1983) found that the low status of women in Northern India prevents them from getting proper health care.

TABLE 1: SEX RATIO (FEMALES PER 1000 MALES), 1901-81

Year	Sex ratio
1901	972
1911	964
1921	955
1931	950
1941	945
1951	946
1961	941
1971	930
1981	935

Source: Padmanabha (1981).

In this paper we investigate some of these issues and show where and how women are deprived of health and family planning in selected villages in Uttar Pradesh (UP).

This lack of access of women to health and family welfare services (and perhaps most other social services as well) can be understood and analysed in the broader framework of women's control of the means of production and their participation in the labour force (Miller, 1981). The research literature provides considerable support for this framework, which assumes that in societies/communities where women play an economically more active role and have control over what they produce, they have higher status and better access to social services (including health care) than in societies where women's economic role is not visible and/or women do not have any control over the fruits of their productive labour (Whyte, 1978). As a corollary, it could also be assumed that in communities where women make a greater or more visible economic contribution, families have a greater incentive to invest in girls' education and health and to assure their survival (Schultz, 1982). In contrast, in societies where women's participation in the labour force is limited and marrying off daughters is expensive because of high dowry payments, females are more likely to be subjected to all sorts of neglect.[2]

---

[2]Perhaps as a consequence, infanticide of girls continues to this day in certain pockets of India (*India Today*, 1986).

MAP 1: STUDY LOCATIONS

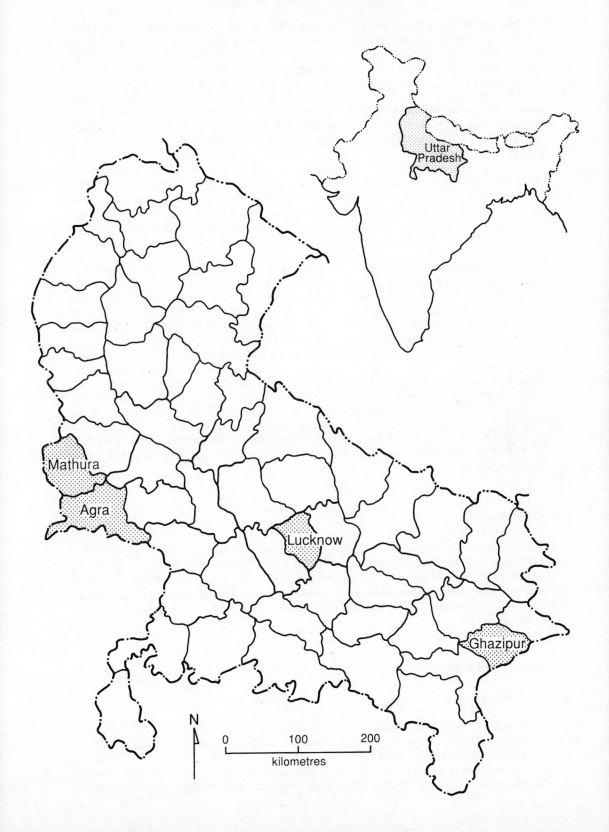

DATA

The study is based on the data collected for one of the ORG/ILO collaborative projects entitled 'Changing roles of women and demographic behaviour'. Part of this study included in-depth analyses of three villages in Uttar Pradesh (UP), a northern state of India which had a population of approximately 111 million in 1981. Two of the villages are located in the western part of UP – one in Agra district and the other in Mathura district. The third village is located in the eastern part of the state (see map). The western part of UP is relatively more developed than the eastern part. However, the state as a whole is one of the least developed in the country and is characterized by high fertility and infant mortality together with low acceptance of family planning among couples.

For this study, trained male and female social scientists were posted in each of the three villages for one year to collect the relevant information (Anker *et al.*, 1982; Khan, 1980). This paper is largely based on the information collected from Krishanpur, one of the two villages in western UP (in Mathura district) situated at a distance of 21 kilometres from an urban centre. Supportive evidence from the other two villages, as well as from studies conducted in other parts of the country, is used to strengthen findings.

The techniques of data collection comprised both quantitative and qualitative assessments so that insights into the process of change or sequence of events when decisions were taken could be understood. Twenty main female informants belonging to 20 households from different caste and class groups were selected. Apart from these 20 main informant families, extensive discussions were held with other villagers during the stay in the village, and at times their activities were also observed and noted. Some of these observations have been included here. During data collection, which extended over one year, the social scientists gradually developed a good rapport with the villagers, particularly with the main informants, and relevant information was collected through detailed discussions and participant observation techniques. We have found that this particular approach yields reliable data. In the beginning, for example, villagers repeatedly told us that there was no discrimination by sex, but over time, through observation, close contact and a high level of rapport, we found that the actual situation was sometimes quite different (Khan and Ghosh Dastidar, 1983).

FINDINGS

The study indicates that discrimination against a woman starts at birth and continues until she breathes her last. We have thus divided our discussion into three broad categories representing the three states of the life-cycle: childhood, adulthood and marriage, and old age. Although the study shows that females are discriminated against in all spheres of life, here our discussion is confined mainly to nutritional and health aspects.

Infancy and Childhood

Food Intake

Our initial discussions with the informants gave us the impression that there was no sex discrimination among children either in breastfeeding or in distribution of food at home, and that both sons and daughters were treated alike. All 20 female informants totally rejected the idea that sons were breastfed more intensely and for longer periods than daughters. We found, however, that this type of discrimination did occur indirectly. In the case of four mothers, the first child was a daughter. They immediately started trying to become pregant for a son, as this would raise their status in the family. Both husband and wife were willing partners in this attempt, and it was also supported by the mothers-in-law. As soon as these women conceived, they stopped breastfeeding their young daughters as they felt this could retard the growth of the foetus. For one daughter milk was stopped when she was just five months old. For the other three, breastfeeding lasted between six and eleven months. In contrast, another three women whose first child was a son showed no such hurry for the next pregnancy. In fact they were trying to avoid the early birth of the next child through abstinence so that they would be able to pay more attention to their sons.

A recent study on breastfeeding, weaning practices and infant mortality in rural Haryana, a neighbouring state of UP, has clearly demonstrated the existence of discrimination in breastfeeding according to the sex of the child (Kumar, 1983). The study (see Table 2) shows that at the end of the fourth month after birth, a significantly larger proportion of daughters (23 per cent) are put on artificial milk than sons (14.3 per cent).

TABLE 2: **BREASTFEEDING PATTERN DIFFERENTIALS BETWEEN BOYS AND GIRLS AT THE END OF THE FOURTH MONTH AFTER BIRTH IN HARYANA STUDY**

Sex of child	Breast-feeding only	Mixed	Artificial bottle-feeding only	Total
Son	155 (40.2)	175 (45.5)	55 (14.3)	385 (100.0)
Daughter	90 (31.9)	127 (45.0)	65 (23.0)	282 (100.0)

$x^2 = 11.66, p < 0.01$

Source: Kumar (1983).

Probing the informants about the distribution of food among children and possible preference to sons brought mixed reactions. Four out of the 20 women spoke quite strongly for discrimination in favour of daughters. Of these four women, Gayetri and Sushma were the most vocal. Gayetri said:

I do not discriminate between sons and daughters. Instead, many times I show preference to girls and offer them the best of whatever is available at home because boys can eat outside whereas girls cannot.

And Sushma:

Girls are much dearer to me. They are with us for a short while only. Afterwards, they will go to in-laws' house. Who knows what they would get to eat there? They can relish eating here only. In contrast, boys would remain at home and eat whatever they like.

Of the remaining 16 informants, 11 said that there was no difference in how they fed boys and girls, while the rest (five) supported better or more nutritious food for sons because they worked hard and needed to grow fast so that they could start earning money as soon as possible.

In none of the informants' families did we notice any differentiation between sons and daughters so far as regular food like *chappati* (bread), rice, vegetable, etc. was concerned. However, in the distribution of more nutritious food like milk, butter and eggs, sons were shown preference. This observation was made not only in informant families, but in other households too. The reasons for this preferential treatment are twofold. First, they look upon sons as their future providers who should grow fast, join the labour force and supplement family earnings at the earliest possible moment. To some extent it is true that in UP villages (and in fact other parts of the country as well) sons start helping their parents at quite an early age, both on the farm and in other cash-earning activities such as minding a shop, working as a labourer/servant, weaving, etc. Thus the faster the physical growth of a son, the more money he can earn at an early age.

Girls on the other hand are regarded as others' property, who will migrate to their husband's house sooner or later. Parents do not want to encourage fast physical growth in their daughers, as this makes them look eligible for marriage at an early age. Villagers believe that a high-calorie diet for girls accelerates the process of attaining puberty. Parents thus avoid certain nutritious foods for their daughers so as to give themselves more time to find a suitable groom and to accumulate/arrange money for a dowry and other marriage expenses. Besides, this practice spares them the worry that the girls might get spoiled and the humiliation of not marrying grown-up daughters in time (Khan *et al.* 1986). We found that for this reason daughters' ages were mostly under-reported. It should be mentioned here that girls also start helping their parents, particularly their mothers, at quite an early age and so it is useful to keep them in the household longer. They look after their younger brothers and sisters, wash utensils, make cowdung cakes, and are even doing the cooking by the age of ten or 12 years, thereby releasing their mothers for other household chores and farm or income-generating work.

Although it was difficult to assess, it seems likely that the freedom of movement of male children adds to their nutritional intake as they have better access to seasonal fruit and raw vegetables. Boys roaming about outside were often seen collecting seasonal fruit or vegetables such as mangoes, carrots, green peas and sugar cane from village fields and gardens. Similarly, those going to school invariably buy peanuts, guava and sweets out of the pocket money received from their parents. In contrast, girls are mainly confined to their homes, as most of them hardly go to school. Observations from Bangladesh also reflect differential calorie intakes according to sex. A recent study from Matlab Thana indicates that male calorie consumption exceeds female calorie consumption by an average of 16 per cent among children under five years and over 11 per cent among adolescents aged 5-14 (Chen *et al.*, 1981).

Treatment During Sickness

In order to assess whether parents discriminated in the treatment of sick sons and daughters, a series of questions was asked of the main informants and other villagers. We also kept track of the number of deaths occurring in the village, including those among children. And, as far as possible, observations were made on the nature and quality of treatment given to sons and daughters.

It was interesting that at first all the informants denied that there was any discrimination in treatment in favour of sons, although our own observations as well as patient statistics collected from the village primary health centre (PHC) showed that boys were given medical attention at an earlier stage of sickness than girls and that the treatment they received was a better quality. When we mentioned these observations to our informants, an overwhelming majority (17 out of 20) still felt that such incidents were in the minority and normally no such discrimination took place. Five of the women in fact reacted quite strongly to these observations. One of them commented:

> Why should girls not be treated in time, or have I to be partial to one when the process of giving birth and the pain we have to bear during delivery is the same for both sons and daughters?

Three of the informants said that while such practices had been common in the past (about 20 years ago), the situation had now changed. In the words of one high-caste woman:

> In our time during sickness sons were treated more seriously. Parents hardly paid any attention to daughters. At that time only one girl was considered sufficient in a family. So the second and subsequent daughters were not treated properly and were allowed to die. But now such discrimination does not exist.

One low-caste woman said:

> In our time much differentiation was made between sons and daughters. A girl's death was preferred to her survival. During sickness they were not given treatment. I myself had suffered too much. Whenever I fell sick, I was given tea only, not treatment. Parents thought I would get well by tea only. It hardly mattered if I died. In those days girls were taken as a burden. The expenditure of bringing up daughters and marrying them off was considered as a futile investment. But now the attitude has changed and girls are less discriminated against. Presently immediate treatment is given, no matter if it is a son or a daughter.

That female children actually do receive discriminatory treatment in sickness is, however, reflected in the statistics collected from the patient attendance register of the PHC responsible for providing health services in Krishanpur and the surrounding areas. In the month of January 1983, for example, we observed the functioning of the PHC for seven consecutive days. In these seven days, a total of 58 children visited the PHC for treatment, out of which 43 (74.1 per cent) were male and only 15 (25.9 per cent) female (Table 3). There is no reason to believe that in the study area, morbidity was less frequent among females than among males. The household census which was taken just before the case studies began also showed that among the 163 persons reported sick in the study village in the previous month, 84 were male and 79 female.[3]

---

[3]Unpublished village census data from study on 'Changing roles of women and its impact on their demographic behaviour'.

TABLE 3: NUMBER OF MALE AND FEMALE CHILDREN TREATED AT PHC DURING OBSERVATION PERIOD

Children	1st day	2nd day	3rd day	4th day	5th day	6th day	7th day	Total
Male	8	6	9	8	5	2	5	43
Female	4	2	1	4	0	2	2	15

Source: Primary Health Centre: Patient attendance register. Block headquarters, Krishanpur, unpublished data.

The local doctors also confirmed that girls were neglected and were not given treatment in time. They cited several examples. One day we ourselves witnessed one such case. One high-caste couple, accompanied by their sick five-year-old son, had come to the village dispensary. The wife, in our presence, asked her husband to get medicine for their sick daughter also. But the husband refused and said 'Don't worry, she will be all right'. When the couple left, the doctor said: 'You can find many such cases'. Another village doctor, while confirming the neglect of girls, added:

Yes, people neglect daughters' treatment. For sons they can take a loan, sell land and spend thousands of rupees to save their life. But for a daughter, even Rs.50 becomes too much.

Our overall observation was that discrimination against girls increases with their number in the family. This is particularly true of high-caste Hindu families who have to pay a large amount of money as dowry on the marriage of their daughters. As a consequence, after the birth of one daughter, or perhaps two, which every family desires, every additional girl is considered a burden and neglected, intentionally or unintentionally. Commenting on this, a village woman said:

In this village girls are not cared for well if they are many. During sickness, no proper care is taken. If she dies, parents console themselves thinking that God had taken her back. But if she survives, it is up to her luck.

In families where there are many daughters, girls generally do not receive attention when they first become sick. This is rationalized by saying that 'nothing has happened to her', or 'it is not a serious matter and she will be all right within a day or two'. However, if sickness persists, treatment is usually given. In contrast to this, boys are given almost immediate attention irrespective of their number in the family. We also observed that in a number of families with many daughters girls were taken to unqualified village doctors. If the situation warranted, for example, if the disease was prolonged and the local doctors were unable to cure it, sons were taken to senior city doctors. Girls' illnesses were never regarded as that serious, though they sometimes proved fatal. During 1981-82, ten children died in the village, out of which seven were female and three male. It was striking that while all the male children were taken to city hospitals for further treatment, none of the girls received similar treatment. There was a popular saying in the village: 'Only fortunates are blessed with the death of daughters as the father would not have to spend on dowry'. One rich person in the village, however, spent thousands of rupees on the treatment of his only daughter who was attacked by paralysis.

Analysis of the reproductive history of 31 women from the 20 informant families reveals a sharp difference in mortality by sex between high- and low-caste families (see Table 4). Among high-caste families, of all the male children born none had died, while the corresponding proportion for female children was as high as 23.5 per cent. Among low-caste families, on the other hand, the proportion of girls who had died (47.6 per cent) was less than the corresponding proportion for boys (63.2 per cent). This suggests that there is not much discrimination by sex among the lower castes. In fact, among the lower castes the main reason for high child mortality is poverty. Male-female discrimination is secondary. The reason is that among low-caste families (in contrast to high-caste), girls are not usually seen as an economic burden to the family. Women, both married and single, work for cash, so girls are seen as a source of income until they marry. To date, dowries are nominal among the lower castes.

TABLE 4: PROPORTION OF CHILDREN DYING AMONG THOSE BORN TO 31 WOMEN BELONGING TO 20 HOUSEHOLDS

Events	High caste		Low caste		Muslims		All	
	Male	Female	Male	Female	Male	Female	Male	Female
Births	30	34	38	42	14	15	82	91
Deaths	0	8	24	20	5	5	29	33
Percentage dying before age 10	0.0	23.5	63.2	47.6	35.7	33.3	35.4	36.3

Source: Khan, Anker, Ghosh, Bairathi and Hein: 'Men and women in Krishanpur village' (forthcoming).

The fact that economic factors lie behind the continued neglect of daughters is illustrated by a study involving the Saharia tribe of Rajasthan, India (Bairathi, n.d.). This study shows that Saharia women participate equally with men in earning a livelihood for the family, and in their community there is a system by which parents receive a bride price when their daughters marry. The Saharia girls are thus not seen as a burden, nor are they discriminated against.[4] In an adjoining village, however, with a non-tribal population where the usual dowry system prevails, neglect of daughters is a common phenomenon. Yet another study from Tamil Nadu, a state in Southern India, indicates that in one community where the dowry system operates in

---

[4]A similar observation was made among the Bhil tribe of Gujarat where daughters are valued because the parents are paid a bride price (based on personal discussions with Mr S.N. Morandar, Research Executive, Operations Research Group, Baroda).

its worst form and women are not encouraged to participate in the market, infanticide of girls is common. According to this report, more than 550 cases of infanticide have been reported during the last ten years from this community of between 100,000 and 200,000 population (*India Today*, 1986).

While we were collecting data for our study, we were able to observe what happened before three girls died in the village. None was given any treatment. When we asked their mothers why, one of them said:

> We are poor. We do not have even enough to eat. If the girl survives, she has to be fed, and then married, on which we have to spend a lot of money. And all these just to send her to another house (in-laws' house).

Other studies confirm this neglect of girls and this discrimination as regards giving them proper medical care. In a prospective study on infant mortality in Haryana in which each birth was followed up during 1981-83, 487 had died before completion of one year, of which 260 (53.4 per cent) were female and 227 (46.6 per cent) male. Neonatal deaths were in fact slightly higher among males than females, although the difference was not significant,[5] but postnatal deaths were much higher among females (61 per cent) than among males (39 per cent). Since postnatal mortality is by and large a consequence of social, cultural and environmental rather than biological factors, the high number of postnatal deaths among girls in Haryana demonstrated that daughters are neglected in this part of the country too.

TABLE 5: DEATHS BY SEX AND AGE AT DEATH, 1981-83, HARYANA STUDY (PERCENTAGES IN PARENTHESES)

Age at death (days)	Male		Female		Total
0-7	97	(53.0)	86	(47.0)	183
8-28	45	(52.3)	41	(47.7)	86
29-365	85	(39.0)	133	(61.0)	218
Total (N)	227	(46.6)	260	(53.4)	487

Source: Kumar and Dutta (1984).

A somewhat similar observation was made in Tamil Nadu by Abel, who found that female infanticide was still continuing in one form or another (Abel, 1984). Four cases of infanticide were verbally reported while he was collecting his data. However, most such cases never come to the surface because of the legal implications. According to the author, many families hold the view: 'When the child is a female why should we bring it up?'

---

[5]Based on biological factors females as compared to males have a better chance of survival. In South Asian countries, however, this is observed only during the perinatal and early neonatal period, where male mortality rates exceed female mortality rates (El Badry, 1969).

In our study village, it was observed that many mothers wanted to give treatment to their daughters but because of their low status in the family, ignorance about good or bad doctors, etc., they could not take the decision to visit a clinic or dispensary for treatment. Such decisions generally rested with the household males, particularly the husband. In the course of this study we came across at least two cases where the mother was eager to provide medical care to a sick daughter but was denied by the husband. In one case a girl had fallen from the roof and become unconscious. On the advice of the village doctor, the wife asked her husband to take the girl to a city hospital, but her husband flatly refused and said it was not serious. The wife submitted to her husband's decision without protest, but continued to weep bitterly. The husband, unperturbed, said to the doctor:

> Kindly do whatever you can. I shall not go to the city. If nothing can be done let her die. I have many daughters.

The couple had three daughters and they belonged to a high-caste family. Fortunately, the child survived due to the prompt treatment of the village doctor.

Adulthood

This discriminatory attitude towards females does not end with childhood. It only changes in form as they grow older. In the following paragraphs we shall see how the adult women in the study village are treated in respect of distribution of food within the family and care during sickness.

Food Intake

Our observations reveal that adult women, who are generally responsible for cooking and serving food in the family (at times assisted by their young daughters), invariably eat less than their due share of food. This is not because of any conscious discrimination against them; it occurs because of cultural norms and practices concerning eating patterns in the family, which give preferences to males in the allocation of food, particularly nourishing food such as milk, curd and ghee.

We observed that not only among the informant families, but in the entire village, women who cook and serve food take their meals last after serving all the family members. It is believed that if the woman who cooks food eats first then prosperity will never smile upon the household. Since food is cooked according to the number of people in the family, the arrival of unexpected guests or a little over-consumption by any of the other members reduces the share of the woman eating last. In the subsistence economy, where households do not have enough food to meet the daily minimum calorie requirements of household members, such an eating pattern affects the health of women very adversely, although it does not create any major health problem in the few big landowning families.

Further, in the distribution of rich food like ghee, curd and milk, it was observed that male family members, particularly the breadwinners, had definite preference. Out of the 20 main informants, 15 said that they eat these rich foods less often and in much less quantity than the males. In these families, male adults have milk and curd regularly, if available, while women consume them occasionally or take ghee at times of special need, for example for one to two months during pregnancy or after the birth of the child. Interestingly, both male and female informants argued that a man should eat more of the rich food as 'he is master of the house'; 'he works hard outside home';

or 'the responsibility of looking after the family lies on his shoulders'. This feeling was shared by the majority of the non-working housewives (12 out of 14) and half of the women (three out of six) working for cash.[6] Even amongst the women with some education most (five out of six) expressed similar views (see Table 6).

TABLE 6: FEMALE INFORMANTS' OPINION ON WHETHER MEN SHOULD EAT MORE, TABULATED BY WOMEN'S CHARACTERISTICS

Opinion	Age group		Working status		Education		Total
	30 or less	30+	Working for cash	Not working for cash	Liter-ate	Illi-terate	
Men should eat more	9	6	3	12	5	10	15
Men and women should eat equally	1	4	3	2	1	4	5
Total (N)	10	10	6	14	6	14	20

Source: Khan et al., 'Women and men in Krishanpur village' (forthcoming).

When we discussed these issues with some of the other village families, they too supported this practice. In the washerman community, for example, the adult males visit distant places during the daytime for wage earning while their women wash the clothes of village farmers. The women start work in the early morning (4 a.m.) and continue until 9 a.m., after which they do household chores. In agricultural seasons, they finish this work quickly so as to join their husbands in farm work. In spite of this hard labour, women rarely consume ghee or milk, whereas their husbands have these regularly, according to a rough estimate consuming between half and one kilogram of ghee every month.

It is interesting to note that in this entire matter of uneven distribution and consumption of nourishing food, women are willing partners. In the village we hardly came across a woman who ever grumbled about getting less food or leftover food or not eating the rich diets which she served to her husband and children. On the contrary, they feel satisfied and enjoy this spirit of sacrifices for the family. Two male informants specifically told us that it was not that male members of the family wanted to eat more than the females. It was the wife who served the best food to her husband, and it was difficult for the males to keep track of who ate how much.

---

[6]Out of these three women earning cash income, two had urban backgrounds and came from well-to-do high-caste families. One of these two was educated up to intermediate standard. Both women sewed at home for cash. The third woman also belonged to a high-caste but a poor family, and had no education; she too sewed at home.

However, we know of one educated male informant (whom we could watch closely) who used to bring *rabri* (condensed milk) and curd from the market and consume the bulk of them himself, sometimes leaving only a small part for the children or other family members.

It appears that the social and economic security for which Indian women depend heavily on their husbands plays an important role in inducing them to behave in this way: without a husband – the breadwinner – they would be nowhere. The teachings of religion, which give husbands a much superior position, also encourage women to offer their husband the best of everything available in the family. Hindu mythology prescribes that women should sacrifice for husband and family. It advises married women to observe a fast on various occasions in the year for the welfare of their husbands and children, but no such fast is recommended to males for the welfare of their wives or family.

It was also found that in families in which there was only one adult woman with no one else to assist her, she ate only after finishing all the household work and serving food to all other family members. As these tasks were performed on an empty stomach, by the time she was free she was totally exhausted, with no appetite for food. We know at least two women who were unable to eat properly due to lack of time and fatigue. In the case of one, her appetite had come down to such a level that she could hardly eat anything, and this ultimately caused her serious complications arising out of malnutrition. It was also perhaps her weakness which led to her having two miscarriages in one year.

Treatment During Sickness

It was found that in sickness married women were usually less neglected than young unmarried girls or female children. We were told that as in the case of a working male, a married woman is in a relatively advantageous position because she is a much-needed member of the family on whom lies the entire responsibility of attending to household chores, cooking, looking after children and husband, etc. Her being sick is therefore likely to upset the whole family schedule and cause serious inconvenience to all family members. Like other females in the household, she is unlikely to receive treatment at an early stage, but she does tend to be given medical attention before the ailment immobilizes her. This neglect is due not only to the carelessness and apathy of the husband but also to the presence of the mother-in-law. In the village we observed a few such cases. Once a Muslim woman visited a village doctor in our presence. In the past year she had had two miscarriages due to a hormonal imbalance, but she had not been given any treatment. On probing, her husband told us that she had not been eating properly for many months, but everyone in the household, including his mother (her mother-in-law), felt that she was all right and nothing was the matter with her. She became weaker but had no respite from heavy household duties. Her husband realized her problems, but could not help her as the other members of the family, particularly his mother, were not taking her illness seriously. It was only when she became totally unfit to perform domestic chores that he was asked to take her to a doctor.

This was not an isolated case. In a joint family in India during the first few years of marriage the son is always afraid that if he takes any initiative in the treatment of his wife or pleads for her to be allowed to rest, he is sure to offend his mother because she will think that her son has more concern for his wife than for herself. And this very feeling can undermine the relationship between the mother-in-law and the daughter-in-law. Such a husband is usually called *joru-ke-gulam* (captive of one's wife). This complex relationship between the son, his mother and her daughter-in-law continues until the mother-in-law, through day-to-day dealings, gains confidence that she is not being neglected and that both her son and daughter-in-law listen to her and care for her.

In India, especially in rural areas, the freedom of a newly married bride is very limited. Her say in family matters and other liberties such as free movement outside the home, talking to other male family members, etc., remain restricted until she becomes a mother of at least one son and moves to the middle age group. Neglect of the health care of young brides thus results not only from the general apathy of males towards females' health, but also from the complex and often strained relationships between mother-in-law and daughter-in-law. It was our common observation that when a daughter-in-law was indisposed the mother-in-law would invariably believe it was an excuse for not working, but when her own daughter was sick she would take it seriously and feel extremely concerned.

The local PHC doctor also confirmed that generally women were not given treatment immediately. So when a patient came to see him he would deliberately tell the husband that her illness was serious so that she could at least get some medical attention. During our visit to the PHC we actually came across one such incident. One woman was suffering from lung congestion. After examining her, the doctor wrote a prescription and warned the husband that her disease was serious and could lead to TB if she failed to take medicine regularly.

Our overall observation was that in the village married women did receive treatment, if belatedly, and that they were a little more 'privileged' than old ladies and young girls, particularly those with sisters.

Who Decides to Call in a Doctor?

It was observed that the decision to call a doctor was generally taken by men, mostly the husbands. Out of 20 female informants, 13 said that they had no power to make or influence such decisions. Hence, until the husband felt that his wife needed medical attention, the doctor was not consulted. In emergencies, for example at childbirth if there was any complication, the female members of the household could make a decision to call a doctor; in all other circumstances such decisions were made by adult males only. In seven families, however, the situation was relatively better with women in need either exercising their own judgement as to whether to call a doctor, or being able to persuade their husbands that they needed to see a doctor for treatment. Two of these women did not even have to wait for their husbands' consent. Both were working women and had considerable influence over their husbands. One of them met the expenses of the whole family by her earnings from sewing. In the remaining six families, there was a very good understanding between wife and husband. The most important factors in giving women power were their age and the nuclear character of the family. Of these eight families, seven were nuclear families without a mother-in-law. Similarly, seven respondents were aged over 30 and had established a good understanding with their husbands. Earlier studies also suggest that as a married couple grow older or as a young bride matures into a mother or mother-in-law, the relationship between husband and wife becomes increasingly egalitarian (Srinivas, 1978:19). Our discussion with the informants showed that 20-30 years ago no woman would have been free to call or consult a doctor without the permission of her husband. They felt that times were changing and women, particularly the young educated ones, were relatively better off than the older generation.

During discussion, none of the 20 informants expressed any objection to being seen or examined by a male doctor. In the village, all the doctors were male, and the informants said that if they preferred treatment by female doctors, they would have to remain sick as there was no woman doctor, even in the village PHC.

Cultural barriers like purdah and restrictions on the movement of females outside the home also restrict females' access to medical aid. On at least five occasions we found that when a female family member fell sick, the husband or other male members, including children, visited the physician and got medicines by simply describing the symptoms. This practice, which was quite common in Bangladesh, sometimes deprived the women of correct diagnosis and treatment (Islam, 1980).

Though the village women had no objection to being treated by male doctors for common ailments, for gynaecological problems at least they preferred to be seen by a woman doctor. Further, they preferred city doctors who were not known to them to local doctors who were known to them. It was interesting to note that in the nearby cities most of the leading gynaecologists were males, but neither the women nor their husbands had any inhibition about being seen by these doctors as they were assured of not being identified. This again was a big change as compared to the situation in rural India 20-30 years ago, when neither women nor their husbands would have been prepared to have such examinations take place unless the life of the woman was in danger. Our discussions showed, however, that there was still a minority of women unwilling to expose their private parts to male gynaecologists. Four out of the 20 informants, for example, were unwilling to be examined by any male doctor for gynaecological problems. At one time one of them had a gynaecological, but due to shyness did not let even her husband know about it until the ailment had become serious and intolerable. When she was taken to a nearby town to consult a doctor who happened to be male, she did not allow him to examine her and got medicines by just describing her symptoms.

Prenatal Care

All the informants, as well as other women in the village, mentioned that ideally a pregnant woman should get rest, good food and some extra attention. They believed that a small quantity of ghee and milk during advanced pregnancy was very useful for the mother and ensured proper growth of the foetus and easy delivery. But in practice they hardly got any. Out of the 20 main informants, seven said that they had consumed a small amount of such foods during pregnancy as their buffaloes were milking. One informant said: 'I take milk if my buffalo is milking, if not I just forget about it'.

Barring some rich landlords and families belonging to business communities, the economic position of most of the families in the village was poor. After meeting all other expenses, there was hardly any money left to buy ghee or milk for the pregnant women. Those who owned cattle invariably sold the bulk of the daily milk to traders to generate cash. The milk the family kept was not enough for all the family members; hence to increase the volume it was mixed with water and served to the family in order of priority, with the head of the household (father) first, then male children, female children and the mother of the children. This practice of mixing water with milk seems to be only 10-15 years old; it started when the milk traders began collecting milk from the villages in order to meet the growing milk requirements of the cities. The villagers commented that this practice is need-based, as the money which they get by way of selling milk is quite useful for buying agricultural inputs or meeting the expenses of daily needs. Otherwise, as one villager commented, 'Who would like to sell pure milk to others and consume water mixed with milk himself or give it to other family members?'. When the cattle are not milking, the family buy a small quantity of milk to prepare tea or for the infants and very young children. Under such circumstances, the pregnant woman has to survive on a routine diet which, by and large, is inadequate even for a non-pregnant woman in terms of calorie value. During discussion about the need for nutritious food, one pregnant woman sarcastically said: 'You talk of ghee and milk? I cannot afford to take even a cup of tea'.

There were instances when even this routine diet was not available to women in adequate quantity because of cultural practices and at times because of the presence of in-laws in the household. One of our informants was pregnant and was suffering from acute malnutrition. She had already lost three consecutive pregnancies. When we suggested she take care of herself, she kept quiet for a while and then said:

At home I have to work from dawn to dusk. We do not take breakfast as we finish our mid-day meal between 10 and 12 noon. I cannot take food unless I have served my husband and mother-in-law. By the time I am through, I am totally exhausted and often don't feel like eating at all. If I do not perform this work who else will do?

On probing about her daily diet, it became apparent that her daily consumption was far below her requirements. Her daily food intake is given below:

1. Two chapattis (about 80 grams of flour) and one dish of vegetables in the afternoon.

2. Two chapattis (about 80 grams of flour) and one dish of vegetables at night.

3. Two cups of tea in a day and occasionally some pulses.

It was found that in general the village household aim to give 1-2 kilograms of ghee to a pregnant woman in the eighth or ninth month in the belief that it will work as a lubricant and ease the delivery of the child. However, all depends on whether the family can bear the cost of ghee (Rs.40 per kilogram).

One of the most serious problems for the pregnant women is the strenuous work which they have to perform at home. They sometimes have to work for as long as 13-14 hours a day. In the village we were able to observe 20 pregnant women – five from informant and 15 from non-informant families. Eighteen of these did everything throughout the pregnancy and two until labour pains started. In the village it was not uncommon to find women carrying heavy loads of fodder on their heads from the fields in the eighth or ninth month of pregnancy. Table 7 presents the time use data of five pregnant informant women on a normal day, and it supports the above observations.

During pregnancy, the village women hardly have any extra medical care – e.g., periodical check-ups, immunization against tetanus, protection against nutritional anaemia, etc. – either from local doctors or from the PHC, from which they could at least get advice and iron tablets free of cost under the Maternal and Child Health (MCH) program. But the women do not seek any medical aid unless they have a serious complaint. Out of 20 informants, only three had visited city hospitals; they had serious complications during pregnancy. But none of the three could say whether they had been given tetanus immunization at the hospital. To the informants by and large, special care during pregnancy meant nourishing food like milk and ghee, rest, light work, etc. They were still guided by old prescriptions, partly because of illiteracy and ignorance, partly due to lack of access to or knowledge about modern health care services. Recently, however, some changes have been taking place. For example, some educated families in the village (including at least one informant family) now insist that the traditional *dai* use of new blade and antiseptic lotion while cutting the umbilical cord. Similarly, in many households (including at least two informant families) a tetanus injection (ATS) is now given to the mother and the child for protection against tetanus.

TABLE 7: **TIME USE DATA OF FIVE PREGNANT WOMEN ON A NORMAL DAY**

Activity	Time spent in hours				
	Kamlesh (3 months pregnant)	Susheela (4 months pregnant)	Shanti (7 months pregnant)	Kamla (8 months pregnant)	Phoolmati (8 months pregnant)
Working for wage/ salary (unskilled)	10.00	-	-	-	5.30
Travelling time to go to work place	-	-	-	-	2.00
Handicrafts	-	-	-	2.00	-
Cooking and serving food	2.15	2.30	2.00	3.00	4.15
Fetching water	0.45	3.00	2.00	1.30	1.00
Other household work like washing clothes, cleaning, dusting, etc.	1.30	2.00	3.00	2.30	2.15
Animal husbandry	-	3.00	2.00	3.00	-
Self care, rest, gossiping, taking food, etc.	2.00	3.00	3.00	2.00	2.15
Making cowdung cakes	-	0.30	-	-	-
Child care	-	-	1.00	2.30	-
Grinding grain	-	3.00	2.30	4.00	-
Sleeping	7.30	7.00	6.00	5.00	6.45

Note: Only time of primary activities included.

Source: Khan *et al.* (1986).

In the 16 deliveries which took place during our stay in the village, both mother and child were given ATS within 24 hours of the birth. However, it was reported that in many cases the injection is given only to the newborn baby and not to the mother. This practice is more common for second and subsequent deliveries. Commenting on this, one high-caste school teacher said:

My wife was given ATS when my eldest son was born. The second time ATS could not be given and nothing happened to her. During the third and fourth deliveries I did not attempt at all.

None of the 20 informants reported any visits from a registered nurse (ANM) for antenatal advice or distribution of vitamin tablets. They were thus denied access to sources of knowledge and services.

The situation presented above is not untypical. Many large-scale sample surveys have revealed similar situations in other parts of the country. Two recent studies covering five states in India have shown that MCH services hardly reach pregnant women in three of the states, Bihar, Uttar Pradesh and Rajasthan, the exceptions being Kerala and to some extent Gujarat (Khan and Prasad, 1983; Mehta *et al.*, 1983). As can be seen from Table 8, in Uttar Pradesh out of 1,800 women who became pregnant during the year preceding the survey (1982), only 10 per cent were checked up by an ANM at home, 10 per cent were given tetanus toxoid, 8 per cent were approached and advised on family planning services, 7 per cent received multivitamins and iron tablets and 4 per cent were referred to primary health centres. A similar situation was observed in Rajasthan and Bihar. In the case of Kerala and Gujarat, the situation was relatively better. In summary, the services of ANMs, who are supposed to visit each home for maternal and child health care, are normally not available to the pregnant women in three out of the five study states.

TABLE 8: **PERCENTAGE OF PREGNANT WOMEN USING VARIOUS MCH SERVICES FROM FIVE STUDIES**

Services	States				
	Bihar[a]	U.P.[b]	Rajasthan[b]	Gujarat[b]	Kerala[b]
Checked up at home by ANM	6	10	9	43	38
Referred to PHC	n.a.	4	6	35	n.a.
Given tetanus toxoid	11	10	11	37	38
Given multi-vitamin and iron tablets	8	7	11	40	39
Given nutritional supplements	5	-	n.a.	n.a.	12
Receiving assistance in delivery at home	9	-	n.a.	n.a.	10
Counselled on FP after delivery	3	8	11	40	26
Total pregnant women (N)	639	1800	1750	1800	638

Sources:
[a]Khan and Prasad (1983)
[b]Mehta *et al.* (1983)

The ANM assigned to Krishanpur hardly visited the village. At the time of delivery, even if there was a complication, she refused to see the case at night. To assist a delivery she charged anything between Rs.30 and Rs.60, depending upon the seriousness of the case. For most of the villagers, this was a large amount. Thus deliveries were mostly assisted by *dais* (traditional birth attendants) and/or by relatives/neighbours (see Table 9). The normal fee charged by a *dai* was Rs.5-10 (US$ 0.4-0.8), plus some grain, e.g., wheat, rice, etc. For poor families this amount was reduced to Rs.2-3 plus some grain.

Table 9 indicates that out of 79 deliveries among our main informants, only four took place in hospital while the remaining 75 took place at home. Out of the 75 home deliveries, only four were assisted by an ANM, while the rest were attended by family members and a *dai*. Other large-scale surveys support the above findings. According to the study referred to above, in Uttar Pradesh about 90 per cent of deliveries take place at home, mostly with untrained *dais*. Another large-scale survey (NIHFW *et al.*, 1982) reports that about 93 per cent of deliveries in rural Rajasthan take place at home, largely with *chamarins* or untrained *dais*. This survey also records that in urban areas of Rajasthan, about 68 per cent of deliveries take place at home and 65 per cent of cases are assisted by untrained *dais*. Yet another survey conducted around the present study village shows that 63 per cent of deliveries are assisted by relatives and neighbours, about 31 per cent by untrained *dais*, and only about 7 per cent by trained professionals (Khan, 1984).

It should be mentioned that there was an MCH centre in the study village. But most of the time it remained closed. It was reported that the ANM maintained a close personal relationship with her superior and thus could skip her duties without any difficulty.

TABLE 9: PLACE OF DELIVERY AND TYPE OF ATTENDANT BY CASTE OF INFORMANT

Caste	Place of delivery		Type of attendant		No.of deliveries
	Institution	Home	Dai	ANM	
High caste	4	58	54	4	62
Low caste	0	17	17	0	17
Total	4	75	71	4	79

Source: Khan *et al.*, 'Women and men in Krishanpur village' (forthcoming).

Old Age

The plight of women usually worsens during old age. In the initial year of marriage a woman suffers because she has little say in family matters and depends for everything on her husband and mother-in-law. When she bears children, particularly sons, her status begins to improve, and she becomes able to influence many family decisions (Srinivas, 1978:19). After the age of about 40 she becomes dominant and rules over other female members of the family, particularly daughters-in-law and at times her own mother-in-law. This is the age at which a woman enjoys the maximum liberty, next only to her husband and the older male members of the family. However, she is usually deprived of this special status if she is vulnerable to desertion by her husband, who can plan for the second marriage.[7]

As she gets older (55-60 years), her position in the family gradually deteriorates. she becomes less active and starts depending more on her children for her economic, physical and emotional needs.   For physical care, she looks to her unmarried daughters, daughters-in-law and grandchildren.   The degree of attention and care she gets depends a lot on her present marital status, whether she possesses property in her own name, what her children are like (particularly her son(s)), and finally the relationship she had with her daughter(s)-in-law when she was at her peak.

It was quite clear from the case studies that an old woman would be relatively better off (though still much worse than when she was in her prime) if her husband was alive, as he would continue to be regarded as the head of the household and his children would pay at least some respect to their mother.   This respect and attention towards parents is much stronger if the father still earns a livelihood for the family or retains family property in his name, which is usually done to ensure family attention.

The death of the husband, however, exposes the widow to many risks.   Her position is slightly better if she owns some property in her own name.   If she does not, she is totally at the mercy of her children, daughters-in-law and other family members.   For such a woman it is crucial whether she has son(s), how concerned and sympathetic they are towards their mother, and how she has behaved in the past with other family members (Khan *et al.*, 1987).

Food Intake

Our observation did not reveal any marked neglect in the distribution of food to older women as compared to young adult women. Older women got the same food as was cooked for the whole family and eaten by other female household members. As far as we could observe, the old women were not neglected in the sense of being given leftovers or less food. However, despite their age, no special care was taken to provide them with nourishing food like milk. In one case out of the five we studied, the old woman had strained relations with her daughter-in-law, and in another case the old lady was staying in her daughter's house and was strongly disliked by her son-in-law. In these two families, the old women were not allowed to enter the kitchen. Food was served to them on the verandah.

Two out of the five older women felt that daughters had more sympathy for their parents, but unfortunately daughters could not be of much help to them once they married into other families. One of the five old women had only one son and she was neglected by him. In contrast, another two older women got help in emergencies entirely from their married daughters; they had no sons.

All five older women believed that having a good-natured son who would care for his parents was a matter of luck and it did not depend on the numbers of sons. We also noticed that among the few older women we observed, those who had two or more sons were relatively better off than those who had only one or no son. Some older women had an uncomfortable feeling that if they continued to stay with one son he might come to consider them a burden. As one old woman commented:

> I have three sons and I keep on visiting each of them alternately. All my daughters-in-law take care of me and they like me. But I don't stay with anybody for a long period, just to avoid the impression that only one of them is feeding me and that I am a burden on them.

---

[7]According to the Indian Penal Code, polygamy is not allowed, except for Muslims. In rural areas, however, this rule is not strictly followed and a second marriage is often reported where the wife has not produced any son. Among low castes having two wives is not uncommon.

In contrast, older men are better off as many of them retain property in their own name and continue to be economically active for their families even in old age. Tradition also gives them considerable support and they command respect from their sons and daughters-in-law. They get better food than older women both because they supplement the family income and because they are male. However, there were cases where old men, too, were neglected when they were physically handicapped or economically inactive and had given their property rights over to their sons.

Treatment During Sickness

In sickness old people, irrespective of sex, suffer. They are no longer active members of the family and have little control over others. Being physically weak, they are in fact at the mercy of others.

Males who own land in their own name and are not totally immobile physically are relatively better off since they can walk to a clinic or chemist shop for medicine. Family members, too, take more care of them if they still control assets. An older woman, in contrast, is in a disadvantageous position because she has no cash nor can she help out greatly in household chores. Her access to doctors or chemist shops is also very limited.

Unless sickness is sudden and serious, treatment is invariably delayed for older men and women, as ailments are considered to be a normal part of old age. Neglect becomes worse when old people are frequently sick or have chronic diseases like asthma or arthritis. Since these people suffer continuously, after a time nobody pays attention to them. In one of the informant families, for example, an old woman was suffering from arthritis. She used to take a particular brand of medicine for relief. For some months this medicine was not available in the village market. The poor woman cried in pain for weeks, but nobody bothered to get it from the nearby town which was hardly 10 kilometres from the village.

In at least six cases (four males and two females) of older persons suffering from chronic diseases, primarily asthma and arthritis, we observed that they were not given any attention. If they complained too often about pain or respiratory problems, it was brushed aside on the grounds that the symptoms were more psychological than genuine. Members of these families felt that the old people were just making a fuss to get attention. Sadly, these feelings were shared by several others in the community. We also observed that old people suffer from loneliness because no one wants to give them company. This is even true of families where aged people get adequate food and medical treatment. Their sons or daughters-in-law speak only a few words to them each day, although grandchildren are sometimes seen taking care of their grandfather or grandmother.

In families where old people are disliked by the parents (as in the case of two informant families), children too show dislike for them. In one of these families the grandson learnt to give injections by making trials on his grandmother.[8] Each time the needle was pushed in she cried in pain, while the rest of the family laughed. Because of continuous neglect, one day she said sobbingly: 'I want to die. Life is a curse for me'.

Our overall observation is that very old people, be they male or female, are generally treated as a burden, particularly if they are sick or handicapped. This is never explicitly said to outsiders, but one can sense it by observing their behaviour.

In day-to-day life, their advice or suggestions are often ignored, more so with women than with men. In a few cases we found that harsh words were also used to silence them.

---

[8]This old lady, aged about 75 years, was a grandmother of the child on the maternal side. Generally, a grandmother on the paternal side cannot be subjected to such cruelty, at least in the presence of her son.

Old people suffer mostly because they are too weak to see to their own personal needs and often no one is available to help them. It is not uncommon to see old men and women waiting for long periods of time for somebody to help them. In old age, it seems, food and shelter are not so much a problem as lack of human caring.

SUMMARY AND CONCLUSIONS

This study has shown that throughout the entire life cycle, men are relatively more privileged than women as regards individual food intake and care during sickness. In the opinion of the authors and others this bias can probably be traced to the higher participation in the labour market and the greater visibility of the economic contribution of men as compared to women.

Although all household members observed in this study ate the same basic meals, males (adults and children) received the lion's share of nutritious food such as ghee, milk and buttermilk that was available to the family as they were considered to be the 'breadwinners' (present and future). Indeed, we found that daughters were often purposely denied these nourishing foods in order to arrest their physical growth and thus prevent them from becoming eligible for marriage at a young age, as this would entail great expense for the family.

An adult married woman does not face this particular restriction, but since she is usually the last member of the family to eat, what remains for her is often leftovers and these are often inadequate for her nourishment. Even if nourishing food, such as ghee and milk, is available, the ingrained spirit of self-sacrifice makes a woman leave it for her children, especially her sons, and her husband, on whom she feels the future of the family rests.

In sickness, daughters and sons in the sample were treated differently, with the neglect in the health care of daughters positively associated with the number of daughters in the household. In contrast, sons, irrespective of their number, received timely and better quality treatment. Neglect of daughters, particularly when the family has more than two, is probably due to the perceived low productive contribution of girls and worry about the large dowry needed for marriage.

Among adult women, married women are relatively more privileged than unmarried women. Although health treatment is usually delayed for all women, this delay is much shorter for a married woman as the family often cannot afford to have her indisposed, especially when she is entirely responsible for household chores. In a joint family, however, even the treatment of a married woman can be greatly delayed, as the sickness of a young daughter-in-law is often not taken seriously by the mother-in-law until the illness makes the daughter-in-law virtually unfit to work. Many times even her husband does not feel able to take her to a doctor, due to a fear of offending his own mother. This situation continues until a woman becomes middle-aged and has children of her own.

In pregnancy, unless there are complications, women do not go for check-ups or immunization. In most cases, deliveries take place at home with the assistance of a traditional *dai* and family members. In the past few years, however, there has been a visible trend to vaccinate babies against tetanus soon after delivery, although frequently mothers are left unprotected. Similarly, some upper-caste families are insisting that the *dai* use a new blade and antiseptic lotion when cutting the umbilical cord. Interestingly, it was found that most women and their husbands in the study were now open to the idea of the women being examined by a male doctor. However, for gynaecological problems, they still insist on a woman doctor. In cases where a gynaecological examination must be done and no woman doctor is available, it is strongly preferred that the examination should be done by a male doctor who is unknown to the family (e.g., a doctor in another town or city hospital).

It appears that, whatever other reasons there may be, this neglect in maternal care can be explained in part by the general lack of knowledge about preventive care measures and the low level of health concsiousness of the masses. The poor performance of public health clinic (PHC) staff further deprives people of knowledge on health matters and of medicines such as vitamin A or iron and folic acid tablets which are available at PHCs.

The majority of the women do not receive a special nourishing diet before or after delivery, as tradition would require, primarily because of poverty. If the family own cattle, a woman gets some milk if the cow is milking; otherwise, like others, she forgets about it.

In view of the village lifestyle, only a few privileged women can even think of resting in pre- or postnatal days. In advanced stages of pregnancy, women in the study area were frequently seen doing all the usual household work and bringing head-loads of fodder from the fields.

Old age is a period of suffering for both men and women. Best off are men who have some property in their own name. Similarly, older women with some assets of their own or whose husbands are alive are relatively well cared for. For an older woman the most important factor in her situation is the relationship she has with her son and daughter(s)-in-law.

Over time, however, some positive changes were observed to be taking place in rural areas. Today, younger couples with schooling are more liberal in their views. And the increased nuclearization of families has given wives more opportunities to mix with their husbands. Women in such families are more independent in deciding what to cook and what to serve to whom, and are even able to persuade their husbands to seek medical help when a child falls sick. Allocation of food among family members in nuclear families is not as skewed, although the males are still better off. Unfortunately such developments are still confined to the better educated families. It is hoped that in time such practices will percolate down to the poorer strata of society.

REFERENCES

Abel, R. (1984), 'Impact of the rural health and development programme on infant mortality', paper presented to Population Council, Gujarat Institute of Area Development, Seminar on the Determinants of Infant Mortality in India, Ahmedabad, 1-4 Oct.

Anker, R. (1982), 'Demographic change and the role of women: research programme in developing countries', in Anker *et al.*

Anker, R. Buvinic, M., and Youssef, N. (eds) (1982), *Women's Roles and Population Trends in the Third World*, Croom Helm, London.

Bairathi, S. (n.d.) 'Tribal culture, economy and health: A study of Saharias of Rajasthan', unpublished study, Department of History, University of Rajasthan, Jaipur.

Chen, L.C., Huq, E. and D'Souza(1981), 'Sex bias in the family allocation of food and health care in rural Bangladesh', Population and Development Review, 7,1:55-78.

D'Souza, S. and Chen, L.C.. (1980), 'Sex differentials in mortality in rural Bangladesh', *Population and Development Review*, 6,2:257-270.

Dyson, T. and Moore, M. (1983), 'On kinship structure, female autonomy and demographic behaviour in India', *Population and Development Review*, 9,1:35-60.

El Badry, M.A. (1969), 'Higher female than male mortality in some countries of South Asia: A digest', *Journal of American Statistical Association*, 64:1234-1244.

Government of India, Committee on the Status of Women in India, (1974), *Towards Equality*, New Delhi.

Government of India, Ministry of Health and Family Welfare (1984), *Year Book 1983-84*, Family Welfare Programme, New Delhi.

Government of India, Planning Commission, *Seventh Five-Year Plan*, 1985-90. New Delhi:para.271.

Hammer, V. (1982), 'The status of women and family planning', paper presented in WHO/Figo Workshop on Concepts of Family Planning in Primary Health Care, San Francisco, 13-14 Oct.

India Today (1986) 'Born to die', *India Today*,(New Delhi) 11,11.

Islam, M. (1980), *Folk Medicine and Rural Women in Bangladesh*, Women for Women Research and Study Group, Dacca.

Khan, M.E. (1980) 'Study of inter-relationships between the status of women and demographic change in Uttah Pradesh, India: A proposal', Working Paper No. 1,Operations Research Group, New Delhi.

Khan, M.E. (1984) 'Determinants of infant mortality in Uttar Pradesh: a micro level study', paper presented to the Population Council, Gujarat Institute of Area Development, Seminar on Determinants of Infant Mortality, Ahmedabad, 1-4 Oct.

Khan, M.E., Anker, R. and Ghosh Dastidar, S.K. (1987), *Plight of Young Widows and Separated Women in Rural India*, Operations Research Group, Baroda.

Khan M.E., Anker, R., Ghosh Dastidar, S.K., Bairathi, S. and Hein, C. (n.d.) 'Women and men in Krishanpur village: gender inequalities and health, work, education and family formation', forthcoming.

Kahn, M.E., and Ghosh Dastidar, S.K. (1983), 'To be an insider: methodological insights from micro level village studies', in *Women, Work and Demographic Issues*, proceedings of ILO/UNITAR seminar, Tashkent, USSR, 11-19 Oct.

Khan, M.E. and Ghosh Dastidar, S.K. (1984) 'Women's perspective in family planning programme', paper prepared for the Division of Family Helath, World Health Organization.

Khan, M.E. Ghosh Dastidar, S.K. and Singh, R. (1986), 'Nutrition and health practices among the rural women: a case study of Uttar Pradesh', *Journal of Family Welfare*, 33,2.

Khan M.E. and Prasad, C.V.S. (1983), *Under-utilization of Health Services in Rural India: A Comparative Study of Bihir, Gujarat and Karnataka*, Operations Research Group, Baroda.

Kumar, V. (1983), 'Inter-relationship between breastfeeding, weaning practices and child mortality', paper presented to ICMR/Ford Foundation Workshop on Child Health, Nutrition and Family Planing, Gauhati, 22-24 Sept.

Kumar, V., and Dutta, N. (1984), 'Community based studies on infant mortality in Haryana: Metholdological issues relating to reporting and causation', paper presented to Population Council, Gujarat Institute of Area Development, Seminar on the Determinants of Infant Mortality in India, Ahmedabad, 1-4 Oct.

Mehta, S., Khan, M.E. Gupta, R.B., Gandotra, M.M. and Ojah, O.S. (1983), 'Role of health service delivery on acceptance of family planning', ICMR, New Delhi, mimeograph.

Miller, B.D. (1981), *The Endangered Sex: Neglect of Female Children in Rural North India*, Cornell University Press, Ithaca and London.

National Institute for Health and Family Welfare (NIHFW) (New Delhi), International Institute for Population Studies (Bombay), Directorate of Health Services (Rajasthan), Registrar General of India (1982), *Baseline Survey on Fertility, Mortality, Family Welfare and Utilization of Health and Family Welfare Services in Rajasthan*, New Delhi and Bombay.

Padmanabha, P. (1981), *Census of India 1981, Series 1, India, Paper 1 of 1981*, Government of India, New Delhi.

Schultz, T. (1982), 'Women's work and their status: rural Indian evidence of labour market and environment effects on sex differences in childhood mortality', in Anker *et al.*, 1982, pp.202-236.

Srinivas, M.N. (1978), *The Changing Position of Indian Women*, Oxford University Press, Delhi.

Ware, H. (1981), *Women, Demography and Development*, Development Studies Centre, Australian National University, Canberra.

Whyte, M.K. (1978), *The Status of Women in Pre-industrial Societies*, Princeton University Press, Princeton.

Chapter 11

THE SOCIAL COMPONENT OF MORTALITY DECLINE: AN INVESTIGATION IN SOUTH INDIA EMPLOYING ALTERNATIVE METHODOLOGIES*

John C. Caldwell, P.H. Reddy and Pat Caldwell

It has previously been reported that mother's education exerts an influence on infant and child mortality that is independent both of the level of medical technology found in the society and of the family's access to it (Orubuloye and Caldwell, 1975; Caldwell, 1979; Caldwell and McDonald, 1982). This finding suggests that social change may have played an important role in the mortality transition and that social factors may explain the failure of health services to be more effective. Clearly an adequate investigation of this proposition means a study not only of mortality but of pre-existing morbidity, an area in which there has been only a limited development of research methodology.

Since 1979, we have been testing the limits of the survey approach in a rural area of South India, and experimenting with the development of supplementary or alternative methods for collecting demographic information. These alternative approaches draw heavily on the methods of anthropology. The continuing work is a joint project of the Population Centre, Bangalore, and the Department of Demography, Australian National University. The original focus of the research had been on changes in marriage and control of marital fertility (Caldwell, Reddy and Caldwell, 1982,1983,1984a,b), but, given long periods of village residence, we had inevitably learnt much about the conditions of health, and by 1981 were in a position to concentrate our interest upon these matters.

The work reported here was carried out in a rural area of southern Karnataka (once Mysore) 125 kilometres west of the city of Bangalore. The study population consisted of one large village with 2,557 inhabitants and eight smaller villages, ranging in size from 62 to 543 persons and totalling another 2,216 inhabitants. The area is traversed by a moderately important sealed road but only the large village is right on it and most of the others are approached easily only by ox cart. The most distant of the small villages is 12 kilometres from the large village. The district has not been provided with a modern irrigation system, although the large village owes its

*First published in *Population Studies*, 37(2)1983, and republished as Chapter 6 in *The Causes of Demographic Change*, The University of Wisconsin Press.

location and size to an ancient tank,[1] which provides water after a year of good rains for the irrigation of 100 hectares of wet land where rice is grown. However, most of the land is used for the cultivation of the subsistence staple crop, *ragi* (Indian finger millet), and the green revolution has had little impact.

Nevertheless, there has been economic and social change. In the large village, the district's weekly market or *shandy* has been increasingly supplemented by a dozen small permanent shops, while the number of retail outlets (tiny stores selling tea, coffee, *bidis* (local cigarettes), soap, matches, etc.) in the smaller villages has doubled during the period of our research. The monetization of the local economy, and the decline of *jajmani* relations (traditional economic relations between landowning families and the service castes characterized by annual payments in grain), is a subject of much comment. In accordance with both central and state government policies, schools have multiplied so that three-quarters of the boys and half the girls are now in school compared with one-third and one-twentieth respectively in 1947 at the time of Independence. Indeed, over the last generation the proportion of brides with some schooling has multiplied 12-fold in the smaller villages, from 3 to 36 per cent. The importance of agriculture as a source of livelihood has declined. In the large village half the adult male workers now regard their primary employment as being outside farming, although the proportion in the small villages is only 8 per cent. Spurred by the expansion of employment in Bangalore and the growth of bus services to it, in over one-quarter of all families at least one male member is now working elsewhere.

The area is well suited to a study of mortality decline. Modern (or allopathic) medicines arrived in the large village in 1929 when the Maharajah of Mysore ordered that a health centre be provided. Since then, a medical practitioner has been stationed there almost continuously and in 1983 a second practitioner (female, as planned) and a small hospital are to be added. In addition, in 1977, the son of a local family of landowners set up in private practice, although his clientele is still very small, being largely confined to relatives and the family's friends and employees. By 1981 a Muslim cloth merchant judged the demand for modern medicines, mostly patent medicines, to have reached the point where he was justified in stocking most of his premises with pharmaceuticals and employing a trained pharmacist for dispensing. The residents of the large village visit the health centre during its official hours of opening on any day of the week, but the majority of people from the smaller villages who come for treatment do so only on Tuesdays when the market is held. The private practitioner now visits the two most populous of the smaller villages once a week, while the government multi-purpose health workers (until recently known as auxiliary nurse-midwives or ANMs) visit each family in all but the smallest village every other month, although, admittedly, their main concern is family planning.

In spite of some uncertainty about exact levels and trends, the overall picture of mortality decline in both India and Karnataka is reasonably clear.[2] In the whole country the expectation of life at birth was certainly lower than 25 years at the beginning of the century, probably over 30 years by 1941, close to 35 years by 1951 and 40 years by 1961, and is probably now at least 50 years. Until World War II, the gains in life expectation had been only about one-quarter of a year for every elapsed year; subsequently the increases have been twice as fast. In Karnataka, expectations of life at birth have tended, at least since 1941, to be between two and four years higher and may now be close to 55 years. However, in the rural study area, the level

---

[1]i.e., a reservoir formed by building an earthen wall across a stream.

[2]For calculations from child survival levels in the Indian censuses since 1951 for the whole country and Karnataka (Mysore) since 1941, cf. United Nations, 1961; the Karnataka Dual Record System, 1977 (Reddy *et al.*, 1980) and Mitra, 1978:22-197.

is still about 50 years, perhaps 52 years in the large village and 48 years in the eight smaller villages. The infant mortality rate in the study area in 1981 was around 115 per thousand live births[3] compared with perhaps 100 in the whole state.

These figures suggest a simple explanation. The smaller villages have less access to Western medicine than the large village, while the latter compares unfavourably with the average for the whole state, which contains urban as well as rural areas; mortality decline is proportional to the penetration of modern medicine. This explanation is far from sufficient. The death rates in the smaller villages, with only very limited access to modern medicine, have fallen by two-thirds since the beginning of the century (when the expectation of life at birth was two-fifths of its present level). Some of the difference can be explained by the success of campaigns against epidemic disease (bubonic plague, smallpox and cholera) during the first two-thirds of the century, and the partial success against malaria,[4] but no estimate of their earlier incidence will explain the whole margin. Nor will these explanations suffice for the gain of perhaps ten years in expectation of life over the past 20 years at a time when the major epidemics had already been brought under control. In addition it is also necessary to explain why modern health facilities in rural areas have had only limited, but increasing, success in attracting patients. Given the levels of sickness and size of the population, the queues at health centres are a fraction of the length that might be anticipated from the experience of countries with lower mortality. Furthermore, the young and very old are underrepresented among the patients.

These are the questions to be answered. Increasingly we have found that the answers are not fundamentally connected with the condition of the medical arts and delivery systems, but with profound changes in the nature of the society. Hence, the pre-existing society, and its very substantial survivals, will be treated here at some length. Earlier we have suggested that social institutions play a major role in determining the degree of success achieved by the application of medical technology (Orubuloye and Caldwell, 1975; Caldwell, 1979; Caldwell and McDonald, 1982), but the investigation is carried much further here. We have also previously suggested the existence of a clash between the beliefs relating to health of members of the more traditional sectors of society and those who have made greater contact with external influences through schooling, but we have not presented a detailed examination of the traditional beliefs to show why resistance to treatment by modern medicine can be so effective for such a long period.

THE RESEARCH APPROACH: FAILURES AND SOME SUCCESS

Although we lived in the larger village and worked in all the villages, we began by taking a census and mapping the area, and were prepared to persist with survey methods as long as our parallel anthropological (or micro) approach did not demonstrate that the surveys had begun to yield information that could not be used. It should be noted that these surveys had been preceded by the principal investigators residing in the locality, so that at every stage an element of in-depth interviewing and participant discussion could be included, the results of which were subject to continuous scrutiny so that the approach, and even the questions, could be continually

---

[3] A longitudinal study of infant mortality carried out two years earlier by research workers in the Bangalore Population Centre in the rural areas of five districts, including that of the study area, yielded an infant mortality rate of 102 (Badari *et al.*, 1979).

[4] By the mid-1960s malaria had apparently disappeared in the study area, as in most of the rest of India. Its incidence is now relatively high with, however, little direct mortality. For most of the period plague, smallpox and cholera were the only notifiable diseases, and hence their trends are best known. There is little evidence to suggest that tuberculosis is declining.

modified. Nightly discussions of each day's findings, stimulated by the interest with
which the group greeted each new finding or insight, prevented us from wandering
too far from local reality. This is often not the case with larger surveys, where the
experience of the interviewer does not percolate upwards (or where there may be no
interviewer) (cf. Reinharz, 1979). In many health surveys in developing countries
there are unwitting major errors because of the nature of the underlying assumptions.
For instance, in South Asia it may be – and frequently is – assumed that all treatment
is undertaken either by allopathic practitioners or their counterparts in the Ayurvedic
or other Great Traditions of medicine (Ramesh and Hyma, 1981). In other studies,
treatment that is not given by practitioners but employs remedies given in the home or
by neighbours is disregarded (Claquin, 1981). Such surveys are not self-correcting
because interviewees and interviewers alike assume that it is this essentially
practitioner-oriented behaviour that is being investigated. Much of the sickness that
does occur is not reported because it is thought to be imbalance, error or sin for which
the appropriate treatment is very different from the matters investigated in the survey.
Respondents identify the survey and its interviewers with the modern world – with
government, the health centre, medical practitioners and the ethos of bureaucrats and
schools – limiting their responses to matters that are appropriate to such persons and
institutions.

The survey approach provided usable information on deaths, if not always on their
timing. Unlike African society, where the discussion of death or the dead may bring
ill-fortune upon the living (Caldwell, 1974), and where mortality is, therefore,
inevitably understated, rural Indians are prepared to co-operate painstakingly in
constructing a record of deaths, provided that the discussions occur at a propitious
time, when the sun is high in the sky, and not at night.

In contrast, different definitions of illness meant that the survey approach failed
miserably when we employed it to measure morbidity. Repeatedly, co-operative, but
clearly sick persons, denied that there was any illness in the house. However, the
information in the survey on attendance at the health centre or treatment by the
private practitioner tallied with the medical records. The information on how long it
took them to seek treatment, the forms of treatment first attempted, and the extent to
which they persisted with the prescribed treatment could be shown both by
observation and the records and conclusions of the staff at the health centre to be very
much less trustworthy. By using a mixture of the survey and the case-study approach
we obtained useful information on the persons who first noted a child's illness and on
the authorization of treatment.

For much of the rest of our investigation there was no satisfactory alternative but
to employ a micro-approach, selecting and modifying anthropological techniques.
Much of the information could never have been obtained but for the fact that we were
well known in the area, and some of the more significant points would have been
overlooked if we and our assistants[5] had not discussed continually where our leads
were taking us. The statements from informants had to be treated with caution: for
instance, Brahmins (inevitably the source of much advice) persistently understated to
us (and doubtless to themselves) the role of sacrifices and the employment of non-
Brahmin priests. A case-study approach was necessary to record the changing
behavioural pattern relating to the purchase of food when home stocks were failing.
Participant observation yielded information about the intrusive role of schools in

---

[5]Staff of the Population Centre and other persons with postgraduate degrees in the social
sciences who had been trained for the project and who progressively accumulated experience
within it.

insisting on the treatment of sick pupils and about the use of *mantras* and *yantras*[6] and the role of specialized temples.   Only organized periods and methods of observation yielded satisfactory information about the physical treatment of children, the liklihood of their being spared from work when sick, and the distribution of food within the family.   The theory behind disease and its treatment – necessary knowledge, if many disorders and their treatments are to be fully noted – can be obtained only from long, probing largely unstructured interviews in-depth.

Once work of such a micro type is carried out within a society some aspects of it can be investigated in larger populations by means of a survey.   Nevertheless, when the investigation goes beyond mortality to include morbidity as well, the survey will always tend to be superficial.   The method is insufficient to study the whole family or neighbourhood because of the atomizing effect of sampling and even of individual questionnaires.   It will yield something less than the truth, because of an insufficient density of questions on any particular matter.   It will obtain an apparent spread of answers from people with the same experience and views, because short answers mean that some people begin reporting the same experience from one aspect and others from another.   It will almost inevitably lose intellectual coherence, because the final analyst will not have played a first-hand role at every level of the investigation. It will contain many questions inherited from previous surveys, unless it is linked to micro-studies for the generation of new hypotheses and hence new questions and new foci of research.   Nevertheless, it may well establish patterns and associations between variables that will provide some support for those hypotheses, and some evidence that detected behavioural patterns exist over a larger population.

The following report on morbidity and mortality is based upon work in nine villages since 1979 using 100 per cent censuses of households and certain surveys, 50 per cent sampling for intensive surveys employing in-depth questions and a case-study approach, repeated in-depth knowledge and reporting on 25 per cent of households (although we came to know many other households almost as well), plus residence in the area and prolonged acquaintance with it.   The report will attempt to substantiate its findings for a broader population by citing confirmatory or opposed evidence from the literature on social science and health in India.

SICKNESS, ITS CAUSE AND TREATMENT

The reporting of mortality presented fewer difficulties than had been anticipated, although there is a greater reluctance to reveal all deaths during an interview held at night than one conducted in daylight.   More serious is a reluctance to report or discuss certain types of sickness.   This is particularly the case when the illness is of a kind not only which is caused by a deity, but where the sickness itself is believed to be a manifestation of the responsible goddess still being within the person.   This is striking in the case of children with chickenpox, as it has been in the past with smallpox.   It also happens when a disorder is regarded as a divine punishment, as in the case of leprosy or skin complaints, and hence not as a sickness at all.   There is clearly underreporting of current morbidity, and almost certainly of past morbidity as well, even though less danger would be involved in such reporting.   It is frequently denied that persons being studied are sick, when quite obviously they are very ill.

---

[6]Chants and charms described in greater detail below.

Much of the reporting in the literature of the treatment of illness implies that healing has been carried out by one of the 'Great Traditions' in medicine, either by those schools indigenous to India (Ayurvedic, Unani or Sidha) or by the opposed modern (or allopathic) medicine.[7]

These implications are often present in surveys (Ramesh and Hyma, 1981), and attention is thus concentrated almost exclusively not only on these methods of treatment, but in any particular region on the disorders in which they specialize. Research in the study area showed that this approach is almost inevitably very misleading. Ayurvedic medicine has changed a great deal during this century because, on nationalistic grounds, the independence movement espoused it and established training colleges which concentrated on medicines and aspects of treatment converging on modern medicine, thus broadening the gap between the Great Tradition and the local religious, magical and herbal treatments that we have called the 'Little Tradition' in healing. Both the medical officer in the study area and his counterpart in the neighbouring district had received more training in Ayurvedic than in allopathic medicine but, while praising the cultural benefits they had received from the former, they practised only the latter because they saw themselves as part of a government or modern system and because the government health services provided them solely with drugs belonging to the allopathic system. As Ayurvedic medicine loses its magico-religious elements, those choosing between it and allopathic medicine are likely to opt for the latter in even larger numbers as being associated with the more powerful materialist tradition. We discovered that the indigenous Great Tradition was of little importance in the study area. There were no Unani practitioners, while the only Ayurvedic practitioner was in the largest village but had few patients; the nearest Ayurvedic pharmacy was 30 to 40 kilometres distant. Consequently the situation reported in this paper is largely the continuing contest between modern medicine and the Little Tradition.

What success either Western or Ayurvedic practitioners have is conditioned to a very considerable extent by the way they are seen as fitting into older systems. More than any other culture, India, even Hindu India alone, is characterized by pluralism, and this extends to healing. The rural areas contain not only government and private practitioners but a range of other persons who play healing roles: local authorities on healing and herbs, both unpaid and paid; priests and saints; those who cast horoscopes or have other astrological knowledge; and midwives. Pluralism extends to trying many systems. A description of a rural area in Northern India will serve also for many of the people in our study area: 'In the lives of most villagers, clinics serve as momentary stopping places on the sick man's pilgrimage from one indigenous practitioner to another' (Marriott, 1955). Undoubtedly more people in the study area have faith in Western medicine than in practitioners trained in Western medicine. Where modern medicine succeeds, it often does so because it assumes that certainty felt by those other practitioners who interpret the divine intention and will. There is still much that is relevant in Carstairs's (1955) observation, made a quarter of a century ago and 2,000 kilometres further north, that patients do not give a history of their complaints because they assume that a healer must know, and in his description of traditional practice: 'when their healers say, "He will recover", they are not expressing a personal opinion but are speaking with the authority of the supernatural power which is the real agent of their cure' (Carstairs, 1955:112). Traditional healers always specify the time that recovery will take; the failure of modern practitioners to do this gives rise to great doubts about their powers. Villagers have traditionally

---

[7]The terms *Great Tradition* and *Little Tradition*, as used first by anthropologists of the Chicago school, referred to the variants of the culture and its religion found on the one hand amongst the learned, in the towns and in the written records, and on the other amongst simple villagers. In this sense Western (or Allopathic), Ayurvedic (Hindu), Unani (Moslem, deriving from Ionian or Galenic medicine) and Sidha (or Dravidian) practitioners are in Great Traditions.

known their healers, who have been in some way part of their personal and family networks, recommended and known by the decision-makers within the family. Most are reluctant to consult strangers outside the area, be they modern or traditional healers, unless the cure is to be effected by a famous saint or at a temple well known for its cures of this complaint or for its general power. In the study area, those with disorders sometimes made long pilgrimages to two temples, one in Andhra Pradesh (Sri Venkateswara) and the other in Kerala (Ayyappan). Hindus may make shorter trips even to the tomb of a Muslim saint.

Simpler disorders have always been believed to have arisen either from an accident or from some kind of physiological imbalance caused by the wrong kind of diet or way of life. In these cases, there is no argument but that herbs or pharmaceuticals or medicines of any kind can help with the cure, given only that change in diet is probably always necessitated. There is a clear field here for modern medicines (as well as Ayurvedic medicines). Where the Western practitioner often fails is by not suggesting changes in diet as well as other treatment. The community has readily accepted aspirin and Vick's Vapour Rub.

The imbalances can be those of diet or behaviour or sexual indulgence. Basic to Indian concepts of simple illnesses and their cures is the division of foods into 'hot' and 'cold' which has little to do with temperatures. Although some kind of balance is important, cold foods tend to be better for the person, but they also tend to be more expensive and to be eaten by the better-off. For instance, milk, curds and most greens are cold while meat, chillies and other spices are hot. There is also a relation with caste: Brahmins say that they eat predominantly cold food in order to achieve calmness, while the hot foods of the lower castes partly account for their base passions and hot tempers.[8] Too much spice can lead to fever, while an excess of cold foods can give rise to influenza. Good health comes from the right kind of life which involves daily bathing, regular elimination, and sexual moderation. Gandhi was very much in the central Indian tradition. Diarrhoea can be caused by too much heat in the body which is likely to arise from eating a disproportionate amount of hot food, or from displacement of the navel which calls for massage as a treatment. Headaches are normally the product of immoderate behaviour. Excessive sexual indulgence weakens a man and can lead to a range of diseases including tuberculosis. The good health of some older men is explained by their adoption of sexual abstinence, and of others by the fact that they eat sufficient cold food to replenish their semen. The eating of meat is injurious because of the heat (*ushna*) it produces. Even disorders as serious as rheumatism can be put down (perhaps correctly) to bodily imbalance: in the study area one man who knew the forest well supplied roots for the treatment of this complaint. Sometimes, illness results from an imbalance of the stars, which can be explained by local astrologers who also offer solutions.

It is in the case of more serious diseases that the traditional culture is very much at odds with the explanations and cures of modern medicine. In South Indian villages the deities which impinge most directly on the lives of most people except the Brahmins are local goddesses, both those of the village and also more regional goddesses concerned specifically with epidemic diseases (Whitehead, 1921:17; Tapper,1979:11). With Aryanization, these female deities have come to be explained as being intermediaries between the villagers and the great gods (Carstairs, 1955:122), and in the study area as forms of Parvati (wife of Siva), although elsewhere they are reported as sometimes being the younger sisters of Hanumantha (the monkey god).[9] These goddesses can cause a range of troubles through their curse (*dosha*): in human

[8]There is in fact a concept of a division of diet into three types by *varna* division (Brahmins, Kshatriyas and Vaisyas, Shudras and Harijans), see Lannoy, 1971:150-151.

[9]Beals, 1976:187. One manifestation of Parvati, who in South India exhibits the characteristics of a regional goddess but who has been incorporated into the Hindu pantheon, is Kali.

beings, plague, smallpox, chickenpox, cholera and typhoid fever; in the fields, plant disease and drought.[10] However, they are not essentially malevolent. They are always female and given to strong emotions and likely to cause adversity if misunderstood, or even if just present. Their essential nature and ancient origin is shown by how closely their names usually approximate to the word for mother. Thus, they are not only the source of disease but also its cure. Disease comes from the goddess being in the house and in the person. Nevertheless, it is always an aspect of the goddess, her devil (*devva*), as in *Kaliammana devva* or Kali's devil. Therefore, one can prevent infection by using various devices to deflect the goddess from the house (for instance, by putting pots of water on the roof, or by writing '*naleba*' or 'come tomorrow' on the door and leaving it there indefinitely), and one can effect a cure by persuading her to leave the body. This may be done by religious ceremonies at a temple and by sacrifices, usually of goats. The temples of the Great Tradition take only vegetable offerings, in contrast to those of the Little Tradition for which expensive animals are often needed (cf. Beals, 1962:47-49). Most members of the village attend her annual festival or special ceremonies at the time of an epidemic. Vaccination against smallpox is permissible if it is thought of as a way of discouraging the goddess from the body, which is quite plausible given the disfiguring vaccination mark in a society which regularly marks bodies to repel evil spirits. Where conflicts did develop, it was usually because there was already smallpox in the village and the vaccinators did not understand the fear that a displeased goddess already within the body might react by killing the person. For the same reasons, villagers have always banned certain foods and treatments of sickness while epidemic disease existed in the the area. In this part of India, goddesses causing epidemic diseases can be led out of a village by means of a series of pots which are moved onward along the road by most of the populace each night (cf. Whitehead, 1921) and which are accompanied by a wooden figure. When an epidemic like cholera, smallpox or whooping cough breaks out in a village, it is not regarded as a sign of the sinfulness of an individual or a family, but of the whole community. Therefore everyone must be involved in finding a solution. It is believed that epidemics break out when many members of a community indulge in immoral behaviour, or neglect to worship the gods at regular intervals. As a forceful reminder the gods spread epidemics, usually through the mediation of a local deity, in the community. Then the whole community reviews the behaviour of its members, and undertakes certain rituals for appeasing the gods and eradicating the epidemics. It might be noted that most villagers do not realize that smallpox is now extinct and Mariamma, the goddess of the disease, is still treated with great respect. One reason is the lack of distinction usually made between smallpox and chickenpox, and the other is that, although goddesses may be quiescent for long periods, they do not die.

A specific type of local god is the snake god which may jealously guard certain areas. Snake bites are fairly common, partly because of the phallic symbolism of both snakes and termite mounds (clearly associated with Siva) and the incautious approach of worshippers to the shrines constituted by snakes living in old termite mounds. Snake bite is invariably regarded as a matter beyond earthly resources, and not a single case has ever been brought to the study area health centre for treatment. There is a local herbalist who employs the bark of a bush which mongooses eat, if bitten by snakes, for curative purposes. Nevertheless, most sufferers regard this treatment as impious and ineffective and employ *mantras* or chants (see below), deciding on the verse by the colouring under the snake's head and the number of stripes. If this fails, they may visit the snake temple to seek, amid living snakes, the help of the god and his intermediary, the priest.

---

[10]cf. on the suffering of crops and human beings from common divine sources, Venkatarayappa, 1962:211-215.

There is another range of disorders which are not the result of the accidental or capricious invasion by a deity, but instead are a planned form of divine punishment for sins and transgressions in this life or in previous lives. Examples of this group are leprosy, skin cancer and tetanus. Those diseases specifically caused by the snake god include dermatitis, impetigo and other skin complaints. Because these disorders are planned punishments rather than capricious happenings, there is much less likelihood that they will be brought to modern practitioners for treatment. There is also a sense of shame which means that such ailments are little talked about and often hidden. Leprosy may be the penalty exacted for failing to adhere rigidly to the laws segregating the castes. The main function of the snake temple is to alleviate these diseases as well as blisters upon the skin and infertility of women.

As sickness becomes more protracted or severe, it is likely to change in classification from the capricious act of a deity to intended divine retribution. In terms of the total impact on mortality, this is most significantly the case with regard to a range of childhood disorders in the area of extended diarrhoea and resultant dehydration and the whole complex of malnutrition which leads to distended abdomens. At first, diarrhoea can be treated as an imbalance of hot and cold food or some similar error, and children can be brought to the health centre or given home remedies. But, as the complaint worsens, it is recognized as being one of the group resulting from the retribution of the gods. In Karnataka it is known as *balagraha*, literally meaning a divine visitation to the child. Necessarily, such complaints must be treated by reconciling the gods. Priests or other local practitioners can perform *mantras* by chanting religious verses, and they can make *yantras* by writing verses or the number of verses on paper, blowing the name of the person upon it, after which the paper is folded, wrapped in string and tied around the neck. The *yantra* may also be metallic, in which case, before placing it around the neck, it may be placed in water which is subsequently drunk. Probably the greatest single failure of modern medicine is to convince the populace that *balagraha* can be treated by medical practitioners. However, it might be noted that some of the healers who employ *mantras* give Ayurvedic or herbal concoctions at the same time. In the study area the sap of certain trees is sometimes employed. It is, of course, true that the local health centre can do little about malnutrition arising essentially from the poverty of the family.

In general, as complaints become more prolonged or the symptoms more serious, or the person appears to be suffering from wasting, the diagnosis is likely to shift from accident or whim to punishment for sin. This is true of a range of surprisingly common liver complaints. Among children, malnutrition appears capable of damaging the liver, and the hardened liver and abdomen are described as one manifestation of *balagraha*; among poor adults, usually of lower castes, liver disorders can arise from the practice of going to bed hungry and stilling the pain with a drink of highly spirituous local arrack. It is possible that as much as one-tenth of all deaths are due to liver complaints.[11] Where no transgression is known to explain a disease, it is assumed to have happened in another life; it is reported from elsewhere that worms in wounds indicate incest in previous life, necessitating purification ceremonies for that sin (Fuchs, 1964:126-127).

The supernatural world is not merely one of gods but also of demons, evil spirits and ghosts. Children are particularly susceptible to spirit invasion, and this explains much of the apparent low level of infant care. Both a casualness about the conditions of birth and a lack of intensive care during infancy denote, in fact, a high degree of concern. Any obvious trouble about the child or any precautions against sickness

---

[11]This estimate is from a government medical officer in the neighbouring district who had specialized in liver disease. See Singh *et al.* (1961:591) for the conclusion that childhood cirrhosis 'apparently rises from genetic inheritance coupled with malnutrition', and Glynn and Himsworth (1944:297) on the clearer relationship between adult liver complaints and malnutrition.

would invite the jealousy of demons and might well result in the death of the child. Precautions include burning spots on the infant's abdomen with the heated ends of broken glass bangles, the placing of black spots (with the soot from the end of a burnt stick), on the forehead – especially in the case of a handsome, young boy – and the wearing of various cords and pieces of copper around the neck or a knotted black thread around the neck or waist. Spirit possession is relatively common, particularly in the case of young daughters-in-law who may even scream at their mothers-in-law and the rest of the household. A beating by a stick tied with fresh green leaves (*peepul*) or a branch retaining leaves may drive the spirit out, but, if this fails, the girl will have to be taken to a temple for treatment by the priest. Magicians also may understand and control evil spirits; sometimes they come from relatively low castes who as hunters have had more contact with wild and magical places.

Closely related are the problems caused by ghosts. These are unsatisfied souls who cannot reach the other world and must stay in the air from which they keep returning to the land of the living because of a range of grievances such as having been murdered, having drowned or committed suicide, or not being accorded proper ceremonial respect after death. They usually trouble their relatives. However, persons carrying meat or travelling alone at night, usually if they look back, can be injured or killed by ghosts haunting the place where they died.

There is also a danger, especially to children, from the 'evil eye' (*drushti*). This is an ancient concept found across much of Africa, the Middle East and South Asia (and older Europe). In India, the possessor of the evil eye has come into its possession by accident, usually because of early severe pollution (such as the eating of faeces when a baby) (Minturn and Hitchcock, 1966:76). The evil eye can cause sickness or death, usually when its owner feels jealousy or greed. This is a major reason for doing little about a pregnancy and making few preparations for a birth or arrangements for postnatal care.

There are also other dangers deriving from hostile persons. Magic, especially if a magician is employed, can be used to harm or kill, and may be countered by a range of measures including those devised by another magician. When adults are sick, especially if vomiting takes place, poisoning by enemies is suspected, and much effort is expended on recollecting what food was given by others or taken at another's house (especially if secret enemies are feared). By this time the poison is believed to have solidified in the stomach and the appropriate herbalist or magician is approached to secure its removal.[12]

PLURALITY AND CHANGE IN TREATMENT

In spite of the traditional explanations and cures for disease, most households in the study area now use the health centre. However, it is clear that they are more likely to do so for some complaints than others, and the maladies omitted include some of the most important causes of death. Furthermore, the visit to the health centre is usually only one of the stratagems employed and it may come late, frequently too late, in the series of steps taken. Partly because of this plurality of methods, not all the treatment recommended by the physician may be employed. More seriously, villages contain substantial numbers of people who clearly require medical attention, but who are not treated because neither they nor their relatives see their problems as medical, sometimes merely because they are old and there are signs indicating the decision that this life has run its course. This is true even when they are identified by the local multi-purpose health worker and told to go for treatment.

---

[12]Parallels with many of the findings reported here can be found in Khare, 1963.

The greater and more efficient use of Western medical facilities is essentially a process of secularizing Hindu society. It is not seen as a turning of the back on the gods or the ghosts, but everywhere there is a slow movement of attitudes to the treatment of specific complaints which transfer marginal cases from the area where Western medicine cannot help to where it may be of some value.

There is no point in transfer taking place too rapidly as the facilities are not available to meet the full potential demand. Karnataka still has only one Western-type practitioner (including those with only one or two years' training in modern medicine plus Ayurvedic training) per 10,000 persons and one nurse per 13,000 persons (Karnataka Government, 1978:191). The relative shortage of nurses is an India-wide phenomenon, arising from the reluctance of parents to have their daughters working away from home and working in an occupation whose members are believed to be immoral and who work in circumstances where ritual pollution is likely.[13] There is still considerable dependence on Christian nurses from Kerala.

Treatment may cost more in practice than in theory, partly because practitioners recompense themselves for outlays in obtaining their positions, and partly because patients offer money believing that a practitioner who is paid and who gives services outside normal hours will try harder. More basic is the concept of the exchange of a gift (*dakshina*) for any kind of service and a deep-seated belief that healers, teachers and priests must be paid. Much of the cost arises from time taken off work, travelling expenses, and buying food while undergoing treatment. Ayurvedic medicine is usually cheaper and local healers much cheaper still. There is much that the health centres cannot do. They do not, in fact, carry anti-venom to counter snake bites or vaccines against rabies, and there is little that they can do about the basic causes of malnutrition (although iron and folic acid tablets for treating anaemia are now frequently given).

In the move toward Western treatment, one important aspect has been the greater degree of Westernization and extent of schooling among the younger generation. The position is more complex than this because these same influences have led to a slow transfer of authority over the treatment of illnesses from the older generation to those of intermediate age. Grandparents have in the past felt very resentful if parents took much initiative at all in caring for the children or even in paying them much attention. Successive treatments are still decided upon by the most authoritative persons in the family network. However, they were once the very old, while now they are quite likely to be the most educated.

There is increasing discussion as to the extent to which that power is employed to provide differentials in treatments to members of the household. Twice as many boys as girls are brought to the health centre in the study area, and there seems to be some evidence that oldest sons are likely to predominate among the boys.[14] However, somewhat surprisingly, the centre treats twice as many women as men. The latter may be evidence of another form of discrimination, because the excess of women among adult patients is entirely explained by much higher levels of anaemia and other nutritional deficiency diseases among women (although menstruation and childbirth

---

[13]Nurses were forced until recently to resign from their profession on marriage, and hence it was widely held that many preferred to retain their incomes by remaining unmarried but having sexual relations with boy friends (see Damle, 1959). Some parents, probably more frequently in North than South India, were also averse to their daughters being in close contact with human waste, afterbirth and corpses, all of which are ritually polluting. The situation is rapidly changing and there is an increasing demand for places in training centres for nurses.

[14]cf. Beals (1976:193), who shows that 73 per cent of money spent on the medical treatment during critical illness of sons is on the eldest, who make up only 32 per cent of all sons, 90 per cent on the two eldest sons (62 per cent of all sons), and 100 per cent on the three eldest sons (80 per cent of all sons).

are undoubtedly aggravating factors). Although differential treatment, amounting to infanticide, has been reported for another part of Karnataka (Beals,1962:81), we found no evidence for this.

THE REDUCTION OF CONTAMINATION AND INFECTION

Probably more than any other society, India has deep and ancient concepts of contamination and pollution. Such concepts have usually operated to allow infection rather than reduce it because of concentration on a different order of priorities.

Pollution is caused by association with persons of lower castes, especially by allowing them contact with one's cooked food or drinking water. It has been pointed out that drinking in tea or coffee shops can be polluting, not because of the possibility of sharing inadequately washed cups but because of the association with people of lower castes with the resultant reduction of production of semem in the body and hence of strength and health (Carstairs, 1955:125). The greatest pollution of all is not contact with infectious disease or with germ-ridden filth but with menstrual blood or foetal remains, and the presence of miscarriage or death.

Proximity to any death endangers one from forces of the supernatural, and funerary ceremonies are mainly aimed at reducing pollution.[15] For everyday pollution, bathing is the most common means of restoring a reasonable degree of purity.

Bathing is undoubtedly cleansing. Yet the avoidance of pollution, such as ignoring faeces and the corpses of animals until such time as the ritually impure may remove them, must have an adverse effect on community health. Some of the better-off people in the villages have latrines but they are often in an appalling condition, obviously a possible source of disease, because fear of pollution means that the family cannot do much about the matter and should not even let their thoughts dwell upon it. Similarly, the insistence that the Hindu kitchen must be protected from defilement by lower castes means that most village cooking is done in an interior, windowless room filled with smoke even though there are usually some holes in the roof. This apparently does lead to a high level of respiratory complaints among women in contrast to the situation found in most tropical societies where food can be cooked and eaten out of doors. The use of village streets as drains and the presence of animals in houses adds to the impression of insanitariness.

Bacterial pollution has undoubtedly been reduced by the improvement of village water supplies. Where water is still drawn from ponds, there is little evidence that the infrequent testing and treatment of the water has been of much avail. There are now some treated and piped rural water supplies, and in the larger village in the study area this facility was available. However, the major improvement has been the provision of tubewells drawing water from sufficient depths for it to be uncontaminated (although in one of the villages the tubewell water has been shown to be impure and dangerous). In all the smaller villages there are now publicly provided tubewells, although the well may be out of action for considerable periods due to mechanical breakdown. Most tubewells can be used by all castes, in contrast to the situation of wells, because the tubewell produces a free jet of water into each person's bucket, so preventing the bucket from ritually polluting the supply as happens in the case of wells or ponds. The government has attempted to ensure Harijan access to tubewells by placing them near or in Harijan settlements. In one village in our study area the non-Harijans still go to an inconvenient, distant and clearly impure pond, rather than share the biologically purer water in a ritually less pure area from the only tubewell adjacent to the Harijan settlement. Non-contaminated water supplies do not mean

---

[15]In Gujarat, villagers use the same word for pollution and mourning (Pocock, 1972:119).

that water is necessarily still uninfected when it is drunk, especially in circumstances where the pollution of drinking water is judged by whose hands touch the outside of the vessel rather than whether the inside has been scalded or disinfected. The evidence on the extent to which originally non-contaminated water is likely to remain in that condition is far from reassuring.[16]   A major source of contamination is probably the insistence on washing everything when preparing meals. Clean plates or cups, and peeled vegetables or fruit, must be washed again, often with water that is clearly far from pure in that it is cold, without soap, and stirred by dirty hands. The lack of cleanliness in washing is partly unavoidable, but also arises from the fact that the washing is at least partly ritual.

THE ROLE OF EDUCATION

Differences in infant and child mortality in the study area are surprisingly small. When other factors are controlled, there are only minor differences by economic status, father's occupation and religion. One of the reasons why Harijan children are not at greater risk is that they are mostly found in the larger village in which there are a major tank, some irrigated land, Brahmin landlords, and hence agricultural labourers. Thus, the Harijans live not only in the village with the health centre but, because that centre and the government colony of officials were deliberately built close to the Harijan colony, they and their illnesses have a high degree of visibility.

On the other hand, there is one powerful determinant of infant and child mortality and that is the education of the children's mother.[17]   In the study area as a whole, where the mother has not been to school, infant mortality rates are close to 130. Where she has had primary schooling, the rate is around 80, and where she has had some secondary schooling it is 70.[18]   The difference is clearly recognized by the community. The single most important reason given by both the educated and uneducated for sending girls to school is that they will be able to look after the health of their families.

It is clear how they do this. First, by dint of their education, or superior education, they are much more likely to be ceded decision-making rights by their parents-in-law. Both the medical officer at the health centre and the private practitioner in the larger village report that they are much more likely to bring their children for treatment and do so earlier before attempting older methods of cure. Furthermore, both maintain that educated mothers are much more likely to persist with the recommended treatment and to return if the sickness persists, rather than try alternative cures. Educated mothers are also likely to share food more equally between the generations and between the sexes.

These changes do not arise primarily from the acceptance of school instructions, but rather from a feeling that the school has enrolled them in a different society, not necessarily wholly Western but certainly transitionally so. They are aware that the health centre, the medical practitioner, immunization of children against disease and taking early action about infant diarrhoea all belong to the same system as their school, the officials, the government and themselves.

---

[16]See Gandhigram Institute of Rural Health and Family Planning, 1977:84-85; similar findings have also been reported from the Matlab research area in Bangladesh.

[17]This has been reported as widespread elsewhere. See Caldwell (1979) and Caldwell and McDonald (1982).

[18]Similar differentials were obtained but not published in a Bangalore Population Centre project in rural Karnataka (see Badari et al., 1979).

NUTRITION

It is very doubtful whether food supplies per head have increased during this century. In fact, most people in the study area believe that the opposite has occurred. However, the important point may be that fewer persons suffer from debilitating periods of extreme crises. At the level of the whole community this is explained by better communications and improved government famine relief schemes.

However, there is evidence that an equally important change has taken place at the family level and arises not only from attitudinal changes, but also from the penetration of the countryside by commerce and the related monetization of transactions. The famine years and the period immediately before the harvest in any year have traditionally been regarded as times of inevitable want, when belts were tightened and the weak occasionally succumbed. It is ever more likely that family income will be used during these periods to buy food from the market, and this is now coming to be regarded as a normal procedure even by farming families who usually grow and store most of their major varieties of food.

Undoubtedly, other changes within the family are also tending to protect the weakest. Women still usually eat last, and daughters-in-law politely serve their mothers-in-law before themselves. The young wife traditionally could not play a role in allocating how much food her husband was to have because, for years after her marriage, it was the husband's mother's task to serve him. Differential feeding was as much a matter of poor communication as of deliberate intent, and men usually did not know what the younger women ate. There have been continuing changes in internal family relations, including a strengthening of the bond between the young husband and his wife. Such changes have almost certainly meant a better internal distribution of food within the family. The internal maldistribution of food within the family has undoubtedly been a major reason for the higher mortality of females in India (cf. India, 1965:330-332; Miller, 1981). However, the greater influence of the young wife may protect her children more than herself, as is indicated by a deteriorating sex differential in mortality.

We made use of responses to direct questions and the research team's observations to try to piece together an adequate picture. The work was not easy, because the direction of our probing was clear and met with some resistance. This is itself important information, for it demonstrates the existence of some belief in equitable distribution, at least among children. Nevertheless, in households where there were both and girls, one-third of the families believed that the boys obtained a disproportionate share of the food, while the research team put the proportion at one-half or higher. We investigated two mechanisms, that which follows from eating separately and in succession, and that which arises from unequal shares, irrespective of eating arrangements.

In half of all households the male household head and any other adult males eat first. In one-fortieth of these cases the wife of the household head also eats with them. In one-seventh of households everyone usually eats at the same time, although the women may stand in the background. In the remainder, eating occurs more capriciously and is determined by who is around when the meal is ready for eating. Eating at the same time is more common in smaller households, or in those where everyone goes to the field together, and is rare in large stem or joint households with more segregation of tasks. In most households boys tend to join any group eating, usually those taking food first. In the case of girls, this is true only for the very young, and at various ages from 6-12 years (peaking at nine years) they join the women. As food tends to run low during the hungrier time of the year, there is certainly a mechanism here whereby many boys tend to receive more food than their sisters.

However, the major mechanism of differential feeding appears to be boys obtaining more, even when both brothers and sisters are eating together. Mostly boys are given somewhat larger shares, usually justified on the grounds that boys need more or are more active. However, another mechanism is to show greater favour to aggression by boys than by girls, so that boys are much more likely to demand extra food than their sisters, and are much more likely to get it once the demand is made. In addition boys do pick up wild foods or obtain something from other houses more commonly than do girls.

It is sometimes suggested that females have more access to food both before and after meals than males, and accordingly we made considerable efforts to investigate this matter. In only one-fifth of households was there any evidence that food was ever eaten during preparation. In 40 per cent of these households it was said that this nibbling of food was done by whoever prepared it (many were nuclear families), while it was done by mothers-in-law only in 38 per cent of cases, daughters-in-law only in 5 per cent, and both in 17 per cent. We also investigated the fate of leftovers, which are found reasonably often in only one-sixth of households, and these the better-off where most members are reasonably fed. These remainders are eaten by the women and children in 40 per cent of cases, often as bribes given to the children to do tasks, by the family at the next meal in 25 per cent, and by the cattle in some cases.

TREATMENT AT THE TIME OF THE STUDY

We found that middle-class or urban Indians, let alone foreigners, cannot disassociate themselves in the minds of villagers from the modern world, its medical practitioners and its hospitals. It is possible to convince rural respondents that one is reasonably neutral with regard to evaluating the kind of activities that the family planning programme should undertake. It is much harder to convince them of genuine empathy in the struggle to appease ghosts and to ward off demons. The survey document itself is so much part of the modern world. Rural respondents felt that, like many officials, what we really wanted to evaluate was the efficiency of modern services and they attempted to help us in this task. We attempted to counter this by probing for conditions and symptoms rather than joining the debate on whether these constituted illness.

Yet this is not the whole problem. A more basic difficulty is that we inevitably asked about sickness, and accordingly were told little about disorders arising from imbalance in the diet, environment or the stars, and much less still about punishments for deliberately or inadvertently transgressing against the divine order. It is practically impossible to obtain an estimate of the full extent of *balagraha* in a survey, even though it is probably the single greatest killer. Many infants were reported as having died without being sick. When asked when they were last sick some, clearly very ill, respondents peered into the past and reported that they had never been sick their lives.[19]

Given this problem, it is still of very considerable interest to note that the median time reported by adults as having elapsed since the last case of sickness in the household was two months for women, four months for men and six months for children. This accords well both with the statistics for attendance at the health centre and the recognition of disorders as illnesses. There is general agreement that invasion by supernatural powers is much more likely for persons under ten years of age, and hence children's illnesses are more likely to be classified as such and, therefore, not to warrant attendance at the health centre. Nevertheless, the survey did confirm the fact that the great majority of families now believe that modern medicine can be effective for a considerable range of disorders, and in these cases they are willing to use modern health facilities.

---

[19]Government health workers, when undertaking surveys, frequently report an overstatement of ill-health, partly as a way of complaining about the lack of facilities. We avoided this partly because we were not so identified and partly because we sought symptoms.

The survey also confirmed that the authorization of health treatment is one of those areas of decision-making where there has been fairly rapid transition during the last 20 or 30 years in terms of the oldest generation ceding power to the younger married generation, with regard not only to the latter's own health but also that of their children. Thus, the effective decision to take children to the health centre was made in almost two-thirds of all cases by parents – who were subsequently overridden by grandparents in only one-tenth of all households. Decision-making in South India is rendered more complex by the fact that grandparents are commonly in charge of the children, while their parents are in the field. Men appear to make decisions about themselves in about three-quarters of all cases, being mostly strongly prodded in the rest of the families by either wives or mothers. On the other hand, women are twice as likely to be sent by their husbands as to make the major decision themselves. Nevertheless, women, especially those with schooling, appear to be attaining a greater role in decision-making about treatment. This change is explained by most people in terms of a strengthening of the conjugal emotional bond between younger couples.

Our examination of individual cases of sickness showed why the passing of more power for noting illness and suggesting treatment is so important. In the case of children's illness, parents first noticed it seven times more often than did grandparents, and mothers ten times more frequently than fathers. However, it should be noted that, even now, mothers suggest the possibility of treatment no more often than do fathers, and make decisions about treatment considerably less than half as often as fathers. Wives identify sickness in their husbands and urge that something should be done about it twice as commonly as husbands do for their wives. When children were sick, our assessment was that mothers were really distressed far more often than any other relative.

In over half of all cases members of households claim that no other curative attempts preceded their first visit to the hospital and the medical practitioner, although clearly they often waited some time before the visit. The fact that sicknesses are often allowed to remain untreated for at least seven days is shown by the much higher attendance of people from outlying villages at the health centre on the day of the weekly *shandy* (or market). When we examined the history of individual cases, we came to the conclusion that mothers who were determined on modern medical treatment for their children were assured of success in about one-third of all households. In another one-third they were not automatically assured of their husband's support but were likely to obtain the treatment if they could convince him. In the balance of households there were real traditional decision-makers, and it was necessary to win the support, or await the decision, of someone who usually made health decisions (more commonly in the stem or joint families which form one-third of all households) (Caldwell *et al.*, 1984b). Power in these households was not the same in the area of health as in the case of economic decisions. With regard to treatment, the patriarch's wife more commonly made decisions than her husband, and there were sometimes even more knowledgeable and influential figures with regard to health, such as the patriarch's sister.

Traditional methods of cure are dominated by *yantras* worn around the neck, and *mantras* (chanted prayers by priests or other wise men), and nearly half the community claim to employ one or the other or both (the anthropological approach suggests a much higher proportion). One-half as many claim to undertake visits to the temples to leave offerings (often rice, curds, coconut, betel nut or flowers), pay for *pujas* (religious services) or make sacrifices of goats, chickens or sheep. Often the visits occur after the illness is over, being the fulfilment of a vow made at the time. Sometimes rice, coconut, eggs, turmeric or limes are not taken to the temple but sprinkled at the crossroads. Many households still obtain herbal medicines or more commonly make their own, but only a handful of families employ Ayurvedic medicines. Most Hindu families participate in some temple ceremonies during the year to protect their families and their villages from ill health. The temple of the village deity has a special significance here, although clearly not that of 60 years ago, when the goddess was seen as virtually the sole defender of the village from threatening disasters from all sides (Whitehead, 1921:46).

Brown glass bangles play a major protective and curative role. (They are also important in temple ceremonies, especially those concerned with fertility, and are the symbol of currently married women). They may be broken so that their ends can be heated in a flame to burn marks on the abdomen of a baby for protection against the evil eye and demons, or adults may have burn marks made on each side of the temple to cure persistent headaches (known as *sondu*). Sores which will not heal may first be cauterized; then a broken bangle is ground on the stone doorstep of the family house and the resultant glass powder is rubbed across the surface of the sore.

The great majority of households denied that there was any discrimination by generation or sex in feeding or in health treatment. One problem is that behaviour which appears to the outsider to be discrimination is justified by household members as meeting specific needs or deserts. It was argued frequently that males needed extra food because they had to do harder work in the field. Similarly, certain foods, such as onions and spices, were omitted, on the grounds of danger, from females diet during menstruation, pregnancy or lactation.

Two-fifths of all households contained some pharmaceuticals which are frequently employed for home treatment. In two-thirds of cases there are only modern types, and in most of the rest of the households they are both modern and Ayurvedic products. The major source of Western-type pharmaceuticals was until 1981 the dispensary attached to the health centre. In that year a cloth merchant, reacting to what he described as a steeply increasing demand, converted his shop to one selling mostly modern pharmaceuticals, together with a few of the better-known Ayurvedic preparations, and brought in a trained pharmacist as dispenser. Almost half the pharmaceuticals examined in the households are described as being for headaches, while around one-quarter are for colds. Some households contain malarial suppressants, pain killers, not meant primarily for headaches, and medicines for asthma and bronchitis. In order of frequency the pharmaceuticals listed were a camphor preparation, Amrutanjan (sold as Vicks in the West and increasingly in India), Anacin and Analgin.

Two constraints on the use of health centres were mentioned. One was the cost in money, and the other the cost in time. One of the reasons why government health facilities have only limited time available for treatment is the proportion of time spent by some medical officers, and many of the multi-purpose health workers, on family planning activities. A visit to an Ayurvedic doctor is usually cheaper, but Ayurvedic treatment can take months with repeated visits; in the study area this involves a considerable journey. However, traditional healers are usually willing to have payment deferred, and they do not assume the formal attitude of modern practitioners which frightens the illiterate and poor.

Many of even the religious measures taken by Hindus have also been adopted by the Muslims in the society. Nevertheless, the evidence in the study area is that the use of modern medical facilities constitutes a considerably larger proportion of all health care among the Muslims than among the Hindus.

A NOTE ON DEATH

The following statement, written a quarter of a century ago, is probably still reasonably accurate:

Both Hindus and Muslims understand the physiological causes of death. It is generally attributed to natural causes, such as disease or old age, but in all cases where the circumstances or manner of death are unusual it is attributed to supernatural factors such as the wrath of gods and ancestor spirits, witchcraft and black magic (Dube, 1955:124).

In the study area, the few Brahmins are the only ones who regularly cremate their dead. Among the rest of the population, in all but one village, burial is the common practice. However, where the circumstances of the death or the nature of the fatal disorder suggested possession or divine vengeance, the body is burnt. It was suggested by some of the richer peasants that they would like to adopt the Brahmin cremation as a sign of their understanding of the best Hindu practices (Sanskritization) were it not for the identification of burning with the destruction of a body rendered impure or unnatural in some way. Deaths in childbirth are always the result of the presence of spirits, sometimes in the child, and the bodies of women who die in this way are always burnt.

The easternmost village is one of a group of about 70 villages where many bodies are exposed on the rocks for birds to consume the flesh. This is strikingly similar to the practice of Parsees. However, such burial methods are apparently ancient in South India and are motivated by a philosophy of the continuing chain of life whereby flesh, rather than decaying, should help produce new flesh. In other areas, in nearby Andhra Pradesh for instance, the same philosophy leads to bodies being placed in rivers so that the fish may be fed. This treatment of bodies in the study area village is a privilege and is reserved only for persons over 40 years of age, who have led a virtuous life and whose death was not of the type calling for cremation.

Of recent deaths, 8 per cent have been cremated (half Brahmins and half because of the nature of the death), 8 per cent have been exposed (all in the village employing exposure, making up half of the deaths there), and 84 per cent have been buried.

Deaths caused real distress in about half of all cases. There was a great degree of acceptance in the other cases on the grounds that the deceased were either very old or very young, and hence death was not something unexpected.

Of the recent deaths, three-quarters of those dying had been seen at some stage by a modern medical practitioner but in only one-third of cases were they patients at the time of death. The reason was the family had decided to seek no more treatment. It is felt strongly that modern practitioners continue to treat and charge, long after they are aware they can do nothing more and, unlike traditional healers, they refuse to predict both the certainty of death and its timing.

A PERSPECTIVE ON HEALTH CHANGE

The persistent decline in mortality over the last 60 years is very far from being a simple case of a progressive increase in the supply of modern doctors and their medicines. The nearest example to that picture is the success of the great campaigns against epidemic disease. Yet there were problems about the acceptance of vaccinations, and theological reasons why acceptance was easier at one time than another.

The progress of modern medicine is even more a question of demand rather than supply. For many diseases the growth of that demand has been made possible only by a reinterpretation of essentially religious concepts of illness and its cure.

The nature of Indian and Hindu society, with a greater degree of pluralism than probably any other society, has been a factor that has permitted much of the change. Yet fundamentally what is happening is a transition from one type of society to another, essentially to a Western type of society. Those who accept modern health services most readily are persons who believe that they have to a considerable extent joined this new and different society.

By far the most potent instrument of change is modern schooling. Mere attendance in institutions which pyramid as far as modern medical schools convince both the educated and their relatives that they have a commitment to a different kind of world, which includes modern medicine as an integral part. There are other conduits for contrasts with Western society or for heightening the belief in an identification with that society. Thirty years ago a practitioner in Northern India reported that modern medical services were accepted most readily by returnees to the village from the town or from army service (Carstairs, 1955:133). This is true today in the study area if one adds to the army service work with the railways, the police or a range of other government employment. Over 50 years ago, two missionary medical practitioners in rural Northern India found that the first villager who felt himself linked to their type of cure was a Christian (Wiser and Wiser, 1971:3). Undoubtedly, the high proportion of Christians in the society and the long contact with the West of the Malabar Coast does much to explain the marked degree of success of health services in Kerala.

The decline in mortality is, then, part of the political, social and economic revolution of the last 40 years. At the official level, independent India has always identified with the new imported society and has given little more than lip service to the most fundamental or indigenous concepts of illness, its cause and cure. If mortality rates are to continue to decline in India, one of the central bastions of its religion and society will have to be successfully assaulted. The concept of pollution will have to be radically changed so that it approximates to circumstances where disease is most likely to be transmitted.[20] Indian society is so flexible that this may well be done without any real awareness of just how sacrilegious that transformation has been. Yet such a change is necessary because it is largely the present interpretation of pollution which makes India more polluted from a bacteriological point of view than most of South-east and East Asia. Sales of soap are rising steeply, but the main reason is the replacement of the services of the *dhobi* by the household washing of clothes. The practice of attaining high levels of 'purity' by plastering floors, walls and grain containers with mud enriched with cow dung has hardly begun to decline.

Changes in the family have already had profound health effects and these will probably accelerate. In a range of matters in the area of demographic decisions the oldest generation has been slowly ceding power to their adult children, and health treatment and feeding practices are in this domain. At the same time, increased buying of food and an intensification of the concept of child dependency has meant that the weakest are less likely to succumb during periodic food crises. There is clearly also a move towards the main decision-maker with regard to a child's safety and health being its mother, and this, too, will undoubtedly help to reduce infant and child mortality rates.

Declining mortality has been part of a profound social revolution, and even a theological one in terms of moving ever more areas of behaviour into the secular domain.[21] There are areas where major reductions in mortality can still be achieved relatively easily. Perhaps the most obvious is that related to antenatal and postnatal care and to infant malnutrition. Family size is beginning to decline, and there is clear evidence from the study area of lower child mortality levels in smaller families

---

[20]Cf. Khare (1962) who points out that food is often abandoned if it is ritually polluted by a human hair or nail clipping falling into it but not if rat faeces, which are not ritually impure, are found in it.

[21]For a parallel process in England, see Thomas, 1971.

(Caldwell *et al.*, 1984a). These arise not mainly from a greater concentration of parental attention originating merely in smaller numbers, but because the family planning programme by its very nature has made a decisive attack on the nature of the traditional family, especially in the area of demographic decision-making. It has also made both parents and the health service workers apprehensive about the possibility of deaths among the children of sterilized parents.

Modern medicine has also made slow but persistent gains when it has been able to demonstrate success. The fact that this has been the case more often in respect of adult disorders than the diarrhoeal or nutritional complaints of children has certainly played a role in confirming that the latter are more certainly the concern of the gods. This has been reinforced by the feeling that infants have only recently come from another world and accordingly still retain links which may draw them back again.

Our study of social attitudes to sickness and its care made two points clear. First, any new injection of modern medical technology or services will not have its full impact at once, but may take many years to achieve its full potential as the interpretation of sickness changes. This change is largely the product of a broad social transformation secularizing many aspects of social life and tending to remove medical explanations and cures from the area of theology. The latter process is probably accelerated by some of the successes of the new technology. Secondly, even if medical technology were to stagnate at its present level, mortality levels would almost certainly decline for many years to come.[22]

There is probably a limit to mortality decline unless nutritional levels can be raised. It may be possible to extend longevity to an expectation of life at birth of 60 years, given sufficient social change, but doubts must remain about how much progress beyond this level can be achieved without very considerable rises in living standards particularly in nutrition.

ACKNOWLEDGMENTS

This research constituted part of a joint project of the Population Centre, Bangalore, India, and the Department of Demography, Australian National University. Most of the funding came from the two institutions, but other support, especially for the analysis, was provided by the Ford Foundation and by a Population Council International Research Award. The authors were the principal investigators of the joint project.

---

[22]Ghana, over the last 20 years, probably provides an example of this. For evidence on the continuing decline in mortality, see Jain, 1982.

REFERENCES

Badari, V.S., Gopal, Y.S. and Devaramani, S.C. (1979), 'Infant mortality in rural Karnataka: findings from a longitudinal study', *News Letter*, Population Centre, Bangalore, 5,5:1-11.

Beals, A.R. (1962), *Gopalpur: a South Indian Village*, Stanford University Press, New York.

Beals, A.R. (1976), 'Strategies of resort to curers in South India', in C. Leslie (ed.) *Asian Medical Systems: a Comparative Study*, University of California Press, Berkeley, pp.184-200.

Caldwell, J.C. (1974), *The Study of Fertility and Fertility Change*, Occasional Paper No.7, World Fertility Survey, London.

Caldwell, J.C. (1979), 'Education as a factor in mortality decline: an examination of Nigerian data', *Population Studies*, 33,3:395-413.

Caldwell, J.C. and McDonald, P.F. (1982), 'Influence of maternal education on infant and child mortality: levels and causes', *Health Policy and Education*, 2:251-267.

Caldwell, J.C. Reddy, P.H. and Caldwell, P. (1982), 'The causes of demographic change in rural South India', *Population and Development Review*, 8,4:689-727.

Caldwell, J.C., Reddy, P.H. and Caldwell, P. (1983), 'The causes of marriage change in South India', *Population Studies*, 37,3:343-361.

Caldwell, J.C. Reddy, P.H. and Caldwell, P. (1984a), 'The determinants of fertility decline in rural South India', in T. Dyson and N. Crook (eds), *India's Demography: Essays on the Contemporary Population*, South Asian Publishers, New Delhi, pp.187-207.

Caldwell, J.C. Reddy, P.H. and Caldwell, P. (1984b), 'The determinants of family structure in rural South India', *Journal of Marriage and the Family*, 46,1:215-229.

Carstairs, G.M. (1955), 'Medicine and faith in rural Rajasthan', in Paul, 1955, pp.107-134.

Claquin, P. (1981), 'Private health care providers in rural Bangladesh', *Social Science and Medicine*, 15B:153-157.

Damle, Y.B. (1959), 'Auxiliary nurse midwives: a study in institutional change', *Bulletin of the Deccan Research Institute*, 19,3/4:237-279.

Dube, S.C. (1955), *Indian Village*, Routledge and Kegan Paul, London.

Fuchs, S. (1964), 'Magic healing techniques among the Balahis in central India', in A. Kiev (ed.), *Magic, Faith and Healing: Studies in Primitive Psychiatry Today*, Collier-Macmillan, Free Press, London.

Gandhigram Institute of Rural Health and Family Planning (1977), *Research Activities, 1964-76: Major Findings and Implications*, Gandhigram.

Glynn, L.E. and Himsworth, G.P. (1944), 'Massive acute necrosis of the liver: its significance and experimental production', *Journal of Pathology and Bacteriology*, 56.

India, Ministry of Information and Broadcasting (1965), *The Gazetter of India*, Government of India Press, Nasik.

Jain, S.K. (1982), 'Mortality in Ghana: evidence from the Cape Coast Project data', *Population Studies*, 36,2:271-289.

Karnataka, Government (1978), *Statistical Abstract of Karnataka 1976-77*, Bureau of Economics and Statistics, Bangalore.

Khare, R.S. (1962), 'Ritual purity and pollution in relation to domestic sanitation', *Eastern Anthropologist*, 15,2:125-139.

Khare, R.S. (1963), 'Folk medicine in a North Indian village', *Human Organization*, 22,1:36-40.

Lannoy, R. (1971), *The Speaking Tree: A Study of Indian Culture and Society*, Oxford University Press, London.

Marriott, McK. (1955), *Western medicine in a village of Northern India*, in Paul, 1955, pp.239-268.

Miller, B.D. (1981), *The Endangered Sex*, Cornell University Press, Ithaca.

Minturn, L. and Hitchcock, J.T. (1966), *The Rajputs of Khalapur, India*, Wiley, New York.

Mitra, A. (1978) *India's Population: Aspects of Quality and Control*, Abhinav, New Delhi.

Orubuloye, I.O. and Caldwell, J.C. (1975), 'The impact of public health services on mortality: a study of mortality differentials in a rural area in Nigeria', *Population Studies*, 29,2:259-272.

Paul, B.D. (ed) (1955), *Health, Culture and Community: Case Studies of Public Reactions to Health Programs*, Russell Sage Foundation, New York.

Pocock, D.F. (1972), *Kanbi and Patidar: a Study of the Patidar Community of Gujarat*, Clarendon, Oxford.

Ramesh, A. and Hyma, B. (1981), 'Traditional medicine in an Indian city', *World Health Forum*, 2,4:495-499.

Reddy, P.H., Shariff, A., Guruswmy, M. and Diwakar, A.V. (1980), *Dual Record System*, Population Centre, Bangalore.

Reinharz, S. (1979), 'The ritual of survey empiricism', in S. Reinharz, *On Becoming a Social Scientist*, Jossey-Bass, San Francisco, pp.50-125.

Singh, A., Jolly, S.S. and Kumar, L.R. (1961), 'Indian childhood cirrhosis', *Lancet*, March 18:587-591.

Tapper, B.E. (1979), 'Widows and goddesses: female roles in deity symbolism in a South Indian village', *Contributions to Indian Sociology*, New Series,13,1.

Thomas, K. (1971), *Religion and the Decline of Magic: Studies in Popular Beliefs in Sixteenth and Seventeenth Century England*, Weidenfeld and Nicolson, London.

United Nations (1961), *The Mysore Population Study*, Population Studies No. 34, United Nations, New York.

Venkatarayappa, K.N. (1962), 'A study of customs in rural Mysore', *Sociological Bulletin*, 11, 1 and 2:208-220.

Whitehead, H. (1921), *The Village Gods of South India*, Association Press, Calcutta.

Wiser, S. and Wiser, C. (1971), *Behind Mud Walls*, University of California Press, Berkeley.

Chapter 12

SENSITIZATION TO ILLNESS AND THE RISK OF DEATH: AN EXPLANATION FOR SRI LANKA'S APPROACH TO GOOD HEALTH FOR ALL*

John C. Caldwell, Indra Gajanayake, Pat Caldwell and Indrani Peiris

INTRODUCTION

It is now clear that the achievement of low mortality depends on a subtle interaction between specific characteristics of a society, whether ancient or the result of recent change, and the level and type of medical inputs. Some of those characteristics have been identified, as, for instance, the level of parental education in ensuring better chances of child survival. What has not been shown so convincingly are the mechanisms employed by populations with these characteristics for using the existing health infrastructure to achieve greater control over mortality. This paper reports on an investigation carried out in Sri Lanka in 1985, and supplemented in 1987, which we believe identified an aspect of society which is of key importance in the conquest of illness and death.

The paper also throws light on the way modern medicine penetrates a society which previously had developed a comprehensive indigenous health system. Medical anthropologists in South Asia have reported radically different findings on whether Western medicine is regarded as just another therapy or, on the contrary, an alien intrusion at odds with indigenous philosophies of treatment and the cultures in which they are embedded. The latter situation was reported for Northern India by Carstairs (1955) and Marriott (1955) who averred that the imported medical system did not fit in with the village cosmology or social system and did not employ the accepted social forms in treatment and so was making little headway. In contrast, Gould (1957) reported shortly afterwards, in another part of Northern India, a ready acceptance of modern medicine where it evidenced its effectiveness. With time, and possibly with a greater penetration of the new system, the latter view has tended to win out. Beals (1976:191) concluded from research in South India that:

*First published in *Social Science and Medicine*, 28(4)1989.

The knowledge of illness possessed by the individual appears to reflect an almost sponge-like acceptance of medical information, regardless of its source ... With the exception of a few factory laborers ... who attempt to conform to modernity in every way, there is no process of conversion from one type of medical treatment to another ... rather, they gradually shift the assignment of particular types of illness from one type of treatment and practitioner to another.

Hanks and Hanks (1955:170-171) reported that in rural Thailand modern medicine was just another curative method.

THE CASE OF SRI LANKA

A previous investigation of countries achieving unusually low mortality levels, relative to what might have been anticipated from their income levels, identified Sri Lanka as having done better than any other country (Caldwell, 1986). By 1986, in spite of an annual per capita income of only US$330 (less than one-fortieth of that of the US), it had attained a life expectancy of 68 years (75 years in the US), and an infant mortality rate of 34 per 1,000 live births (Population Reference Bureau, 1986). That study had directed attention to a range of circumstances which seem to be related to unusual success in achieving good health and which were found to a marked degree in Sri Lanka: a high level of female autonomy, mass education for at least a generation with the important indicator being the level of female schooling, grass-roots democracy with a significant radical tradition, and substantial governmental intervention in providing primary health care together with a range of other social services with such aims as establishing a nutritional floor and ensuring particular care around the time of birth. It was concluded that there was a symbiotic relationship between education levels and the density of health services and that a parallel increase in both was the most effective way to reduce mortality. The extraordinary fall in mortality in Sri Lanka between 1946 and 1953, when 12 years were added to the life expectancy, was taken as a prime example of how the rapid increase in health interventions could capitalize on a major investment already made in education.

Nevertheless, that study did not demonstrate the specific mechanism whereby mortality has been so successfully reduced. It did not show how a poor and predominantly rural population behave in order to stop themselves and their children from dying. That is the purpose of this paper which reports on the employment of both survey and micro-approaches to demographic field research among almost 2,000 families in seven widely scattered and socio-economically contrasting localities in south-western Sri Lanka. We had previously experimented with this approach to understand the mechanics of mortality control in South India (Caldwell, Reddy and Caldwell, 1983), but the Sri Lankan work focused far more intensively on health and was carried out in a society which had been unusually successful in achieving that control.

There has been a number of studies in both Sri Lanka and India to examine the use of different types of health service both by kind of illness and frequency of treatment, as well as more macroscopic examinations of the health infrastructure and investment in it (e.g., on Sri Lanka, Wirz, 1954; Simeonov, 1975; Jesudason, 1976; West, 1981; Department of Census and Statistics, 1973; Obeyesekere, 1976; Waxler et al., 1983; Gunatilleke, 1985; Perera, 1985; Meegama, 1986; and on India, Gould, 1957; Khare, 1963; Neumann et al., 1971; Bhatia et al, 1975; Bhardwaj, 1975; Caldwell et al., 1983). The present study attests to the explanatory value of such indices. However, in the search for effective measures to save human life, it places even greater emphasis on the awareness of danger, the quickness of identification of illness and consequent action, the appropriateness of first action, the readiness to change ineffective actions, and the persistence of efforts until success against mortality has been achieved. It relates these matters both to education and other characteristics of the society and to the health facilities available. We became increasingly convinced that the explanation of unusually low mortality is to be found in this complex of activities.

PROBLEMS IN INTERPRETING THE SRI LANKAN SITUATION

The Sinhalese society of south-west Sri Lanka has long been culturally characterized – almost dominated – by its fight against sickness and by the range of treatment available. One example is the exorcist *thovil*, or 'devil dance', which is related to the dancing that Sri Lankans and tourists watch in the Kandyan and other *peraheras*. So central to the culture is its interest in healing that anthropologists who sought to study the society often increasingly concentrated on its indigenous medical system (Wirz, 1954; Kapferer, 1983). These indigenous treatments are often taken to be the antithesis of Western medicine, and yet the experience of two areas which take indigenous treatment very seriously, Sri Lanka and Kerala, suggests that they may pave the way for the rapid adoption of imported treatments. The reason is probably the very great extent to which the societies are conditioned to look for ill health or unusual symptoms and to react to them. There is little fatalistic acceptance of illness, and there is an individualistic responsibility on all to note its existence. It may be no accident that the only other society in South Asia with a comparably strong tradition of indigenous medicine, Kerala, has also recently been able to employ modern health services to achieve unusually low levels of mortality.

The other area of debate is the role of Ayurvedic medicine, the ancient therapy of Hindu India, and, to a lesser extent, Muslim Unani and Tamil Sidha medicine, all of which are practised in Sri Lanka. Ayurvedic medicine is often mistakenly regarded as being essentially religious and hence as being defensively supported by the culture in which it is found (probably because in India it is associated with the Hindus and perhaps because of the association between its name and the Hindu scriptures or Vedas, yet the root of both terms is merely the Sanskrit word for 'knowledge'). Certainly, Ayurvedic medicine draws on ancient ideas about health and sickness, especially on the role of the bodily humours and their balance, but, since the writing of its classical medical texts during the first millennium, its practitioners and devotees have regarded it as essentially secular and the best use of existing physiological knowledge (Dunn, 1976:148). We have found little agreement among respondents in India and Sri Lanka when we have suggested that there is a religious element in adherence to Ayurveda. This has been partly obscured by the extent to which cultural nationalism in both India and Sri Lanka has led to governmental intervention to promote Ayurvedic healing to the extent that in Sri Lanka a separate ministry has been created.

Among Sri Lanka's traditional healing systems, it is Ayurvedic medicine which is most akin in attitudes to pragmatic science and which, far from offering resistance to Western medicine, is likely to pave the way for it and even to absorb many of its treatments. This has clearly been shown in India where the main reason for Ayurvedic practice in many rural areas is the lack of provision of Western services or of knowledge of Western medicine by the local Ayurvedic practitioners (Gould, 1957; Bhardwaj, 1975; Bhatia et al., 1975; Caldwell et al., 1983). The same receptive attitude to Western medicine has been reported in Sri Lanka not only among patients but also among final year students at the Ayurvedic Medical College and among doctors in the Ayurvedic Hospital (Obeyesekere, 1976). Yet in Sri Lanka there is a persistent theme that Ayurveda is not only surviving but flourishing. This, as we will show later, is probably not the case – in contrast to the production of herbal medicines at home or more religious or magico-religious practices – and may well reflect the lack of recent data. Jesudason (1976:237) cited Simeonov (1975:2), quoting the Sri Lankan Ministry of Health's 1962 *Proposal for Setting Up an Asian Health Organization* as stating that the 'overwhelming majority of the people of Ceylon has continued to love and approach Ayurveda despite two centuries of unilateral, intensive and relentless indoctrination in favour of allopathy.' He also drew on the *1969-70 Socio-Economic Survey* (1973) to show that 22 per cent of treatment was by indigenous systems (Department of Census and Statistics, 1973:237) and then argued that this must be an underestimate in view of the fact that estimates prepared for the Health Manpower Study reported in Simeonov (1975) indicated 38 per cent of the demand for medical care being met by Ayurveda. However, these data were collected in an eclectic fashion and cannot be taken to be representative. Perera (1985:97) reported that Ayurveda is still widely practised in Sri Lanka and cited the 1947 Committee on Indigenous Medicine to the effect that 'over 70 per cent of the population... resort to it in times of illness.' We shall show later just how complex is the whole situation with regard to treatment, but that by 1985 only 5 per cent as many people sought their first treatment from Ayurvedic as from Western doctors (although as many again treated themselves with Ayurvedic medicines as went to Ayurvedic doctors) and very few indeed did so for life-threatening illnesses. Our findings are in line with the trends reported in most of the cited sources, except for the 1975 Medical Manpower Study, and evidence the transition from a situation where rural populations had until 1945 little access to Western medicine to one whereby nearly all do so. The earlier situation, as it existed in the 1940s, has been described well by Wirz (1954). The indigenous methods usually relieved anxiety and often pain, but their failure to contain mortality is shown by life expectancies in the 1920s of little over 30 years (Nadarajah, 1976:148) in a country richly endowed with a panoply of indigenous health systems and a population energetically employing them. The subsequent dramatic reduction in mortality was achieved by the spread of Western medicine until it was almost universally obtainable and by the development of a society that was able to make effective use of it. To discover how this system works so efficiently was the focus of the research described in this paper.

One final preliminary point of considerable importance should be made. When Sri Lankan social scientists explain the reduction of mortality in Sri Lanka, they place emphasis on the development of the modern health system together with the social welfare and educational systems (e.g., Meegama, 1981, 1986). In terms of explaining how a given society achieved change, this is completely logical. Nevertheless, in this paper we wish to adopt a different perspective. Our focus is on how Sri Lanka, given its medical and social infrastructure, achieved such low mortality. What interactions were involved, and can they be replicated in other societies? The important point is that, good as the Sri Lankan health coverage is, it is very far from providing the whole explanation. This is brought out by comparing for 1980 Sri Lanka with other countries with a similar ratio of population to doctors (i.e., 7-8,000 persons per doctor as reported in World Bank, 1984:264): Ghana, Haiti, Kenya, Philippines, Sudan, Thailand, Yemen PDR, Zambia and Zimbabwe. These nine countries are characterized by approximately the same ratio of both doctors and nurses to population (the latter ratio is particularly close if the Philippines is excluded). Yet their average annual per capita income is 75 per cent higher than Sri Lanka and their average life expectancy almost 15 years shorter. Clearly Sri Lankans employ their health system more efficiently, and our research aimed at finding out how this was done.

THE RESEARCH PROGRAMME

During 1985 a joint research programme of the Demographic Training and Research Unit, University of Colombo, and the Department of Demography, Australian National University, carried out an investigation of demographic change in the south-west, lowland area of Sri Lanka. (During the first half of 1987 further work was undertaken in the Sri Lankan highlands which has yielded additional insights exploited here but for which there are not as yet usable statistical data.) It was not the right time for a national study, and, in any case, there was much to be said for concentrating on the Sinhalese heartland which is fairly homogeneous. Furthermore, this area has given rise to much of the ideological and other change of the last 100 years and is somewhat ahead in its mortality decline (Gajanayake, 1988:79-88).

The research employed both survey and micro-approaches, the latter involving local residence and participant observation; for fuller explanations of the techniques, see Caldwell, Hill and Hull (1988) and Caldwell, Reddy and Caldwell (1988). The research approach differed from that adopted for previous work in India (Caldwell *et al.*, 1982). The latter was undertaken in a single village area with repeated periods of study over several years. The Sri Lankan research was an attempt to combine this intensive approach with the survey's ability to cover a wider area. Accordingly in 1985 we worked in seven localities, accumulating both quantitative data and more intimate knowledge of 1,974 households and 10,964 persons living within them. The research area was chosen to be as representative as possible: two villages reasonably distant from large towns (in the north-east of the Gampaha District and in the extreme south of the Kalutara District), a semi-urban area within commuter range of Colombo, a middle-class section of Colombo, a Sinhalese squatter community in the outer part of Colombo, and two slum areas near the centre of Colombo (one almost completely inhabited by Sri Lankan Moors, or Muslims). One point is of social and demographic significance. The semi-urban area peripheral to Colombo had few residents as economically well off as a significant proportion of the Colombo middle-class area, but neither did it include any substantial number of poor, while richer Colombo contains, in gullies back from the roads onto which the wealthy houses front, many poorer families, some of whom provide services for the rich. The research team consisted of 15 persons with university training in social sciences and was predominantly female.

Although the addition of population for seven localities, in each of which the entire population was studied, can in no sense be regarded as constituting a representative sample, this procedure can be helpful in that it provides a single 'central' measure and will in the paper be employed to supplement statistics for the separate areas. The totalled population was 67 per cent Buddhist, 12 per cent Christian, 17 per cent Muslim, and 3 per cent Hindu, compared with national figures of 69, 8, 8 and 15 per cent. The figures are partly affected by the concentration on the south-west and partly by the inclusion of a Muslim slum instead of a Tamil one (the Hindu proportions will rise when the 1987 study is added). The sex ratio of the population was 102 males per 100 females compared with 104 in the 1981 census. The proportion under 15 years of age was 32 per cent compared with 35 per cent in the 1981 census (which is compatible given the fact that the study was undertaken four years after the census in the region with the lowest fertility). Of those who were school age or older, 28 per cent were still receiving education, three-quarters of this group being under 15 years of age. Of those not being educated, 12 per cent had no schooling, 30 per cent only primary schooling, 28 per cent lower secondary schooling, 27 per cent upper secondary beyond three years, and 1 per cent tertiary education. Comparatively few households, even in the rural areas, depended mostly on farming for their income. This is of the utmost importance for understanding both changes in health treatment and social change more broadly. Not only has there been a diversification of rural employment but there is a great deal of daily and weekly commuting by husbands, wives or adult children to work in the larger towns and especially in Colombo. There is little of the isolation of near-subsistence farming, for almost everyone has contact with the larger society and regards urban facilities, including health facilities, as part of a common system.

Applying indirect methods of demographic analysis to the data on child survival, we obtained the estimates shown in Table 1 (these are essentially indices as life expectancy is merely the model life table equivalent of child mortality, and even infant mortality estimates are based on survival rates of both infants and older children).

The health segment of the research was essentially behavioural and was carried out by social scientists with some public health experience and knowledge. The aim was to discover when the people studied believed that they or their relatives were ill, what they thought was wrong, what they did, and how long they took to take each successive action. The well-tested life history approach was employed for charting the course of illnesses, but the usual problems of retrospective data collection were minimized by securing information both on current and past illness and treatment. The former provided fewer cases for study than the latter but allowed a comparison to be made between current events under observation and the reporting of past, but usually recent, events. This comparison was highly reassuring with regard to the quality of the retrospective information, especially as it related to the important measurement of time taken to react. The principal investigators spent the full research period in the field providing intensive supervision for 15 Sri Lankan young women graduates in the social sciences who had earlier undergone specific training for the project both outside and in the field. All recorded information was checked and collated as the project continued and households were subject to repeated visits. For this type of research the important point about the nature of illness is what the sufferer or the family believes it to be. Nonetheless, it is of interest to note that most of the respondents employed modern terms for their illnesses, either because the afflictions had been identified by modern health practitioners before or during our visit or because past experience had familiarized them or their community with such identification. A glance at Table 2 will show that the most common illnesses raise few problems in this regard. In any case, this is in reality a minor point because the research reported here makes no attempt to establish the pattern of Sri Lankan disease, but concentrates on awareness of illness and subsequent action taken.

The mortality level for all areas is around three years below the official 1981 estimates for the whole country and the infant mortality rate almost 30 points higher. This difference is probably partly explained by the inclusion in the study of a disproportionate number of slum and squatter areas in order to examine how economically disadvantaged populations fared in the social welfare state. The table shows clearly that the major mortality differentials in south-west Sri Lanka are no longer urban-rural ones. The villagers are very much part of the overall scene. The large differentials are by socio-economic status, especially in Colombo. It should be noted that the Sinhalese squatter area exhibited significantly lower mortality than the predominantly Moorish slums even though incomes were no higher, education was little higher, and health facilities were no more accessible. The explanation is probably partly that the inner slums were more congested and polluted, but partly also that the Muslim women there had less control over health decisions and that families were not characterized by the acute Sinhalese awareness of the onset of sickness and the need to do something about it.

TABLE 1: ESTIMATES OF MORTALITY IN STUDY AREAS, APPROXIMATING THE 1981 SITUATION

	All areas	Villages (two areas)	Central Colombo predominantly Muslim slums (two areas)	Outer Colombo Sinhalese squatter area (one area)	Colombo middle class area (one area)	Colombo periphery predominantly middle class commuting area (one area)
Life expectancy (years)	66	71	56	64	72	74
Index (all areas = 100)	100	99	81	90	109	100
Infant mortality rate (per 1000 births)	58	46	93	64	37	30
No. of persons studied	10956	4009	1897	1498	1705	1847

Note: The mortality estimates are based on Brass child survival methods (cf. Brass and Coale, 1968:104-122).   The model life tables employed are the United Nations Latin American set (cf. United Nations, 1982:118-159), in accord with the conclusions of that volume regarding the Sri Lankan mortality structure by age. Because of the late age at marriage and child-bearing, the estimates are based on child survival to women 20-24, 25-29 and 30-34 and are subsequently averaged. They approximately represent mortality levels about four years before the 1985 study.

TABLE 2: ANALYSIS OF MOST RECENT USE BY FAMILIES OF EACH TYPE OF TREATMENT, 1985 (N = 1616 FAMILIES)ᵃ

	Home medicine	Hospital or dispensary	Western doctor	Ayurvedic doctor	Exorcism	Yantras	Mantras	Temple, church, mosque
(1) Ever used	75%	82%	86%	43%	15%	25%	17%	42%
Users only								
(2) Median time since last usedᵇ	This year	This year	This year	One year ago	Four years ago	One year ago	One year ago	One year ago
(3) Median distance travelled (km)	Home	3km	2km	5km	Home	Nearby	Nearby	Under 1km
(4) Cost:								
(a) No cost involved	27%	62%	1%	44%	1%	1%	3%	16%
(b) Median cost (where cost involved)ᶜ	Rs.2	Rs.5	Rs.22	Rs.10	Rs.600	Rs.150	Rs.25	Rs.25
(5) (a) Most frequently treated 10 complaints (in order) (1)	Cold, cough	Fever	Fever	Rheumatism, aches	Possession	Malign influence of the planets	Fever	Malign influence of the planets
(2)	Fever	Cold, cough	Cold, cough	Cold, cough	Malign influence of the planets	Fever	Malign influence of the planets	Pregnancy
(3)	Headache	Stomach upset	Stomach upset	Headache	Stomach upset	Possession	Headache	Fever
(4)	Stomach upset	Worms	Worms	Asthma	Mental illness	Nightmares	Fits, convulsions	Measles
(5)	Rheumatism, aches	Asthma	Asthma	Stomach upset	Influence of devils	Fits, convulsions	Stomach upset	Stomach upset
(6)	Rashes, sores	Rashes, sores	Rashes, sores	Fever	Evil spell	Asthma	Rheumatism, aches	Mumps
(7)	Asthma	Rheumatism, aches	Rheumatism, aches	Limb pains	Fever	Mental illness	Toothache	Cuts, injuries
(8)	Toothache	Cuts, injuries	Cuts, injuries	Swollen limb	Nightmares	Stomach upset	Menstrual disorders	Asthma
(9)	Cuts, injuries	Childbirth	Chest pains	Cuts, injuries	Cuts, injuries	*Balagiri dosaya*	Possession	Rashes, sores
(10)	Mumps	Diarrhoea	Diarrhoea	Chest pains	Asthma	Headache	Nightmares and *balagiri dosaya*	Chicken pox
(b) Proportion of first 10 complaints of all complaints	93%	68%	78%	71%	62%	67%	56%	43%

ᵃOne rural village omitted because this question added only for later studies.
ᵇOn average, 'this year' covered less than six months.
ᶜAt the time of the study US$1 = Rs.25.

THE PUBLIC HEALTH CONTEXT

Much stress has been placed on the non-curative aspect of the Sri Lankan health miracle (cf. Meegama, 1981). From the nineteenth century prosperity allowed the import of additional food, while from the end of World War II government intervention ensured that all had a minimal sufficiency in food. There was a growing awareness of the need for cleanliness, sparked by the campaign against hookworm in the second decade of this century and reinforced by the government subsequently institutionalizing public health measures. Infant deaths have been prevented by the increasing use of midwives and health institutions for delivery and by antenatal and postnatal home visits by public health midwives.

As our research progressed we became convinced that the situation was almost certainly more complex than this. Such a view has been argued in the case of the post-World War II mortality decline where the initial assessment that it was almost entirely the product of the DDT campaign against malaria gave way to the view that much of the change could be attributed to the parallel rapid spread of rural health services.

Given the level of income, Sinhalese society certainly places an emphasis on cleanliness, both in frequent bathing and in wearing neat and washed clothing. This emphasis on cleanliness is not a new development, and has its parallel among the Malayalam society of Kerala. Travellers have noted such cleanliness in the two areas at least since the time of Marco Polo, and it probably owes at least something to high rainfall and ample access to water.

The research programme devoted substantial effort to studying related aspects of cleanliness and hygiene. The results were surprising and certainly suggested that domestic public health measures are not the main explanation for Sri Lanka's low mortality.

A higher proportion of families appear to be exposed to possible contaminated water than was the case in our South Indian study (where much of the water came from deep tubewells). Almost three-fifths of all water still comes from surface wells (which, in the villages, are the almost universal source). Of these wells, almost 40 per cent had no surrounding wall or even the smallest lip to stop surface water flowing in. During the wet season contamination from surface water clearly occurs on a large scale. Furthermore, given the high water table in much of the coastal low country, the wells are often shallow and are presumably therefore exposed to subsurface contamination. There are problems about protecting water supplies: only 29 per cent of the families had their own water supply, the remainder sharing wells in the village and communal taps in towns. There was frequently a casualness about the source of water and the quality of the water that had been collected that we had not expected and that was not in keeping with either the interest in health or the level of personal fastidiousness. It is widely believed that any spring water is pure.

One might anticipate that the casualness about water collection would be offset by the subsequent treatment of the water, especially in view of the continual pressure from the Ministry of Health for the boiling of water. Most families know that the government and local doctors and nurses feel strongly that they should boil their water, whether obtained from rural wells or the sometimes suspect water supply of Colombo city. Yet only one-fifth of the families in the study normally boiled their drinking water. A higher proportion boiled water for the sick, especially those with diarrhoea or other gastrointestinal complaints, possibly a case of locking the door after the horse has bolted. Most families boiled water for infants, partly as a result of very strong pressure from the public health midwives. These figures overstate the protection given by boiling water because many of the families who do boil water subsequently cool it down for drinking by adding cold unboiled water. The main reason for failing to boil the water is not the trouble or the cost or scarcity of fuel (reasons most commonly advanced in India) but the unacceptable change in the quality of the water. It is said not to be as good, not to quench the thirst, not to taste the same, and not to be refreshing. Only one-fifth of respondents, when asked what boiling did to water, said anything about killing germs or the agents of disease. Undoubtedly some of the hostility to boiled water derives from the South Asian suspicion of hot foods and of imbalance in what is eaten and imbibed. The government now recognizes this resistance and is conducting a campaign to purify wells by dropping pellets into them.

It might be added that only 6 per cent of houses, almost all urban middle class, employ hot water for washing the dishes and pots. In contrast 90 per cent now use soap and detergent instead of the gravel or sand once used. The use in the West of hot water for scalding when washing up undoubtedly derives from the difficulties of removing animal fats used in cooking, in contrast to the Third World tropics where the use of vegetable oils poses no equivalent problem. Yet this tradition of scalding presumably was of hygienic value in the West.

Only one house in 70 studied possessed a flush toilet. However, 63 per cent now have water seal toilets which have been strongly advocated by the government, 19 per cent use cess pits, 3 per cent buckets, and most of the remaining 14 per cent the surrounding area of trees and bushes known as the 'jungle' (which stems from the Sanskritic origin of the word). Considerable attention has recently been paid by the international demographic and health communities to the significance of the type of toilet facility in Sri Lanka because of the demonstration by the 1975 World Fertility Survey of an association with infant mortality. This may well have been spurious because of the inability to control adequately for economic and behavioural factors that make families more likely, for instance, to acquire a flush toilet. Furthermore, our research showed just how unreliable these statistics are as a guide to the fate of faeces. In rural areas the water seal toilets are only easily flushed with water during the wet season when water is often drawn from the closer wells and from higher water levels in the wells. During the dry season there is often great difficulty in keeping up the water supply (which the research team failed to do in one of the two remote village localities), and recourse is frequently had to the jungle. In poor urban areas the water seal toilets are frequently communal and often offensive (half the study households either shared facilities or employed communal ones).

We found some soap in nearly all houses, although half had only a single tablet. Nearly everyone washes their hands after defaecating (with the exception of some of the unsupervised small children), but only a minority use soap. Similarly, nearly all families encourage the washing of hands before eating but only one-third use soap.

There is no evidence a majority of Sri Lankans are particularly careful about these aspects of domestic hygiene. Yet our retrospective data showed a continuing fall in the proportion of child deaths contributed by diarrhoea and a very low level of diarrhoea at the time of the study (2 per cent of illness from which people have most recently recovered and 1 per cent of sickness found at the time of the investigation). The most likely solution to this mystery is that quick action to cure existing cases of diarrhoea has broken the chain of infection and reinfection.

Yet there is an individual and household fastidiousness about many aspects of cleanliness and houses are usually tidy and well kept. More importantly still for behaviour in the areas of both hygiene and the use of curative services, there is an awareness of sickness and of its dangers and a willingness to demand action. This is often very individualistic and does not have to await attention by senior members of the family, as is often the case in much of India (Caldwell *et al*, 1983:200-201) but less so in Kerala (Sushama, 1989). Part of the explanation is ancient and lies in a certain emphasis on individuality and a strong emphasis in Buddhism on mitigating sorrow and pain. Some is related to the Sinhalese traditional beliefs in a wide variety of influences causing distress, disability and sickness, and the need for detecting, identifying and combating such malignancy. The Buddhist Reform Movement of the second half of the nineteenth century, the most potent moulder of modern Sinhalese society, broadcast its appeals to the individual, and its most significant moral leader, Anagarika Dharmapala, laid considerable emphasis on responsibility for maintaining and reattaining good health. The unusually high levels of education – partly a product of the movement's strong advocacy of education – have played a major role in the demand for health services and the willingness and ability of the population to make effective use of them. Sri Lanka has, relative to per capita income, the world's highest level of female education.

The micro-approach field work described here cannot itself attribute the exact responsibility among all these influences for the creation of a health awareness and a willingness to act quickly in terms of identifying and attempting to combat ill health in Sri Lanka society. It can attest that the seven localities studied did have the characteristics and that they existed to a degree that was not the case in other areas of our previous research experience in Ghana (Caldwell, 1966), Nigeria (Orubuloye and Caldwell, 1975) or Karnataka in India (Caldwell et al., 1983), although again, there appear to be parallels with Kerala (Sushama, 1989). The impression we receive from the very considerable anthropological and health literature in mainland South Asia is that the Karnataka experience was typical of much of the region, and indeed that most studies further north evidence, if anything, a slower reaction to ill health. There was, in Sri Lanka, a feeling of responsibility for action in regard to health that was striking. Clearly it has played its role in the area of public health. It is responsible, for instance, for co-operation with the government to the extent that nearly all studied children had been immunized (although the threat to refuse entrance to school for the unimmunized is also important). Nevertheless, as we saw it in action, its most important manifestation was in the early detection of any kind of sickness, the quick action thereafter taken, the awareness of whether treatment was achieving success, and the willingness to take further action if that seemed necessary. We have commented on the difficulty found among the less educated and lower castes in India in following correctly prescribed treatment, in maintaining it for the instructed duration, and in reporting back to medical personnel of higher status that the treatment they recommended has failed (Caldwell et al., 1983:197-198). These problems are relatively unimportant in Sri Lanka, where educational levels are higher (and even illiterate persons have been influenced by the ethos created by mass education), the society more egalitarian, and the democratic and radical traditions older. Indeed, a real problem in Sri Lanka is not failure to report the lack of success of a treatment but premature complaint before it has been fully tried. The lack of a rigid referral system also renders it easy to change doctors or to go directly to specialists provided that the family can afford it.

The essential point is that the nature of the society is clearly of transcendent importance in making the health system work effectively as it was in bringing such a comprehensive scheme into existence in the first place (covered elsewhere, Caldwell, 1986). How, then, do Sri Lankans use the systems that are available?

THE MEANS OF TREATMENT AND THEIR USE

We had been taught by our experience in Karnataka, India, that it is very difficult for highly educated researchers, and especially foreign ones, to elicit from villagers or slum-dwellers information on all types of treatment especially when some types are treated derisively by medical personnel (Caldwell et al., 1983). Therefore, we adopted the approach of first using field work to identify all forms of treatment employed on a significant scale, and subsequently adopting a Kinsey-like approach in assuming that the behaviour had taken place and requesting the details.

Some of the findings are summarized in Table 2, but, in order to be able properly to interpret that table, some preliminary points should be made. The term 'Western medicine' has not been imposed by the researchers but has long been used in Sri Lankan English (the Indian equivalent, 'allopathic medicine', is rarely used by Sinhalese), although 'English medicine' and 'doctor medicine' are also employed.

Western private doctors are not all fully qualified, and there are many persons practising Western medicine with homoeopathic or lesser training, sometimes in clinics owned but not operated by a fully trained doctor and bearing his name and qualifications on the notice board. Since 1977 hospital doctors have been allowed to practise privately (often in their houses on hospital grounds) after hours, and, although we have tried to include all such treatment under 'Western doctor', misunderstandings have probably led to some cases appearing under 'Hospital'. Ayurvedic practitioners include persons ranging from those trained in medical colleges, to those who regard their job as hereditary, to the self-appointed with varying degrees of skill. Those Ayurvedic doctors who treat fractures or snake bites are usually specialists in these applications. There are many people who practise exorcism or *thovil* (which may be with or without the devil dance), or who make *yantras* (protective copper, gold or palm leaf talismans engraved with mystic diagrams or letters, see Wirz, 1954:206-299), or who chant *mantras* (formulae or occult verses, often referring to Buddha, which are used when conducting the *thovil*, making the *yantra*, creating a charm upon water or medicinal oil or in any other occult practice); some are specialists and some undertake all activities. Visits or vows to the temple (or church or mosque) may be to the usual place of worship, or to a specialized one far away (such as annual visits to Kataragama in south-east Sri Lanka, where Hinduism and Buddhism interact, in order to receive general protection from misfortune, or visits to sacred places with more specialized reputations for cure), or to an individual monk with reputed curing powers. Home medicine includes domestic herbal recipes, the making of Ayurvedic medicines on instruction or from knowledge, the giving of pharmaceuticals, or a mixture of any of these activities. It often also includes the use of 'charmed' water or medicinal oil, thus understating the resort to *mantras* with which the charming is achieved. More generally, there may well be an understatement of the employment of *yantras* and *mantras*, and probably also of exorcism (part of the problem is that we were identifying treatment while many of the *yantras* that we pointed to in family discussion were preventive rather than curative).

Sri Lankan health treatment is now dominated by home treatment and the use of Western doctors and hospitals. The former tends to be for complaints that do not need immediate specialized treatment or have already had such treatment but are chronic. The ailments first treated at home are dominated by colds and coughs, fevers (often mild rises in temperature), headaches and gastric upsets, which together make up almost three-quarters of the cases first treated at home. Far from demonstrating a dangerous disregard for more expert treatment, the speed and near-universality of home treatment is rather evidence of the extent to which all health changes are noted and acted upon, for in much of the poorer world, mild complaints of this kind would more often than not go unheeded. Kleinman (1980:183) recorded a similar situation in Taiwan in the 1960s when, although life expectancy was already over 65 years, 93 per cent of disorders were treated first in the home and 73 per cent only there. In Sri Lanka once the disorder has been noted and treatment has begun, more specialized outside help will be sought within a few days if the symptoms do not disappear. The home treatment is also a tribute to the comprehensive pharmacopeia that has been developed and maintained over the centuries and which is known to all households. Most families can select leaves, flowers, roots, seeds or bark from the garden or the forest, or can buy them from herbal shops or specialists. They also buy Ayurvedic and Western pharmaceuticals, including some widely sold preparations that are unique to Sri Lanka and fall somewhere in between (e.g., Siddhalepa), and draw no hard distinctions between them. At the time of interview at least two-thirds of the households had stores of modern pharmaceuticals of which analgesics were the commonest. Not only is the rapid resort to home medicines associated with a willingness to turn soon, if unsuccessful, to alternative treatments, but with an immediate change in attitude to the sufferers with a greater likelihood that they will be relieved of work or made to rest.

When treatment is examined in terms of the nature of complaints, we find that contemporary Sri Lanka does not make the contrast which has become part of conventional wisdom, namely that Western medicine concentrates on what is life-threatening or what it can easily cure while Ayurveda increasingly specializes in chronic complaints that Western medicine can do little to cure (see, for instance, Obeyesekere, 1976:217-223). The important point is that, as the first resorts, home treatment, Western medicine and Ayurveda are employed for a very similar list of physical disorders. Sri Lankans are slightly more likely to turn to Ayurvedic practitioners for rheumatism and arthritis, asthma and swollen limbs, but, even with these complaints, most go first to Western doctors, partly as a result of the long-term trend in this direction and partly, perhaps, because modern medicine is a little more effective in these areas, especially in bringing relief, than used to be the case. Ayurveda is still preferred for fractures and snake bite, although its predominance in the latter area is presumably now a measure of the fact that many hospitals do not stock antivenenes. Sri Lankans may also turn first to Ayurveda in the hope of avoiding the knife, as Noten (1985:82) observed with regard to lancing boils or more serious operations.

The real contrast is between these treatments on the one hand and the use of exorcism, *yantras* and *mantras* on the other (with vows at temples, churches or mosques in an intermediate position because they usually take the form of promising future actions if cures take place by whatever method of treatment has been adopted). These ancient approaches are important in the psychological areas but their prior use is probably not life-threatening except perhaps in some cases of fits and *balagiri dosaya*. Some of the former, especially the considerable incidence of them a week or two after birth, may have been tetanus (although perhaps little could have been done anyway, and their incidence seems to have declined, presumably because of the immunization of pregnant women). *Balagiri* (literally 'infant seizure by a demon', and possibly related to the *balagraha* of South India, an infant disorder attributed to sins in a previous life (cf. Caldwell *et al.*, 1983:194) may also be an exception in that its characteristics are that the afflicted infants cry continually, stare at the ceiling, and are probably in need of medical diagnosis.

There has been a massive and continuing trend toward Western medicine, at least as the first method of treatment outside the home. This has continued during the period that the government has given financial and moral support to Ayurveda. Even many, who maintain that Ayurvedic medicine treats the whole body and ensures a more permanent cure, turn first to Western medicine even though they regard it as curing the symptoms rather than the underlying causes, or as acting too quickly rather than giving the body time to restore itself properly.

Given that more and more people regard Western medicine as the most likely agent of a quick cure, Table 2 provides most of the rest of the explanation for its increasing dominance. Once the Ayurvedic doctors and other indigenous healers preferred by the family were found at shorter distances and their services, except for exorcism, could usually be obtained more cheaply. The spread of Western medicine, and of free government services through dispensaries and hospitals since the Second World War has radically changed that situation. Ayurvedic treatment, combating on the whole the same ailments as Western medicine, is now on average dearer than dispensaries and hospitals and is likely to be further away than Western doctors. This is largely explained by the collapse of the ancient Ayurvedic profession passed from father to son. We were told again and again of the educated sons of Ayurvedic doctors who wished to seek occupational success in the modern sector of the society and economy, and of their fathers who encouraged it because the arrival of Western hospitals and doctors had so eroded their clientele. The conversion of the population to Western medicine over the last half century as the facilities provided by government spread, was accelerated by the widespread advertising of medicines by pharmaceutical companies, announced with complete self-assurance and little regard for tradition, a process which has also been noted in Taiwan (Unschuld, 1976:312) and Hong Kong (Topley, 1976:258).

The greater average distances travelled nowadays to Ayurvedic doctors require some explanation, especially as there are four times as many Ayurvedic as Western doctors, or three times as many if the latter group is enlarged to include medical assistants.[1] In terms of services provided, the modern system certainly averages more patients per practitioner, but this is not an explanation of the relative distances travelled. Furthermore, there is a greater tendency, when seeking traditional healers, even Ayurvedic practitioners, to travel to the specific one who is most trusted, or who is believed to specialize most successfully in a specific complaint, whether it is bone-setting or the illnesses of the very young; when going to a hospital or modern doctor, most people visit the nearest, at least in the first instance. The perhaps surprising finding that the average family travels a greater distance to the Ayurvedic practitioner of their choice, than to modern medical facilities, was confirmed by the anthropological segment of the field work.

One last puzzle remains. Why are private doctors thriving in a situation where they offer the same system of treatment as the hospitals but are much more expensive? Table 2 offers one clue in that they are often nearer to the sick family. But a specific investigation of this problem in the area peripheral to Colombo showed that this was a trivial deterrent to hospital use, cited as the primary reason for using a private doctor by only 7 per cent of families. The single greatest case against hospital treatment, cited as their main reason by 39 per cent of persons going to private doctors, is the long queues and the fact that their time is more valuable than the money charged by the doctors for relatively quick service. Almost as important a reason, given by 36 per cent, is poor service: hospital doctors and other staff often treat them cursorily, doctors do not listen to the description of their ailments, and even give medicines that are not the best cures. Indeed most families hold both views about the free government outpatient service. Since 1977 many hospital doctors seem to have reinforced these views by implying to patients that they will receive better treatment if they see them in their private consultancies outside their official hours. In contrast there is little dispute that really sick persons are in the safest hands when they are admitted to hospital. Even so, most people have a clear concept of a hierarchy of effectiveness in government services, and many bypass local dispensaries for district hospitals, while others go straight to specialist hospitals in Colombo (cf. West, 1981:106).

The crux of the matter is the order and speed of treatment and this was investigated both by examining the treatment of all persons currently sick in households and the succession of treatments of the last person in each household to have been sick and to have been successfully treated.

THE CURRENTLY SICK

Around one-fifth of the households included at least one person who was identified by the family as currently sick. In comparison with the age distribution, infants are overrepresented by 2.4 times and the population over 55 years of age by 2.2 times. Up to ten years of age, females are just as likely as boys to be identified as sick; between ten and 55 years they are 1.7 times as likely to be so identified; while thereafter the ratio falls to 1.2. Indeed, males 10-54 years of age make up 34.5 per cent of the surveyed population but only 19.5 per cent of the identified sick. There may also be a macho element here. Given that similar proportions flow through to

[1]Health Service statistics for 1981-1986 provided by the Ministry of Health and Ministry of Indigenous Medicine, 1987:9.

medical treatment, there may also be an explanation here for the improvement of female mortality relative to that of males over the last quarter of a century (Langford, 1987), although the declining birth rate is undoubtedly also an element. Most of the treatment of adult women is primarily decided by themselves, and, while it owes something to the relatively good position of Sinhalese women, other factors are undoubtedly the availability of free services (which means that action does not have to await decisions on money) and the frequent consultations between women of reproductive age and the public health midwives.

Of the persons currently sick the ailments fall into two groups: 71 per cent from one or other of ten ailments (the balance from 90 other ailments), and, of these, just over half have transient complaints like colds, fevers, gastric upsets and cuts, while the remainder suffer from such chronic complaints as asthma, bronchitis, rheumatism, arthritis, skin disorders, high blood pressure and heart problems. Most of the latter do not reappear in our analysis of patients who have recovered. Diarrhoea was not important, although, in retrospective records covering infant deaths to all surviving women, it had accounted for 12 per cent of mortality. There was agreement from the respondents that diarrhoea had been a greater problem in the past.

TABLE 3: THE TREATMENT OF THE CURRENTLY ILL

		First treatment (N = 432)	Second treatment (N = 170)
(1)	Type of treatment		
	Home treatment: Home made preparations	19%	3%
	Ayurvedic prescriptions	7%	13%
	Pharmaceuticals	4%	3%
	Hospital or dispensary: Outpatient	37%	23%
	Admission	2%	2%
	Western doctor	28%	44%
	Ayurvedic doctor	2%	9%
	Yantras, *mantras*, exorcism, charms, offerings	1%	3%
(2)	Length of treatment: under one week	41%	76%
	Over one week	59%	24%
(3)	Median cost	Rs.20	Rs.30
(4)	Why discontinued:		
	Treatment not successful[a]	37%[a]	39%[b]
	Treatment too expensive, far, difficult or disliked[a]	2%[a]	2%[b]
	Treatment continuing	60%	57%[b]
	Just recovering	1%	2%

One village excluded: analysis of one currently ill person per household.

[a]Nearly all these categories proceeded to a second treatment.

[b]92 per cent of these categories proceeded to a third treatment.

TABLE 4: THE FIRST TREATMENT ADMINISTERED TO THOSE WHO WERE SICK BUT HAVE RECOVERED, BY TYPE OF TREATMENT (N = 1601)

	Home-made medicine	Pharma-ceuticals	Ayurvedic treatment	Hospital	Western doctor	Mantras, yantras, thovil	Other
(a) All ailments with over 20 cases (No. of persons and percentage of all identified ailments in parenthesis)[a] (% treatment adopted)							
Fever (474; 30%)	34%	14%	1%	20%	31%	1%	–
Cold, cough (337; 21%)	58%	9%	2%	16%	15%	–	–
Stomach upset (103; 6%)	38%	4%	5%	20%	33%	–	1%
Headache (81; 5%)	37%	28%	6%	9%	16%	2%	–
Rheumatism, arthritis (68; 4%)	27%	4%	29%	19%	19%	2%	–
Asthma (57; 4%)	11%	7%	5%	26%	49%	2%	–
Skin troubles (45; 3%)	13%	7%	7%	31%	42%	–	–
Worms (42; 3%)	14%	2%	2%	33%	48%	2%	–
Bronchitis (41; 3%)	27%	5%	–	22%	44%	–	–
Cuts, injuries (36; 2%)	25%	–	3%	47%	25%	–	–
Diarrhoea (31; 2%)	19%	3%	–	32%	48%	–	3%
Chest pains (31; 2%)	7%	3%	3%	36%	48%	–	–
Toothache (29; 2%)	24%	35%	7%	10%	24%	–	–
Vomiting, nausea (22; 1%)	46%	–	–	14%	36%	4%	–
All ailments	33%	10%	5%	22%	29%	1%	–
(b) Duration of treatment							
Median	2 days	2 days	2 weeks	1 week	1 week	1 day	
75 percentile	3 days	3 days	4 weeks	2 weeks	2 weeks	3 days	
(c) Why treatment discontinued							
Cured, symptoms disappeared, condition improved	52%	57%	77%	73%	87%	66%	
Patient not better (or worse)	47%	43%	20%	24%	11%	34%	
All other reasons	1%	–	3%	3%	2%	–	

[a]Excludes ten cases unidentified.

Possibly the strongest reason for including Table 3 is that it shows the pitfalls found in analysing current sickness data, at least in terms of the matters of greatest interest in this analysis. Among those currently ill, 54 per cent have chronic complaints (and another 15 per cent are also probably in the category). The proportion among those who 'were sick but have recovered' (i.e., Table 4) is only 15 per cent (the anomaly that there are any is explained by respondents including individual attacks of such disorders as asthma or epilepsy which were subsequently brought under control). Because of the inclusion in Table 2 of the chronically ill, it is easy to miss a central feature of Sri Lankan treatment, namely the impatience with therapies that do not work and the willingness to try something else. Thus almost two-thirds of patients are shown as being treated for longer than a week.

The table does underscore not only how important home-made preparations are for first treatment but also how readily they are given up if the patient does not soon improve. It also shows a search for therapies which will work, with a significant shift from first to second treatment from the free hospital outpatient treatment to private doctors, often with the accusation that the hospital doctors were fobbing them off. At the same time there is also a movement from Western to Ayurvedic medicine, with a rise in Ayurvedic treatment, both by doctor and home prescriptions, from 9 to 22 per cent, and a rise as well in religious and occult treatments. This shift was largely confined to those with chronic ailments. Even so, it does appear that there has been a long-term trend toward at least the initial treatment of the chronically ill (and the mentally ill as well) by Western practitioners either because of greater faith in the whole Western system or because of its increasing ability to deal with some complaints where it previously possessed no effective or quick response.

THOSE WHO HAVE BEEN SICK AND HAVE RECOVERED

The effectiveness of the Sri Lankan response to illness is best examined by recording the whole cycle from the onset of the disorder until recovery. In order to secure the widest possible representation of family reactions, we obtained data from each family on the most recent illness-recovery cycle to be completed. These data were analysed in Tables 4, 5 and 6, beginning with the important issue of the first treatment. We had originally intended to measure the gap between the first identification of illness and first treatment in elapsed days, but the survey categories proved inadequate because most action occurred during the first day. Indeed, when home treatment was the first therapy, remedies were often tried within the first hour. This speed of response was probably the single most important finding of the research programme.

Most of the explanations for the extraordinary Sri Lankan health achievement are probably found in Table 4. Nearly all disorders were reasonably clearly identified by the families (i.e., all but ten or 99.4 per cent) either from their own knowledge or because health services had told them, or at least the illnesses were given a name readily understood by all and usually in keeping with the viewpoint of the health service (see the methodology section). This is in marked contrast to the situation in those parts of either Africa or India where we have undertaken field research, and may be the *sine qua non* of low mortality. Home treatment is common. However, it is dominated by minor complaints and is typically resorted to for only a day or two. During that period at least half the ailments are cleared up, probably mostly regardless of the treatment as is suggested by the high success rate achieved by *mantras* and *yantras*. Pharmaceuticals, which are most commonly analgesics, are chiefly important for the treatment of headaches and toothaches. The one group of ailments for which home treatment is likely to persist is that comprising complaints which are known traditionally as 'Gods' Diseases' and for which it is believed Western treatment is harmful. These are very largely the childhood infectious diseases. The widespread failure to secure modern medical assistance is presumably of little harm.

After a week or two, uncured patients are likely to be transferred even from the more institutionalized forms of treatment (the apparent greater persistence with Ayurvedic doctors is solely a product of the higher proportion of chronic ailments they treat). The transfer may be at the instigation of the patient or relatives or may be an initiative of the healer. Referral is commonly practised by Ayurvedic doctors and also private doctors, especially those without full modern qualifications. This is an important explanatory factor in Sri Lanka's achievement of low mortality and requires explanation. One factor is undoubtedly the Sri Lankan sensitivity to the importance of life which has been briefly discussed earlier. There is another factor which appears to be important but which seems to have been ignored in analyses of the situation in Sri Lanka and elsewhere, and that is the official reaction to death. The registration of both deaths and births was commenced in 1867, made compulsory in 1897, and appears to have been fairly comprehensive in the first decade of the present century when the registered death rate for 1906-1910 was 31 per 1,000 (Nadarajah, 1976:123). For most of this century the police have been likely to suspect something was wrong if a family failed to register a death. Death notification on this scale and the obligation to establish the cause of death inevitably means suspicion of unnecessary death and an aversion on the part of both healers and families to being associated with it. Sri Lanka has gone further, and 60 year ago enacted the Sudden Death Ordinance establishing a system of competent lay persons, appointed rather in the way Justices of the Peace are, to enquire into sudden or unnecessary deaths. Now that most deaths occur in institutions the system only partly operates, but it established an attitude against the occurrence of deaths arising from the incompetence of healers or the carelessness of families. The police are also likely to make enquiries about the circumstances of even non-violent deaths when they appear to have been unnecessary. This attitude to death is quite different from that found in most of South Asia and Africa where neither healers nor relatives are usually questioned either by officials or public opinion about deaths from natural causes and where it is rarely regarded as unnecessary that sickness should end in death. Without this attitude, partly cultural and partly the product of governmental intervention, it is most unlikely that mortality could have reached the existing low levels.

There are two further points which should be emphasized. The first is that the speed with which treatment is secured is facilitated by the capacity of Sinhalese women to make such decisions. We studied this in the Colombo periphery where we found that 47 per cent of sick children taken for treatment beyond their homes were taken solely on the decision of the mother in contrast to only 8 per cent of the decisions being taken by the father alone and 45 per cent being joint decisions.

There is now a strong social pattern of seeking better treatment if the patient is not improving. This is facilitated by the density of population and services in the south-western lowlands, and by the hierarchy of governmental services culminating in the most specialized health institutions in Colombo. It is assisted also by the extraordinary mobility of the population who have made travelling almost a way of life and who are willing to spend a substantial fraction of their incomes on the government and private buses which crowd the roads of this part of Sri Lanka. This partly arises from the fact that few families, even in rural areas, derive their income solely from their own farm, with the result that a very mixed economy means familiarity with towns, urban ways and commuting. There is none of the apprehension of distant and different institutions that one finds among many small farmers and agricultural labourers in India.

Urban-rural and socio-economic differentials in treatment have greatly diminished. Indeed, such low mortality would probably have been unattainable if this had not occurred, and it is a tribute to the provision of modern services throughout the rural areas and near the urban slums. It is among slum dwellers and in the city shanty towns that the first resort to Western medicine is highest (at 61 per cent). This is possible because of their access to hospital outpatient treatment. Among the other groups, home treatment continues to be very important as the first response to sickness. The reason is that the rural population (among whom it is 42 per cent) have continuing access to the plants needed for home preparations while the urban and middle class keep more pharmaceuticals in their houses. But these are initial reactions and within a couple of days the contrasts in treatment are minor.

There remains one interesting contrast as is shown in Table 5.

TABLE 5: FIRST TREATMENT BY AGE

	Under 1 year	1-44 years	45 years and over
Home treatment	28%	44%	39%
Western treatment	59%	52%	49%
Indigenous treatment	13%	4%	12%
All treatments	100%	100%	100%

As we have anticipated, those over 45 years of age are more likely than younger persons to use traditional healers, although the number who do so is not great and the gradient in Western treatment is not steep. Similarly, infants are usually taken at once for treatment rather than being given home remedies. What is surprising is that as many infants as old people are treated first by indigenous methods. This arises from a persistence of the South Asian belief that very young children still remain part of the other-worldly situation from which they have emerged and are more likely to suffer from complaints that no simple materialistic health system can assist (cf. on South India, Caldwell et al., 1983:194). Infants in Sri Lanka are believed to be susceptible not only to balagiri dosaya[2] (seizure by a demon characterized by persistent crying and staring at the ceiling) but also to rathagaya (literally 'red pain' and characterized by the baby suffering pain and developing a red hue, preventable and curable by an Ayurvedic paste) and fits arising from too much phlegm (adjustable by Ayurvedic treatment), while being peculiarly susceptible to evil eye (which was believed in by 70 per cent of the respondents). Small girls are in particular mystic danger around two months of age when their ear lobes are pierced. Nearly all health measures taken for these problems are indigenous and many preventive. It is possible that some infant mortality is caused by delays arising from first treatment being given by indigenous healers for these troubles, but in most cases we examined, parents move on quickly to second treatments.

The key to Sri Lankan low mortality is treatment and persistence with it. There is little of the failure to follow the recommended treatment that exists, especially among the illiterates, in rural India (Caldwell et al., 1983:198). An important aspect of that persistence is judging whether the treatment is effective and so changing healers when it is not. This is clearly brought out by Table 6.

---

[2]Derived from the Sanskrit dosham meaning 'fault', 'flaw' or 'trouble' (see Lozoff et al., 1975:356). In India childhood doshas normally arise from pollution but in Sri Lanka from the action of supernatural beings (Obeyesekere, 1976:206).

TABLE 6: SUCCESSIVE TREATMENT OF THOSE WHO HAVE RECOVERED

Order of treatment	Persons receiving treatment No.	Per cent of those originally sick	Median duration	Proportion recovered	Proportion proceeding to next treatment
First	1601	100.0	5 days	70%	30%
Second	475	29.7	7 days	83%	17%
Third	80	5.0	5 days	86%	14%
Fourth	11	0.7	5 days	100%	–

The Sri Lankan approach whittles down non-chronic cases (i.e., as measured by this definition of recovery) to about one person in 150 still ill after a fortnight. The interaction between the patient and the patient's relatives on one hand and the healers on the other means a change in unsuccessful treatment and healers on average about once every five days. The relatively low success rate during the first treatment is wholly explained by home treatment.

TABLE 7: TREATMENT BY STUDY AREA

	Villages	Central Colombo predominantly Muslim slums	Outer Colombo Sinhalese squatter area	Colombo middle class area	Colombo periphery predominantly middle class area
First treatment:					
Duration	3 days	6 days	7 days	5 days	3 days
% Western treatment	42%	60%	60%	51%	43%
Second treatment:					
Duration	4 days	7 days	7 days	6 days	4 days
% Western treatment	82%	69%	91%	89%	85%

If the analysis is correct, then it would be sustained by the examination of areas displaying mortality differentials. This is carried out in Table 7. This is confined to the first two treatments after which over 95 per cent of the sick are reported as cured. Two significant points stand out. The first is that in the two poor Colombo areas treatment change is slower. The second is that, although the better off and better educated areas are conspicuous in their first resort to home treatment, by the second treatment it is the central Moorish slums that are persisting with such methods. The lesser sensitivity of this area to the need for change in treatment and the lesser reliance on Western treatment as the ultimate defence almost certainly goes far toward explaining higher mortality, and especially higher child mortality, in the area. Woods and Graves (1976:347) came to the same conclusion in central America, when, seeking to explain mortality differentials in a highland Guatemalan town, they reported: 'Ladinos incorporate the services of a doctor earlier in the curing process. Hence their illness episodes tend to be shorter than those of their Indian counterparts.'

THE LESSONS

Sri Lanka has an effective system for ensuring that the great majority of people do not prematurely die. With an expectation of life at birth around 68 years, it exceeds all other countries of South Asia by more than a decade. It has reached this level without an unusually high level of per capita income (less, for instance, than Pakistan with a life expectancy 18 years shorter) or ratio of doctors to population (again, significantly lower than Pakistan (World Bank, 1984:264). The explanation lies in the nature of the society, its educational levels, and a comprehensive social welfare and health system.

It is hard to prove just how much health has improved. It is probable than health has improved very greatly, and certain that the assessment made a dozen years ago that 'The morbidity pattern in Sri Lanka has not changed much in the last 30 years' (Simeonov, 1975:139) cannot be read to imply that a Third World disease pattern still prevails.

What is true is that the chances that the sick will die have been dramatically reduced. This has been done within a social welfare framework of subsidized food for the poor, free governmental health services, household visits to pregnant women and nursing mothers by public health midwives, the institutional delivery of most babies, and other services. The health services have been characterized by density rather than by hospitals with high levels of medical technology.

Yet our study suggests that the ultimate mechanism whereby such phenomenally low death rates have been achieved is the use made by a population highly sensitive to illness and the need for treatment of a modern medical system that is accessible to all.

That sensitivity to the need for treatment has ancient roots. Yet it has been greatly increased by education and other social and political change. It was this sensitivity that employed an effective political system to bring the modern health system into being. That sensitivity could not earlier employ the comprehensive indigenous health system to reduce mortality to any significant degree. It appears certain that very low mortality has been achieved solely because of the modern health system, but that the system would not have been very effective on its own. What has made the Sri Lankan system peculiarly effective is the way the population employs it. The major social input needed to bring mortality down, and especially the significance of maternal education in reducing infant and child mortality, has bee noted before (Caldwell, 1979; Caldwell and McDonald, 1981; United Nations, 1985). In South India, we discovered some of the mechanisms, with, for instance, the greater persistence of educated mothers in continuing with the prescribed treatment and in reporting when it was failing.

However, in Sri Lanka the whole society, even the minority with no schooling, has been affected by the penetration of education. In these circumstances, the great majority of people follow the prescribed treatment. What distinguishes this society in terms of health advance is the fact that most sickness is recognized very early and some action is taken. That action may often take the form of ineffective home remedies, but even these are accompanied by extra attention for the patient and often imposed rest.

Subsequently, the ultimately effective action is the continued seeking of effective treatments if the first attempts are not successful. If the ailment is life-threatening, the successful treatment is almost always back-stopped by Western medicine. Where it is not, and where it is chronic, resort may often be made to Ayurveda which may well provide superior relief. However, there is no simple division and increasingly sufferers from chronic complaints try to seek assistance from Western healers.

The evidence is that low mortality cannot be attained without a comprehensive system of Western treatment, and that this will not be employed effectively without a society highly sensitized to the need for healing and the advantage of taking quick action. The social side of the formula may be more difficult to achieve in most countries than the health system. Education is most important but it is probably not sufficient alone for adequately sensitizing the community. An important part of that sensitizing is the health personnel because people are often reluctant to employ a system which inconveniences them or fails to win their confidence. Even in Sri Lanka this is one reason why the private Western system is an important supplement to the government system.

ACKNOWLEDGEMENTS

The Sri Lanka Demographic Transition Project is a collaborative research programme of the Demographic Training and Research Unit, University of Colombo, and the Department of Demography, Australian National University. Field work was funded by the collaborating institutions, data analysis by the Rockefeller Foundation, and some travel by the Ford Foundation.

REFERENCES

Beals, A.R. (1976), 'Strategies of resorts to curers in South India', in C. Leslie (ed., *Asian Medical Systems: A Comparative Study*, University of California Press, Berkeley, pp.184-200.

Bhardwaj, S.M. (1975), 'Attitude toward different systems of medicine: a survey of four villages in Punjab-India', *Social Science and Medicine*, 9:603-612.

Bhatia, J.C., Vir, D., Timmappaya, A. and Chuttani, C.S. (1975), 'Traditional healers and modern medicine', *Social Science and Medicine* 9:15-21.

Brass, W. and Coale, A.J. (1968), 'Methods of analysis and estimation', in W. Brass, A.J. Coale, P. Demeny, D.F. Heisel, F. Lorimer, A. Romaniuk and E. van de Walle, *The Demography of Tropical Africa*, Princeton University Press, Princeton, pp.88-150.

Caldwell, J.C. (1966), Four chapters in W. Birmingham, I. Neustadt and E.N. Omaboe (eds), *A Study of Contemporary Ghana*, Vol. 2, Allen and Unwin, London.

Caldwell, J.C. (1979), 'Education as a factor in mortality decline: an examination of Nigerian data', *Population Studies*, 33, 3:395-413.

Caldwell, J.C. (1986). 'Routes to low mortality in poor countries', *Population and Development Review*, 12, 2:171-220 (Chapter 1 of this book).

Caldwell, J.C., Hill, A.G. and Hull, V.J. (eds) (1988), *Micro-approaches to Demographic Research*, Routledge and Kegan Paul, London.

Caldwell, J.C. and McDonald, P.F. (1981), 'Influence of maternal education on infant and child mortality: levels and causes' in *Proceedings of the International Population Conference, Manila, 1981*, Vol. 2, International Union for the Scientific Study of Population, Ordina, Liège, pp.79-96.

Caldwell, J.C., Reddy, P.H. and Caldwell, P. (1982), 'The causes of demographic change in South India: a micro-approach', *Population and Development Review*, 8, 4:689-727.

Caldwell, J.C., Reddy, P.H. and Caldwell, P. (1983), 'The social components of mortality decline: an investigation in South India employing alternative methodologies', *Population Studies*, 37, 2:185-205.

Caldwell, J.C., Reddy, P.H. and Caldwell, P. (1988), *The Causes of Demographic Change: Experimental Research in South India*, University of Wisconsin Press, Madison.

Carstairs, G.M. (1955), 'Medicine and faith in rural Rajasthan', in B.D. Paul (ed.), *Health, Culture and Community: Case Studies of Public Reactions to Health Programs*, Russel Sage Foundation, New York, pp.107-134.

Department of Census and Statistics (1973), *Socio-Economic Survey of Sri Lanka 1969-70: Rounds 1-4*, Government of Sri Lanka, Colombo.

Dunn, F.L. (1976), 'Traditional Asian medicine and cosmopolitan medicine as adaptive systems', in Leslie, 1976, pp.133-158.

Fernando,D. (1985), 'Health statistics in Sri Lanka, 1921-1980', in S.B. Halstead, J.A. Walsh and K.S. Warren (eds), *Good Health at Low Cost*, Rockefeller Foundation, New York, pp.79-92.

Gajanayake, I. (1988), 'Infant mortality in Sri Lanka', *Journal of Biosocial Science*, 20,1:79-88.

Gaminiratne, K.H.W. (1984). 'Trends in causes of death in Sri Lanka: 1971-1979', *Population Information Centre Research Series Papers*, no.1, Ministry of Plan Implementation, Colombo.

Gould, H.A. (1957), 'The implications of technological change for folk and scientific medicine', *American Anthropologist*, 59:507-516.

Gunatilleke, G. (1985), 'Health and development in Sri Lanka: an overview', in Halstead *et al.*, 1985, pp.111-124.

Halstead, S.B., Walsh, J.A. and Warren, K.S. (eds) (1985), *Good Health at Low Cost: Proceedings of a Conference held at the Bellagio Conference Center, Bellagio, Italy, April 29-May 3, 1985*, Rockefeller Foundation, New York.

Hanks, L.M., Jr. and Hanks, J.R. (1955), 'Diphtheria immunization in a Thai community', in Paul, 1955, pp.155-185.

Jesudason, H.A. (1976), 'Population growth and health needs', in *Population of Sri Lanka*, ESCAP Country Monograph Series, No.4, Economic and Social Commission for Asia and the Pacific, Bangkok, pp.234-251.

Kapferer, B. (1983), *A Celebration of Demons: Exorcism and the Aesthetics of Healing in Sri Lanka*, Indiana University Press, Bloomington.

Khare, R.S. (1963), 'Folk medicine in a North Indian village', *Human Organization*, 22, 1:36-40.

Kleinman, A. (1980), *Patients and Healers in the Context of Culture: An Explanation of the Borderland between Anthropology, Medicine and Psychiatry*, University of California Press, Berkeley.

Langford, C.M. (1987), 'Sex differentials in Sri Lanka: past trends and the situation recently', paper prepared for the Workshop on Differential Female Mortality and Health Care in South Asia, jointly sponsored by the Bangladesh Association for Maternal and Neo-natal Health and the Social Science Research Council of New York, held in Dhaka, January 4-8, 1987.

Leslie, C. (ed.) (1976), *Asian Medical Systems: A Comparative Study*, University of California Press, Berkeley.

Lozoff, B., Kamath, K.R. and Feldman, R.A. (1975), 'Infection and disease in South Indian families: beliefs about childhood diarrhea', *Human Organization*, 34, 4:353:358.

Madan, T.N. (1969), 'Who chooses modern medicine and why', *Economic and Political Weekly*, 4, 37:1475-1484.

Marriott, McK. (1955), 'Western medicine in a village of northern India', in Paul, 1955, pp.239-268.

Meegama, S.A. (1981), 'The decline in mortality in Sri Lanka in historical perspective', *Proceedings of the International Population Conference, Manila, 1981*, Vol. 2, IUSSP Ordina, Liège, pp.143-164.

Meegama, S.A. (1986), 'The mortality transition in Sri Lanka', in Population Division, Department of International Economic and Social Affairs, United Nations, *Determinants of Mortality Change and Differentials in Developing Countries: The Five-Country Case-Study Project*, United Nations, New York, pp.5-32.

Ministry of Indigenous Medicine, Sri Lanka (1987), 'Special report': health and medical services', People's Bank, Colombo, *Economic Review*, 12, 9.

Nadarajah, T. (1976), 'Trends and differentials in mortality', in *Population of Sri Lanka*, ESCAP Country Monograph Series no.4, United Nations, Bangkok, pp.123-153.

Neumann, A.K., Bhatia, J.C., Andrews, S. and Murphy, A.K.S. (1971), 'Role of the indigenous medical practitioner in two areas of India – a report of a study', *Social Science and Medicine*, 5:137-149.

Noten, A. (1985), *Health Care in Monaragala: Health Care and Its Utilization in a District of the Dry Zone of Sri Lanka*, Colombo Research Paper Series 5, Department of Sociology, University of Colombo, Colombo, and Institute of Cultural and Social Studies, Leiden University, Leiden.

Obeyesekere, G. (1976), 'The impact of Ayurvedic ideas on the culture and the individual in Sri Lanka', in Leslie, 1976, pp.201-226.

Orubuloye, I.O. and Caldwell, J.C. (1975). 'The impact of public health services on mortality: a study of mortality differentials in a rural area in Nigeria', *Population Studies*, 29, 2:259-272.

Paul, B.D. (ed.), (1955), *Health, Culture and Community: Case Studies of Public Reactions to Health Programs*, Russel Sage Foundation, New York.

Perera, P.D.A. (1985), 'Health care systems of Sri Lanka', in Halstead *et al.*, 1985, pp.93-110.

Population Reference Bureau (1986), 1986 *World Population Data Sheet*, Washington DC.

Rao, S.L.N. (1976), 'Mortality and morbidity in Sri Lanka', in Demographic Training and Research Unit, *Population Problems of Sri Lanka (Proceedings of a Seminar)*, University of Sri Lanka, Colombo, pp.27-47.

Sarkar, N.K. (1957), *The Demography of Ceylon*, Ceylon Government Press, Colombo.

Simeonov, L.A. (1975), *Better Health for Sri Lanka: Report on a Health Manpower Study*, WHO Regional Office for South-East Asia, New Delhi.

Sushama, P.N. (1989), 'The causes of fertility decline in Kerala'. Unpublished Ph.D. thesis, Australian National University, Canberra.

Topley, M. (1976), 'Chinese traditional etiology and methods of cure in Hong Kong', in Leslie, 1976, pp.243-265.

United Nations, Department of International Economic and Social Affairs (1982), *Model Life Tables for Developing Countries*, United Nations, New York.

United Nations, Department of International Economic and Social Affairs (1985), *Socio-Economic Differentials in Child Mortality in Developing Countries*, by B. Mench, H. Lentzner and S. Preston, United Nations, New York.

Unschuld, P.U. (1976), 'The social organization and ecology of medical practice in Taiwan', in Leslie, 1976, pp.300-316.

Waxler, N.E., Sirisena, W.M. and Morrison, B.M. (1983), 'Infant mortality in Sri Lankan households: a causal model', mimeograph.

West, K.M. (1981), 'Sri Lanka: exploring the use of the TBA as a low-cost means for family health', in A. Mangay-Maglacas and H. Pizurki (eds), *The Traditional Birth Attendant in Seven Countries: Case Studies in Utilization and Training*, World Health Organization, Geneva, pp.97-130.

Wirz, P. (1954), *Exorcism and the Art of Healing in Ceylon*, E.J. Brill, Leiden.

Woods, C.M. and Graves, T.D. (1976), 'The process of medical change in a highland Guatemalan town', in F.X. Grolling and H.B. Haley (eds), *Medical Anthropology*, Mouton, The Hague, pp.331-382.

World Bank (1984), *World Development Report 1984*, Oxford University Press for World Bank, Washington DC.

HEALTH PROGRAMMES

Chapter 13

CAN COLLABORATIVE PROGRAMMES BETWEEN BIOMEDICAL AND AFRICAN INDIGENOUS HEALTH PRACTITIONERS SUCCEED?*

Edward C. Green

In 1977 the World Health Assembly of the World Health Organization passed a resolution promoting the development of training and research related to traditional medicine. The following year in Alma Ata, WHO and UNICEF issued additional resolutions supporting the use of indigenous health practitioners in government-sponsored health programmes. Such programmes were initially directed at traditional birth attendants (TBAs) as distinct from traditional healers. The first well-documented collaborative programme involving traditional healers in Africa predated the resolutions (having started in 1954) and focused on psychiatric care (Lambo, 1967, 1973). More recent programmes have focused on primary health care, especially on the 'appropriate health technologies' of child survival such as oral rehydration therapy (Warren et al., 1982; Green and Makhubu, 1984; Green, 1985, 1987; Hoff and Maseko, 1986; Warren, 1988). Others have been restricted to screening and referral of patients to government clinics (MacCormack, 1986). However, official national-level collaborative programmes of any sort are still rare in Africa.

Nearly ten years after Alma Ata, Last (1986) lists the remarkably diverse coalition of interests that have with varying degrees of advocacy promoted or supported some sort of collaboration between indigenous practitioners and African health professionals:

Governments (whether parties, bureaucracies or military men) who need both to cut costs and maintain popular support; WHO (or a section within it) urging these governments on with ideas and international pressure; psychiatrists puzzled by solutions to patients' problems in other cultures and pharmacologists on the look-out for new compounds; idealists seeking to develop a truly national medicine and skeptics weary of the medical profession, its claims and its drug companies; radicals of varying persuasion, backing for example the countryside against the town or the 'folk' against the

*First published in *Social Science and Medicine*, 27(11)1988.

bourgeoisie; or realists who simply remark that 'primary health care' is already, *de facto*, the province of traditional medicine and therefore want local knowledge and skills recognized for what they are.

To this diverse group could be added a number of Western anthropologists, public health professionals, and assorted scholars.

In spite of support from such groups, a recent survey by Good (1987a) of on-going, planned, or defunct collaborative programmes involving African traditional healers could only list five, with two of which the present author has been involved. Of these, T.A. Lambo's pioneer Aro project is no longer functioning. The programme in Araromi, Nigeria appears to be in either the planning or the earliest implementation stage; the programmes in Benue and Lagos states, Nigeria (counted as one programme by Good because both focus on family planning and have common sponsorship) have been designed and began implementation only in February 1988 (although some 40 healers in Lagos state have been trained in family planning and primary health care in an earlier stage under different sponsorship); and the well-documented PRHETIH project in Ghana and oral rehydration project in Swaziland are both stalled as of this writing. Only two district-level projects recently spawned by PRHETIH appear to be functioning at present, in Dormaa and Berekum, Ghana (Warren *et al.*, 1982); Berekum was not listed by Good.

True, these setbacks may be temporary. There is a number of people in Techiman-Bono district, Ghana, in Swaziland, and in Nigeria dedicated to getting collaborative programmes resumed or started, and perhaps time is on their side. Still, there is not a lot to show ten years after Alma Ata. Evidently there are some powerful counter-forces at work. There has already been discussion of these by Pillsbury who, after surveying national health systems throughout Asia, Latin America and Africa in 1982, noted:

... little progress has been made in actually utilizing indigenous practitioners, especially healers, in these national systems. It appears in fact that in the entire developing world there are only one or two countries in which traditional healers have actually been incorporated, as traditional healers, in the national health care system (Pillsbury, 1982).

Pillsbury asked why, in the presence of policy support from WHO as well as many national governments and international donor organizations (Pillsbury, 1979) for incorporating indigenous health practitioners, there has been so little progress in implementing such policy.

The present paper will confine its investigation to sub-Saharan Africa and will explore the various factors that appear to constrain the implementation of the Alma Ata resolutions. It will also present arguments and evidence that suggest ways to overcome or circumvent the constraining factors. Discussion will focus on traditional healers as distinct from traditional birth attendants. Since the author has seen no evidence of genuine 'incorporation' of traditional healers in African national health systems, this term will be dropped in favour of terms such as collaboration or co-operation, which more accurately describe the programmatic objectives found in Africa's pilot projects involving healers.

One constraining factor is the logical development of health programmes over time: government officials and their foreign advisers begin with the manpower that is immediately available and supervisable, namely government employees. It would be unrealistic to expect that indigenous practitioners – even if they outnumber Western-trained health personnel by hundreds to one and offer far better rural outreach – would be developed as health service providers before Western-trained personnel in either the public and private sectors. However, if this were a significant constraining factor, there should be evidence that governments are now turning   increasingly to traditional health manpower, evidence which is difficult to find (Pillsbury, 1982; MacCormack, 1986; Janzen, 1986).

A more basic factor may be 'cultural distance' between indigenous practitioners and medically educated Africans and their expatriate advisors: the two groups embrace distinct and perhaps intrinsically incompatible world views or paradigms of illness.   In the words of one observer, traditional healing practice is 'frequently premised on supernatural and other belief systems that are distinctly alien to and not easily comprehended by modern-sector practitioners' (Pillsbury, 1982:1827). Resistance to, or rejection of, magico-religious belief systems has been particularly strong in Africa because health care has largely been in the hands of missionary groups which offer competing religious belief systems quite apart from the scientific paradigm.

Still, there seem to be areas of at least potential congruence. As Janzen puts it:

... the point of greatest convergence between African medicine and Allopathic medicine is between the collective, community-oriented movements of the former, and the community oriented primary health care programmes of the latter. From the former there come health precepts such as balance, rhythm, coolness, purity, and plenitude, and from the latter essential prerequisites of these states such as adequate and clean water, infant care, sewage facilities, adequate nutrition, and good housing, all organized within local communities (Janzen, 1986:50).

Another important factor inadequately documented in the literature seems to be economic and prestige competition between the two sectors. Many traditional healers have developed financially-lucrative practices, some of which are located in urban areas where Western-style medicine is available. Such healers may take patients away from physicians, as can be seen in Lagos where a number of healers have earned enough to build multi-bed hospitals with modern equipment and to own one or more expensive cars.

The wealthy, successful traditional healer stands as a rebuke to the biomedically trained physician who practises in the same neighbourhood.   Traditional birth attendants, on the other hand, are not as threatening. They often perform their services without cash compensation, their activities are usually limited to childbirth and events immediately surrounding it,[1] and their prestige does not typically rival that of doctors or nurses.   This helps explain why there are far more collaborative programmes throughout Africa involving TBAs than those involving traditional healers (Bannerman et al., 1983).

Resentment of indigenous practitioners by African medical professionals has probably grown in recent years due to the development among African healers of what can only be called professionalization. In this context, the term refers to the institutionalization of more standardized, empirically-based indigenous training of healers; the (usually self-initiated) adoption of aspects of Western medicine or other non-indigenous medicine such as homoeopathy; and, especially, the formation of professional associations of traditional healers.

According to a 1985 WHO report, there are healers' associations now operating under official auspices, at either national or district levels, in at least 23 African countries: Ghana, Nigeria, Zimbabwe, Swaziland, Zambia, Benin, Central African Republic, Congo, Guinea, Ivory Coast, Madagascar, Niger, Rwanda, Cameroon,

---

[1] I am using the WHO definition of TBA as a person who assists the mother at childbirth and who initially acquires the necessary skills by working with other TBAs or is self-trained, a definition that has been adopted by other researchers, e.g., Lewis et al., 1985.

Togo, Senegal, Mali, Liberia, Zaire, Uganda, Kenya, Tanzania, and Burkina Faso (WHO, 1985). Malawi and Botswana, and probably other African countries, also have healers' associations that may or may not be operating officially. National associations of traditional healers are usually made up of many thousands of healers, sometimes with a few 'modern sector' advisers such as physicians, university professors or civil servants.[2] The inclusion of such advisers can be seen as a survival strategy: associations boasting – and sometimes led by – a professor with a Ph.D. are harder for governments to dismiss as backward or inconsequential. A characteristic of the healers that comprise these associations is that they are especially interested in learning more about modern/Western health care, they want to work in co-operation with the modern sector through involvement with ministries of health, they want to change the popular image of traditional healers as 'primitive witch-doctors,' and they want to become as respectable among government officials as they typically are in their own communities.

Last (1986) has discussed this rise in professionalism among African healers as a reaction to the post-colonial development of the biomedical professions. African physicians, whose own rise of professionalism has meant to them decolonization, Africanization of jobs, and meeting the European on equal terms, have tended to regard traditional healers as something of an anachronism, as a throwback to a time when Europeans may have believed that 'second-best' was good enough for Africans. In short, traditional healers have been regarded by African physicians as a threat to their own professionalism. Therefore they have often opposed initiatives that would result in official recognition of, or increased power among, indigenous healers.

> As a result, what we are now seeing, is a kind of 'second generation' of traditional healers who have adapted their methods to meet the competition, and organized themselves to defend their right to practice against criticism from an expanding medical profession. The prize is recognition from the government, and ultimately a share in the salaries, supplies and buildings provided by government (Last, 1986:11).

It should be noted that MacCormack holds a quite different view of healers' associations. In fact she regards 'requiring that practitioners form an association and present themselves with a well-organized hierarchy of officers where there is no cultural tradition for doing so' as one of several 'tactics used to exclude traditional practitioners from primary health care training' (MacCormack, 1986:153). She further observes that healers' associations might simply become organizations of 'junior professionals,' subordinate to the medical professions, that might be legislated against at any time. While there may be truth in this, at least regarding the motives of some physicians and government functionaries, it has been this author's observation that healers who join and participate in an association tend to feel that strength in numbers offers them genuine political power in the wider society.

There are reasons beside professional elitism and fear of economic and status competition that help explain why the medical establishment may resist opportunities to co-operate with or extend recognition to indigenous practitioners. These include misunderstanding about the nature of traditional health beliefs and practices, and a genuine concern that indigenous practitioners practise in ways that may be harmful to patients. When the author was involved in advocating and designing a collaborative programme for healers in Swaziland – one focusing on diarrhoeal disease and ORT –

---

[2]Chavunduka, 1986. As another example, the most recent chairman of the Lagos Board of Traditional Medicine has a Ph.D. and is a professor of pharmacology (at this writing, new elections for Chairman are under way).

he had to face the issue that a number of healers gave herbal enemas to children with infectious diarrhoea, thereby exacerbating dehydration and threatening the lives of children. The counter to critics of the would-be programme took the form of a question: if healers are engaged in practices detrimental to public health, do not health and government officials have a public health responsibility to try to change these practices, rather than ignore them?

Eventually workshops focusing on child diarrhoeal disease were conducted with traditional healers, and a year later there was evidence that healers were abandoning traditional enemas and adopting ORT in cases of child diarrhoea (Hoff and Maseko, 1986; Green, 1989; Hoff, 1986). However, as of this writing, all workshops for healers in Swaziland have been suspended due to problems concerning government recognition of the national association of healers.

For their part, African government officials tend to regard indigenous practitioners as a somewhat embarrassing anachronism, especially when dealing with donor organization officials or other outsiders. Traditional healers in particular project an image of the backward, the primitive, the heathen, even of the illegal. It should be remembered that most colonial regimes supported medical missionary efforts to illegalize or severely curtail the practices of 'witch-doctors'. Today, Western-educated African elites would prefer to pretend that 'witch-doctors' are a thing of the past rather than a genuine force to be reckoned with. Western scientists sometimes reinforce the attitude that traditional institutions stand in the way of progress. One such scientist, who feels that 'emotional self-indulgence' helped push the WHO resolution through regarding indigenous health practitioners, believes that

if the economic development of a country is the goal, the transformation of a society's social structure and of its traditional institutions is a precondition; in this process, traditional medicine is marginal at best or a hindrance at the worst (Velimirovic, 1984).

Political ideology may also bias government officials against indigenous practitioners. As Last (1986:13) notes, Marxist governments such as those of Mozambique and Tanzania may oppose healers '... on grounds that healers were, and potentially still are, part of the old "feudal" system, unproductive, giving support to chiefs, furthering "superstition" and liable to exploit the poor in their need'. Traditional healers, as guardians of the traditional moral and religious order, may also be viewed by Marxists as reactionary purveyors of 'the opium of the people'.

Whatever the reigning political ideology, physician attitudes and biases influence government policy. As Good (1987b) observes,

... the biomedical establishment is powerfully represented in African health ministries. It often disassociates itself from popular and progressive initiatives, and is always powerful enough to determine what changes and programmes are acceptable. Furthermore, if a proposal to promote cooperation between biomedicine and traditional medicine comes from a foreign (non-African) source it can easily be dismissed on the grounds that 'they don't know our problems', or 'they want us to be satisfied with second-class health care'.

In fact foreign donors, planners, and administrators usually have little or no understanding of or access to African healers or the world view they represent. Access to healers may well be subject to the approval of ministries of health that represent local medical establishment views, therefore access may be difficult to obtain. The author has been told by a high Ministry of Health official in West Africa that he did not believe his country still had traditional healers, except perhaps in remote rural areas. His office happened to be in an urban neighbourhood possessing many prominently-advertised clinics run by traditional healers. The neighbourhood also had an active branch of the national tradition healers' association.

It should be stressed that some African Ministry of Health officials dedicate much time and energy to arguing the case for collaboration with healers and to establishing pilot programmes to demonstrate that collaboration works. Unfortunately, rapid personnel turnovers and the common practice of shuffling individuals within and between ministries has the effect of diminishing the influence of officials whose continuing support and involvement may be crucial to sustaining collaborative programmes. The same can be said of foreign researchers and advisers involved in establishing and supporting such programmes, since they seldom stay in the same country for more than 2-4 years.

Finally, as noted already, Western development planners and other professionals (including some Africans) tend to think of traditional systems − whether relating to health care, land tenure, communal ownership, kinship obligations, or ancestor veneration − as archaic and dysfunctional, as a way of life to be overcome if there is to be progress and development. What such a view fails to recognize is that traditional systems may be well suited to the social, psychological, and other needs of participants in these systems; that traditional systems may be a great source of comfort to Africans undergoing rapid culture change, providing security and continuity in an unpredictable, changing world; and that traditional systems tend to be genuine functioning systems whereas the same cannot as yet be said of the modern-urban alternative.[3]

In fact, many African healers who are themselves successfully adapting to rapid culture change serve as what might be called change-brokers, guiding and reassuring Africans who are 'torn by the conflicting expectations of their changing worlds', as Ulin (1974) described the situation in Botswana. In Swaziland, healers broker change by preparing magical medicines designed to help school children pass O-level examinations, help adults succeed in business, or help influence judges favourably in civil court cases. The last example stands as a classic Malinowskian case of people resorting to magic to influence events in a realm over which they believe they have no control, in this case Western jurisprudence.

In Nigeria, Yoruba healers − especially herbalists (*onisegun*) − are providing both traditional and non-traditional, improvised methods to meet a recent surge in demand for preventing unwanted pregnancies, a demand probably influenced by accelerated urbanization and cash-dependency in an economy crippled by depressed oil prices. The Planned Parenthood Federation of Nigeria (PPFN) is aware of at least 20 distinct methods of fertility regulation used by Yoruba herbalists, some of them relying on Western manufactured products. It should be noted that the Lagos Ministry of Health and the Lagos branch of the PPFN have been training a small number of Yoruba herbalists in modern family planning technology since 1984 (Green, 1989). Training workshops for healers are designed and co-ordinated by the Lagos Board of Traditional Medicine, a body formed by the Lagos State Ministry of Health and comprising both traditional healers and scientifically-trained professionals. It is significant in light of the issues raised in this paper that herbalists participating in the training have been officially referred to as traditional birth attendants rather than traditional healers.

In addition to their change-brokering skills, indigenous practitioners have several other important advantages over Western-trained health care personnel. These advantages have been pointed out by anthropologists and others so often that they need only be outlined here. African healers are accessible, affordable, and culturally appropriate and acceptable, thereby fulfilling the major criteria for effective service

---

[3]The author is indebted to Harriet Sibisi for this idea.

delivery[4] (Asuni, 1979; Ademuwagun, 1979; Lorenzelli, 1985). They have credibility as well as respect and prestige in local African communities, otherwise people would not seek their advice and pay for their services. African healers make little distinction between body, mind, and spirit in therapy; the whole person is treated. The holistic perspective of African healers has led to considerable insight and success in treating a wide variety of illnesses that have a psychosomatic component. While there is a movement in modern medicine toward recognizing the psychosomatic component in *all* illness, most physicians lack both the training and the requisite familiarity with patients' social and family situation to deal effectively with patients' psychosocial problems (Green, 1980).

It is clearly advantageous to develop collaborative health care programmes with healers who have their own sources of income rather than with 'logically chosen volunteers' that often lack any sort of health care interest or background, regular cash income, or prestige or at least credibility as health advisers in their own communities. In any case, the morale problems associated with cash income and community acceptance that often plague the usual type of community health worker (cf. Jancloes, 1984) seem unlikely to cripple programmes involving traditional healers.

Perhaps the most powerful argument in favour of collaborative programmes is that public health goals probably cannot in the foreseeable future be realized in Africa without some sort of participation in goal attainment on the part of indigenous healers. The numbers simply are not there: the number of Western trained medical personnel, the number of clinics and hospitals in rural areas, and the amount of money available to ministries of health are all inadequate to existing needs. If anything, numbers work in the other direction: sub-Saharan African populations are growing at rates of between 2.5 and 4.0 per cent annually, requiring corresponding increases in medical personnel facilities just to maintain current inadequate levels of service.[5] Furthermore the recent scourge of AIDS promises to tax health budgets and personnel to an unprecedented degree (Sabatier, 1987; Good, 1988; Green, 1988). Thus economic and manpower arguments in favour of collaboration can only become stronger in years to come

In view of all these factors, it would seem that if the co-operation of indigenous practitioners can be enlisted in public health programmes, there can be no more potent impetus for improvement in the public health. Although actual collaborative programmes have been few and far between, surveys of African healer attitudes and limited programmatic experience have consistently shown willingness on the part of the healers to learn more about Western medicine and to co-operate and collaborate with Western-trained practitioners (Messing, 1976; Osborne *et al.*, 1977; Rubel and Sargent, 1979; Green and Makhubu, 1984; Last, 1986; Chiwuzie *et al.*, 1987). Prestige and recognition appear to be fundamental incentives underlying healers' willingness to co-operate. Healers may well enjoy prestige in their local communities, but collaboration with physicians or government officials bestows a respectability and recognition in the modern-urban sector that indigenous practitioners have come to value. This prestige, along with any skills acquired in Western medicine as a result of contact with Western-trained practitioners, enables a healer to attract more clients and expand his or her practice. It is easy to understand

---

[4]Among donor agencies, the US Agency for International Development (USAID) has been open to supporting programmes involving traditional healers since at least 1979, cf. Pillsbury, 1979. USAID has supported several healer training programmes in Africa by providing not only funding, but technical support from medical anthropologists and others.

[5]For supporting statistics, see various country reports for sub-Saharan Africa prepared by the Futures Group, Washington, D.C., under the AID-funded Resources for the Awareness of Population Impacts on Development (RAPID) project.

why the relatively few healers who have participated in government-sponsored training courses prominently display any certificates or diplomas that testify to their training.

Another incentive to healers is the possibility of earning money through sale of commodities promoted by health ministries or donor groups such as oral rehydration salts or condoms. However, collaborative programmes for healers in Africa seem to have thus far limited commodity sales to very inexpensive items with little potential for profit margin – or as sceptical African physicians have commented to the author, for profiteering.

A survey of Swazi healers showed that if they were to choose which aspects of Western medicine they could learn about, they would choose X-ray technology, blood transfusions and injections of antibiotics (Green and Makhubu, 1984:1073). Instead of these mysteries of modern medical science, healers who participated in government-sponsored workshops learned about mixing sugar-salt solution to rehydrate children with diarrhoea. A plan to develop healers as promoters and distributors of packaged oral rehydration salts was defeated by physicians and health officials who felt traditional healers could not be trusted with modern 'medicine'.

This anecdote is not meant to demean the importance of inexpensive child survival technologies but rather to illustrate the eagerness of traditional healers to have contact with government health programmes at any level, and the extreme reluctance on the part of many African physicians and government officials to share power. MacCormack (1986:153) has made a similar observation, noting that medical techniques and the use of drugs '... are the very skills physicians are least likely to relinquish if they perceive themselves as being in competition for patients and general social status'.

What, then, are the prospects for the Alma Ata resolution of ten years ago becoming a reality in Africa? The history of the allopathic medical profession in wealthier countries – perhaps especially the United States – has been one of consolidating a monopoly of power and stamping out competition from homoeopaths, naturopaths, osteopaths, chiropractors, herbalists, and any other 'heterodox', competing health care systems (Cassidy et al., 1985). In fact US physicians have spent a good deal of time and energy guarding their power prerogatives against incursions from nurses and auxiliary health care personnel (Kotelchuck, 1976). If this provides any clue to prospects for physicians sharing economic and political power in Africa, the outlook is not hopeful, especially since indigenous practitioners out-number physicians by hundreds to one. While it seems unlikely that physicians will share power with healers voluntarily, it may be possible for healers to assert political power through their newly-formed professional associations in such a way that Western trained health personnel have no choice but to recognize and collaborate with indigenous practitioners. It may also be that African governments will eventually have to adopt a stronger human resource development orientation that realistically assesses all available manpower, then leads to the development of policies and health service delivery programmes in light of this.

The goal of co-operation and intersectoral collaboration has not been, and obviously should not be, the displacement or replacement of modern biomedicine with traditional medicine. It should be partly the preservation of medical pluralism, i.e., the availability of more than one system of medical therapy that most Africans currently and of necessity rely on. It should also be, following the arguments and directives of the late King Sobhuza II of Swaziland, the eventual development of a syncretistic system that can combine the best features of biomedicine and traditional medicine in order best to serve human needs. Perhaps syncretism can never develop very far due to a basic incompatibility between the two paradigms of illness and the supporting world views, but pilot project experience suggests that intersectoral co-operation can be achieved and there is no reason to suppose co-operation cannot be extended to all areas of public health concern, including AIDS and other sexually transmitted diseases, nutrition, child immunization, and alcoholism.

It may well be that the ten years that have elapsed since Alma Ata have not been enough time to make real inroads into the entrenched interests of Africa's new medical establishment or the colonial legacy of elitist attitudes towards traditional beliefs and practices. Perhaps it should not be surprising that a human resource development orientation toward primary health care takes more time to develop. We should be in a better position to assess the viability of the Alma Ata resolutions on their 20th or 25th anniversary. Unfortunately, while Africa waits, much life-preserving primary health care will remain inaccessible to too many Africans.

ACKNOWLEDGEMENTS

The author would like to thank D. Michael Warren and Charles Good for valuable comments they provided for an earlier draft of this paper. Any shortcomings in the paper are, of course, the author's responsibility.

REFERENCES

Ademuwagun, Z.A. (1979), 'The relevance of Yoruba medicine men in public health practice in Nigeria', in D.M. Warren *et al.* (eds), *African Therapeutic Systems*, Crossroads Press, Waltham, pp. 153-157.

Asuni, T. (1979), 'The dilemma of traditional healing with special reference to Nigeria', *Social Science and Medicine*, 13:33-39.

Bannerman, R.H., Burton, J. and Wen-Chieh, C. (1983), *Traditional Medicine and Health Care Coverage*, World Health Organization, Geneva.

Cassidy, C., Baer, H. and Becker, B. (1985), 'Selected references on professionalized heterodox health systems in English-speaking countries', *Medical Anthropology Quarterly*, 17:10-18.

Chavunduka, G.L. (1986), 'ZINATHA: the organization of traditional medicine in Zimbabwe', in Last and Chavunduka, 1986, pp.29-49.

Chiwuzie, J. *et al.* (1987), 'Traditional practitioners are here to stay', *World Health Forum*, 8:240-244.

Good, C.M. (1987a), 'The community in African primary health care: problems of strengthening participation and a proposed complementary strategy', paper presented to the Takemi Program in International Health, Harvard School of Public Health, Boston, June.

Good, C.M. (1987b), *Ethnomedical Systems in Africa: Patterns of Traditional Medicine in Rural and Urban Kenya*, Guilford Press, New York.

Good, C.M. (1988), 'Traditional healers and AIDS management in Africa', in Miller and Rockwell, 1988.

Green, E.C. (1980), 'Roles for African traditional healers in mental health care', *Medical Anthropology*, 4:489-522.

Green, E.C. (1985), 'Traditional healers, mothers and childhood diarrheal disease in Swaziland: the interface of anthropology and health education', *Social Science and Medicine*, 18:1071-1074.

Green, E.C. (1987), 'The integration of modern and traditional health sectors in Swaziland', in R. Wulff and S. Fiske (eds), *Anthropological Praxis*, Westview Press, Boulder, pp.87-97.

Green, E.C. (1988), 'AIDS in Africa: an agenda for behavioral scientists', in Miller and Rockwell, 1988.

Green, E.C. (1989), 'Collaborative programs for traditional healers in primary health care and family planning in Africa', in C. Fyfe and V. Maclean (eds), *African Medicine in the Modern World*, pp.115-144.

Green, E.C. and Makhubu, L. (1984), 'Traditional healers in Swaziland: toward improved cooperation between the traditional and modern health sectors', *Social Science and Medicine*, 18:1071-1074.

Hoff, W. (1986), 'Training traditional healers to assist in the control of childhood diseases in Swaziland', paper presented at the National Council for International Health Annual Meeting, Washington DC, 10-13 June.

Hoff, W. and Maseko, D.N. (1986), 'Nurses and traditional healers join hands', *World Health Forum*, 7:412-416.

Jancloes, M. (1984), 'Could villages do better without their volunteer health workers?', *World Health Forum*, 5:296-300.

Janzen, J. (1986), 'The meeting of allopathic and indigenous medicine in the African context', manuscript, published as 'Hippocrate del deserto, Galen della savanna', *Kos: Rivista di Cultura e Storia delle Scienze Mediche*, 3,20:39-61.

Kotelchuck, D. (1976), *Prognosis Negative: Crisis in the Health Care System*, Vintage Books, New York.

Lambo, T.A. (1967), 'Experience with a program in Nigeria', in R. Williams and L. Ozarin (eds), *Community Mental Health: An International Perspective*, Jossey-Bass, San Francisco, pp.97-110.

Lambo, T.A. (1973), 'Services for the mentally handicapped in Africa', *Royal Society of Health Journal*, 93:20-23.

Last, M. (1986), 'The professionalization of African medicine: ambiguities and definitions', in Last and Chavunduka, 1986, pp.1-19.

Last, M. and Chavunduka, G.L. (eds) (1986), *The Professionalization of African Medicine*, Manchester University Press, Manchester.

Lewis, J., Janowitz, B. and Potts, M. (1985), 'Methodological issues in collecting data from traditional birth attendants', *International Journal of Gynaecology and Obstetrics*, 23:291-303.

Lorenzelli, M., (1985), 'Collaboration between traditional and modern medicine: problems and prospects', paper presented to National Council on International Health Conference, Washington DC, June.

MacCormack, C. (1986), 'The articulation of Western and traditional systems of health care', in Last and Chavunduka, 1986, pp.151-162.

Messing, S.D. (1976), 'Traditional healing and the new health center in Ethiopia', *Conch*, 8:52-64.

Miller, N. and Rockwell, R. (eds) (1988), *AIDS in Africa: The Social Impact*, Mellon Press, New York.

Osborne, O. *et al.* (1977), *Continuities between the Practices of Traditional and Scientific Botswana Health Care Practitioners*, African American Scholars, Inc., Washington DC.

Pillsbury, B. (1979), *Reaching the Rural Poor: Indigenous Health Practitioners Are There Already*, AID Program Evaluation Discussion Paper No. 1, Washington DC.

Pillsbury, B. (1982), 'Policy and evaluation perspectives on traditional health practitioners in national health care systems', *Social Science and Medicine*, 16:1825-1834.

Rubel, A. and Sargent, C. (1979), 'Parallel medical systems: papers from a workshop on the healing process', *Social Science and Medicine*, 13B.

Sabatier, R. (1987), *AIDS and the Third World* (revised), PANOS Institute and Norwegian Red Cross.

Ulin, P. (1974), 'The traditional healer of Botswana in a changing society', *Rural Africana*, 26:123-130.

Velimirovic, B. (1984), 'Traditional medicine is not primary health care: a polemic', *Curare*, 7,74-75.

Warren, D.M. (1988), 'Utilizing indigenous healers in national health delivery systems: the Ghanaian experiment', in J. van Willigen, B. Rylko-Bauer and A. McElroy (eds), *Making our Research Useful: Case Studies in the Utilization of Anthropological Knowledge*.

Warren, D.M. *et al.* (1982), 'Ghanaian national policy toward indigenous healers: the case of the primary health training for indigenous healers (PRHETIH) program', *Social Science and Medicine*, 16:1873-1881.

World Health Organization (1985), 'Report on the consultation on approaches for policy development for traditional health practitioners, including traditional birth attendants', WHO, Geneva.

Chapter 14

WILL PRIMARY HEALTH CARE REDUCE INFANT AND CHILD MORTALITY?

A CRITIQUE OF SOME CURRENT STRATEGIES, WITH SPECIAL REFERENCE TO AFRICA AND ASIA*

W. Henry Mosley

INTRODUCTION

For almost three decades after World War II, the health care efforts of most developing countries were directed towards building medical systems similar to those in wealthy countries. This strategy, involving the development of sophisticated medical schools and hospitals with a network of health centres, was consistent with the 'trickle down' development philosophy of the period. Coupled with this, there were efforts to stamp out traditional medicine as well as tribal dressers and dispensers as 'unscientific medicine' and 'vestiges of colonialism'. This approach continues to have popular appeal among national policy makers, particularly the medical profession and the political elite, since they are the main beneficiaries of the Western medical systems that have evolved.

In the past decade, however, there has been a growing awareness that this approach was not only becoming increasingly costly, but also failing to reach the majority of the population, particularly in the rural areas. This led to a reassessment of strategies to meet basic health needs by national and international agencies, culminating in the Alma Ata Conference in 1978 (WHO and UNICEF, 1978). The Alma Ata Declaration asserted that health is a human right and that health care should be accessible, affordable and socially relevant. The basic strategy termed Primary Health Care (PHC) involves community participation and the use of paramedical

*First published in J. Vallin and A. Lopez (eds) (1985), *Health Policy, Social Policy and Mortality Prospects*, Ordina, Liège.

personnel using simple but effective and appropriate technologies. Components of PHC include not only health promotion and personal curative and preventive services, but also education, water, sanitation, agriculture, and related economic development activities.

It would seem that a new philosophy and a new strategy for health care is needed for Africa. Among the 48 countries on the continent, 29 are among the 46 least developed countries in the world with a per capita GNP of $500 or less, and 38 have life expectancies at birth of under 50 years (World Bank, 1981). Most have an extreme shortage of highly qualified medical manpower, with average population to physician ratios ranging from 10,000 to over 40,000. For rural areas the ratios are often at least ten times higher. Even where large numbers of nursing personnel, midwives, and medical assistants have been trained, the health centres and dispensaries from which they operate cover only a small proportion of the rural population.

THE COMPONENTS OF PRIMARY HEALTH CARE (PHC)

Before considering the implications of PHC for mortality reduction, it is essential to distinguish between the rhetoric associated with PHC and its evolving reality. As originally defined at Alma Ata, PHC included the following components:

1. Active participation by the community; this implies that the local community would exercise some control over the contents and implementation of the programme.

2. Be socially relevant to the local context; Western medicine should augment, rather than replace, traditional health systems.

3. Involvement of other sectors such as education, housing, water, sanitation and agriculture.

4. Health services and health promotion should be largely operated by paramedical personnel.

5. Use of simple but effective technologies.

A review of the recent literature and national health plans suggests a growing tendency to minimize or ignore some of these components. It is important to document these trends since they will determine the structure of PHC programmes in the future, and thus have a substantial influence on any potential impact that PHC may have on mortality in developing countries.

Community participation may be considered first. This assumes that in most developing countries local communities exist in some autonomous and democratic form in the rural area and can be readily mobilized to manage their own collective welfare in an egalitarian fashion. In fact, this is rarely the situation in most traditional societies. Ronaghy and Solter (1974) provide a graphic description of how the powerful elite blocked an attempt to get democratically chosen candidates for a 'barefoot doctor' programme in rural Iran. Similarly, the Gonoshastra Kendra Health Programme in rural Bangladesh has met strong resistance from the village elite in their efforts to serve the needs of the poor (Chowdhury, 1981).

Generally, the path of least resistance for a PHC programme is to simply accommodate to the existing power structures at the local level. In some situations this may be satisfactory; for example, reasonably successful PHC projects in Kenya, Nigeria and Indonesia were implemented through health committees building on existing political power structures (Were, 1979; Haliman, 1981; Akpovi et al., 1982). In other cases, however, building a system on the local elites can be counterproductive. In rural Java, for example, only 6 per cent of the village health workers could be classified as 'dedicated' – that is, their performance 'approached the standards set in the training manuals' (Rienks and Iskandar, 1981).

While there are intrinsic difficulties in gaining true community participation at the local level, the principal difficulty lies in the highly centralized control that is exercised by the bureaucracies of national governments in most developing countries. This over-centralization of authority weakens administration at the peripheral level which plagues most developing countries. Moreover, bureaucratic control could effectively destroy PHC programmes even before they commence or at least compromise them into programmes that bear little resemblance to the original concept.[1]

The reason seems straightforward. PHC rests on a political commitment to a new rationale and strategy for programming the limited health care resources any country has available (Montoya-Aquilar, 1977; Gish, 1982). However, most health bureaucracies are already locked into an urban-biased, hospital-based, high-technology system that is essentially self-perpetuating, administratively and politically (World Bank, 1980). As a result, PHC, rather than being a revolutionary force for change, is more often simply added as another appendage to an assortment of vertical programmes. As such, PHC does not compete for the allocation of funds, and may even be operated with almost no funds at all if it is built around inexpensive technologies and volunteer workers!

A second element of PHC that seems to be fading is social relevance, that is, attention to cultural values and the existing traditional health care systems in the respective countries (Bidwell, 1980). China provides the classical example of how traditional and Western medicine can be effectively combined. In other developing countries, the health benefits provided by traditional practitioners range from bone-setting to psychiatric care (WHO, 1978; Choffat, 1980; Kapur, 1980; Ahluwalia and Mechen, 1980). Nonetheless, rather than taking existing health systems and determining what elements of Western medicine can be usefully added, developing countries are often 'swallowing whole' the Western system including expensive technologies like foetal monitoring and intensive care units. Thus the introduction of sophisticated hospital-based technologies is rarely subjected to a 'field trial' for a risk-benefit-cost analysis which these same countries would insist on for a rural health project such as training their own traditional practitioners to use antibiotics and other drugs.

Interestingly, although most health bureaucracies have difficulty with the integration of traditional and Western medicine, their populations do not. Rather, in many developing countries most people take an eclectic approach to health care and disease treatment, and use both Western and traditional medicine, often simultaneously, depending upon a variety of personal, social and cultural factors (Kochar et al., 1977; Assad and Katsha, 1981). Indeed, in India, where for 25 years national commissions and conferences have been struggling unsuccessfully with the issue of integration, traditional practitioners had already made the shift; more than 75 per cent of the drugs they are using are Western medicines (Taylor, 1982).

By failing to take into account the existing health care system, even the most logically conceived strategy for PHC can become virtually impotent or even counterproductive (Unschuld, 1975). In Egypt, for example, where for many years traditional midwives were registered and given some training and incorporated into the health care systems, this 'outmoded' system was revised in 1969 and replaced by fully qualified midwives. By 1980, despite the fact that there were enough qualified midwives to attend almost all deliveries, over 80 per cent were still attended by traditional practitioners (Hamamsy, 1973; Nadim, 1980). However, since these

---

[1]See, for example, *Egyptian Experience in Primary Health Care*, Ministry of Health, Republic of Egypt, Cairo (undated).

practitioners are no longer 'recognized' (licensed) by the government, their practices have not improved and as a consequence, the incidence of neonatal tetanus remains extremely high. Similarly, in the Sudan, young women selected by a programme to be trained as midwives, but subsequently considered by the community to be insufficiently experienced, were in many cases led to earn a livelihood by performing female circumcisions (El Dareer, 1981). Unfortunately, training manuals for village level workers are often written with a Western medical bias which takes no account of local health-related factors, and thus greatly hinder the introduction of some effective technologies to the community (Rienks and Iskander, 1981).

Intersectoral involvement is also largely neglected for a variety of reasons. The lack of additional resources which other sectors would often need to use to support PHC is a major difficulty. Additionally, there is the more general problem of the failure of administrative lines of authority to transcend bureaucratic barriers to the actual implementation of many intersectoral activities.

Without these three principal elements, PHC essentially becomes a top-down strategy to reach the community with some simple but theoretically effective preventive and curative technologies using various types of village level workers. While this is admittedly a narrow and constrained definition, there seems to be a growing consensus that not only accepts but implicitly endorses these limits. This can be seen in a variety of PHC proposals ranging from 'crash' health manpower planning (Marera *et al.*, 1980) to 'selective' or 'optimal packages' of PHC interventions based on either subjective judgements (Walsh and Warren, 1980; Gwatkin *et al.*, 1980a), or on explicitly specified computer models (Grosse, 1980; Barnum *et al.*, 1980), or on a growing body of what might be called trial and error field experiences with community based programmes (Parker, 1982).

With this as a background, PHC in this analysis will be confined to preventive, curative and promotive activities that will normally be the responsibility of the formal health sector and are designed to: (a) reach the mass of the population; (b) use relatively simple technologies; and (c) be provided predominantly by paramedical personnel. This can include water, sanitation, health education and food distribution programmes, in contrast to secondary and tertiary curative care provided by hospitals dominated by physicians.

HEALTH CARE AND MORTALITY IN AFRICA – A KENYA CASE STUDY

While several African governments are taking the initiative to develop a lower cadre of health worker for community level activities, there is insufficient experience or data to assess any impact on mortality. There have been two longitudinal, comprehensive, integrated rural health research projects however; the Danfa Project in Ghana (Univ. of Ghana and UCLA, 1979) and the Calabar Project in Nigeria (Weiss, 1982). In both cases, detailed documentation of the performance of the various service delivery activities has been produced yet the evidence for any health impact from the projects is questionable. For the Danfa Project problems of data quality as well as long-term health trends confound the demographic interpretation. In the case of the Calabar Project, the limited coverage of the target population together with the relatively small change in traditional patterns of health behaviour produced by the project were the main constraints. Some documentation of other PHC initiatives in Africa is available but is generally anecdotal, or based on uncontrolled observations, making critical analysis impossible.

Given these limitations, the recent child mortality trends and differentials in Kenya will be examined instead with a view to assessing what has been the connection between national development strategy and child survival. This analysis will consider not only the formal health system, which largely comprises secondary and tertiary care facilities, but also more comprehensive social and economic policies in terms of their impact on child mortality.

In many respects, Kenya is a microcosm of Africa. Its 17.5 million inhabitants are spread from the dense settlements in the hot, humid, malarious coastal plains and lake basin areas to the more scattered villages in the central highlands; sparse nomadic tribes wander in the vast arid plains (Hickman *et al.*, 1973). Despite these differences, trends and differentials in child mortality seem to be more closely related to economic conditions.

On the basis of macro-economic indicators at least, Kenya appears to have made good economic progress since independence in 1963. The Gross Domestic Product (GDP) grew at an average annual rate of almost 6 per cent from the early 1960s through to the middle of the 1970s; although since then economic growth has fallen substantially with the general sluggishness of the global economy (Barkan, 1979; Central Bureau of Statistics, 1980a). Nonetheless, there has been considerable regional inequity in the pattern of investment in national development, with the bulk of resources going to the most productive areas, especially the Central Highlands (Migot-Adholla, 1979; Wright, 1982). This has perpetuated colonial policies and aggravated regional economic disparities, particularly in the agricultural sector.

With regard to education, particularly primary education, the situation has been more equitable, due largely to the magnitude of investment, currently about 20 per cent of the annual national budget (Central Bureau of Statistics, 1980b). Kenya has achieved primary school enrolment ratios approaching 85 per cent for both sexes in recent years. The coverage of the population by schools is also very high: for example, a 1974 rural household survey found that 80-90 per cent of households were within two kilometres of a primary school (Central Bureau of Statistics, 1979a).

The health sector, on the other hand, only receives about 6-7 per cent of the national budget (Central Bureau of Statistics, 1980b). Over two-thirds of this is spent on urban hospitals, while only about one-tenth is available for rural health services (Government of Kenya). As a result, there is only one health facility for 10,000-20,000 persons in the rural areas, and only 10-15 per cent of the rural population are within two kilometres of these facilities (Central Bureau of Statistics, 1979a). The majority of facilities are understaffed and constantly short of essential drugs (Family Health Institute, 1978).

The population of Kenya has doubled in the 19 years since independence (Central Bureau of Statistics, 1979b) due to a sustained high (and perhaps rising) birth rate – estimated at 54 per 1,000 – coupled with a falling death rate which has now reached about 14 per 1,000. The current growth rate of 4 per cent per year was the highest recorded in the world in 1980 (Population Reference Bureau, 1980). Although mortality shows some striking social differentials, fertility has so far shown relatively little variation by any social indicator, and thus is not a significant factor in explaining mortality change (Central Bureau of Statistics, 1980c).

Indirect estimates of mortality before the age of two years ($2q0$) from the 1962, 1969 and 1979 census yield rates of 174, 157 and 125 per 1,000 respectively (Central Bureau of Statistics, 1969; Kibet, 1982). As a result of this remarkable decline, Kenya now has one of the lowest infant mortality rates among Sub-Saharan African countries: 87-90 per 1,000 (Mott, 1982). Social differentials in child mortality reveal a large effect of mothers' education from both the 1969 and 1979 census data. For mothers with no education, the number of children dying before age two was 163 per 1,000 in 1979; for women with 1-7 years education, the rate was 104 per 1,000, while for mothers with eight or more years of education, the rate was 61 per 1,000 (Kibet, 1982). This is a 36 per cent decline in child mortality with primary education, and a 63 per cent decline with secondary education, compared with the levels for uneducated women. A similar effect was evident from the 1969 census data (Central Bureau of Statistics, 1969).

TABLE 1: ESTIMATED EFFECT OF CHANGES IN EDUCATIONAL LEVEL OF WOMEN ON CHILD MORTALITY

| Year | Percentage of women aged 20-24 with: | | | Child deaths by age two | | Estimated ratio of death rate to rate in 1962 based on educational level of women[b] |
	No education	1-7 years of education	8 or more years of education	Rate per 1000 population[a]	Ratio of death rate to rate in 1962	
1962	84	15	1	174	1.00	1.00
1969	61	34	5	157	.90	.90
1979	35	47	18	125	.72	.76

[a]From census data.
[b]Estimate based on the proportion of women in each education category, and the relative risk of death by education level as noted in text.

TABLE 2: SOCIO-ECONOMIC AND DEMOGRAPHIC INDICATORS BY PROVINCE, KENYA

Province	Percentage of population[a] living in province	Number of health facilities per 100000 population[b]	Percentage of households below poverty line[c]	Child deaths by age 2 per 1000			
				All	No education	1-7 years	8+ years
Central	15.3	6.2	18.2	67	94	63	42
Eastern	17.8	5.2	28.5	103	128	96	51
Rift Valley	21.1	7.0	38.8	108	125	94	58
Coast	8.8	9.0	43.5	177	200	126	75
Western	12.0	2.6	51.6	152	173	142	86
Nyanya	17.3	3.4	55.6	174	204	158	85
North East	2.4	5.1	[d]	135	139	120	43
Nairobi	5.4	–	[e]	93	138	101	53
Kenya	100.1	–	38.5[f]	125	163	104	61

[a]From 1979 census data.

[b]70 per cent of these are one-person rural dispensaries offering only very limited curative services. Every province has a provincial hospital, and there are 40 district-level hospitals.

[c]ILO estimate based on a household consumption criterion of 2200 Kenyan shillings annually.

[d]This province which is largely inhabited by nomads was not included in the survey.

[e]Metropolitan area – not included in the rural household survey.

[f]This is only for the rural population included in the survey.

Sources: Kibet (1982): Family Health Institute (1978); Senga et al. (1980).

Given these findings and the remarkable advancements in primary education since independence, one may ask how much of the decline in child mortality since 1962 is attributable simply to changes in the level of education among women of childbearing age. Indirect estimates of child mortality derived from census data are based on the responses of women to questions about child survival (Hill and Trussell, 1977). To estimate survival to age two, only information about educational change among women aged 20-24 is of interest. The estimated effect of changes in educational level of women on child mortality is examined in Table 1.

From the table, it is apparent that all of the observed mortality decline between 1962 and 1969, and about 86 per cent of the decline between 1962 and 1979, was due solely to an improvement in the education level of mothers. Over the latter period 1969-1979, 78 per cent of the change in child mortality can be accounted for by the education variable alone.

In Kenya, however, there are large regional variations in child mortality which cannot be fully explained by maternal education. As Figure 1 indicates, the districts with highest mortality based on the 1979 census lie along the eastern sea coast and western lake basin areas, while the lowest levels are found in the central highlands. Child mortality rates range from 216 per 1,000 in the South Nyanya District in the western lake basin region to 49 per 1,000 in the Nyeri District in the central highlands. Nairobi and Mombasa, the two major metropolitan centres, have intermediate child mortality levels of 93 and 120 per 100 respectively.

There is an impressive parallel between the regional differentials in child mortality and the regional disparities in national development discussed earlier. A more objective assessment is given in Table 2 which shows educational differentials in child mortality by provinces, and, for six of the seven rural provinces, gives an indication of the average economic condition of families based on the percentage of households having an income below a poverty line as determined from a 1974 rural household survey (Senga et al., 1980).

Two points are immediately evident from these data. Firstly, the relative magnitude of child mortality differentials by mother's education is roughly the same within each province, irrespective of the overall mortality level. Indeed, even a more detailed analysis by district shows that this effect of mother's education persists (Kibet, 1982). Secondly, the inter-provincial mortality differentials are generally maintained even within education groups and are strongly correlated with variations in the level of household poverty.

The correlation of child mortality with the level of poverty in each province can be seen separately for different levels of mother's education in Figure 2. The correlations are striking: for mothers with no education, $r = 0.88$; for mothers with 1-7 years, $r = 0.96$; and for mothers with eight years or more, $r = 0.97$. The estimated regression lines are revealing also. Increasing poverty has a greater impact on mortality levels for children of women with the least education, and this effect declines with increasing education. Thus at high levels of poverty, the absolute mortality differentials are greatest. At the other extreme, by projecting these regression lines to 'zero poverty' (as defined here), educational differentials in mortality would theoretically disappear at a child mortality rate of about 16-19 per 1,000, a level typical of the developed regions of the world.

Overall, these data suggest that the child mortality differentials between the regions of Kenya can largely be 'explained' by just two factors: maternal education, and level of household poverty. Given that the six provinces covered in this analysis include over 96 per cent of the rural population, it seems reasonable to conclude that the patterns and trends of economic development can probably account for most of the national decline in child mortality since 1962.

FIGURE 1: CHILD MORTALITY BEFORE AGE TWO YEARS IN KENYA, BY DISTRICT – 1979 CENSUS

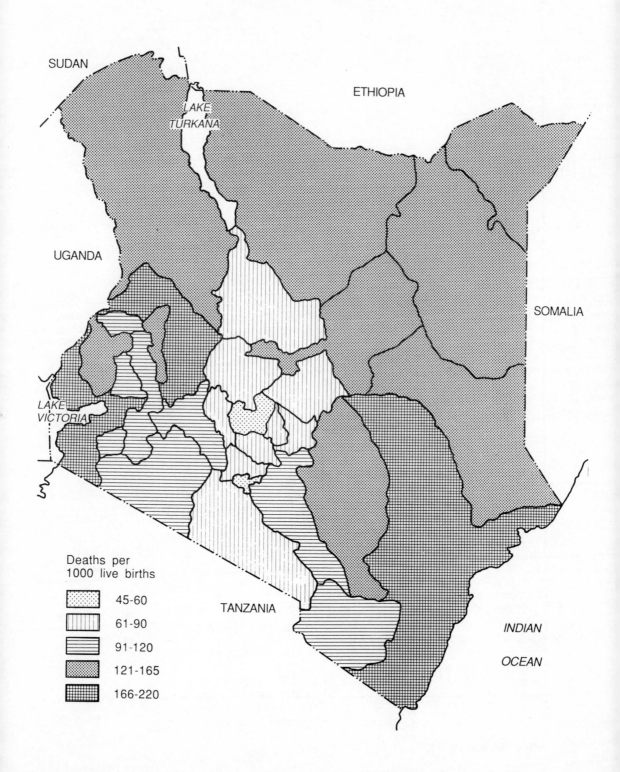

Deaths per
1000 live births

- 45-60
- 61-90
- 91-120
- 121-165
- 166-220

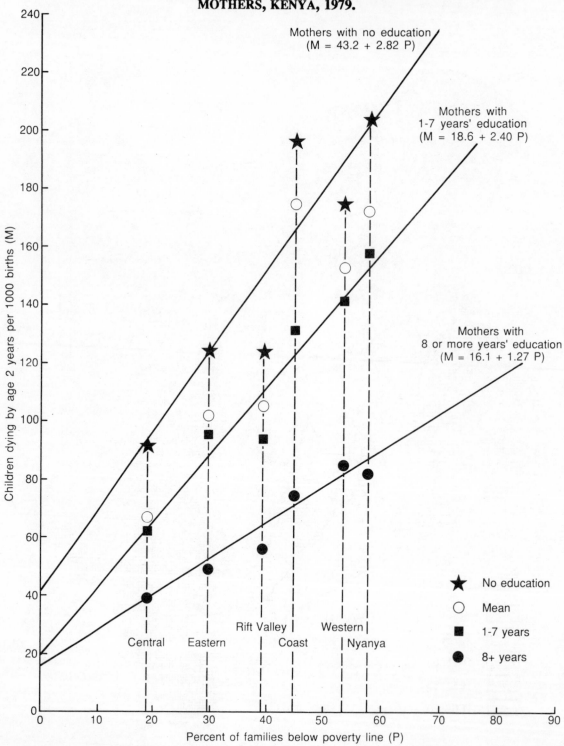

FIGURE 2: CORRELATION OF CHILD MORTALITY WITH LEVEL OF POVERTY IN 6 RURAL PROVINCES ACCORDING TO EDUCATION LEVEL OF MOTHERS, KENYA, 1979.

Mothers with no education
(M = 43.2 + 2.82 P)

Mothers with 1-7 years' education
(M = 18.6 + 2.40 P)

Mothers with 8 or more years' education
(M = 16.1 + 1.27 P)

Children dying by age 2 years per 1000 births (M)

Percent of families below poverty line (P)

Central   Eastern   Rift Valley   Western
                      Coast   Nyanya

★ No education
○ Mean
■ 1-7 years
● 8+ years

Source: Same as Table 2.

TABLE 3: POPULATION CHANGE AND CHILD MORTALITY IN NAIROBI AND MOMBASA METROPOLITAN AREAS AND ADJACENT RURAL REGIONS, 1969-1979[a]

Region and city or rural district	Population		Number of child deaths per 1000 before age 2					
	1979 Census (000)	Per cent increase since 1969	Estimate from		Per cent change 1969-79	By education of mother in 1979		
			1969 Census	1979 Census		No education	1-7 years	8+ years
Central highlands								
Nairobi (urban)	827	62.5	96	93	−3.0	138	101	53
Kiambu (rural)	686	44.3	95	70	−26.2	103	69	45
Muranga (rural)	648	45.6	113	68	−39.8	87	65	47
East Coast								
Mombasa (urban)	341	38.1	142	120	−16.1	138	119	78
Kilifi (rural)	430	40.1	213	212	−0.5	223	135	66
Kwale (rural)	288	40.2	188	190	+1.1	200	148	68

[a]Data from 1969 and 1979 censuses.

It is of interest also to examine what are the urban-rural differentials in child mortality. In Kenya at least, urban areas must be examined individually and with reference to their own regional settings, given the vast regional differentials in patterns of development. In the analysis shown in Table 3, the two major metropolitan centres, Nairobi in the central highlands, and Mombasa on the east coast are contrasted with their respective adjacent rural areas which are comparable in their ecological settings but contrasting in terms of urban amenities.

Among the rural districts, Kiambu and Muranga in the Central Province, the area which derived greatest benefit from Kenya's development programme over the past decades, enjoyed a decline in child mortality of 26 per cent and 39 per cent respectively between 1969 and 1979. On the other hand, for Kilifi and Kwale District in the Coastal Province, where little attention has been paid to development, not only is child mortality three times higher than in Central Province, but there has been no improvement in survival during the decade. As a result, population growth has been slower and the mortality gap between the two regions has widened.

A comparison of the two urban areas indicates that although Nairobi has better child survival than Mombasa, when examined by educational groups the advantage is limited to women with some education. This may arise in part from the very different economic character of the two cities. Mombasa is primarily a seaport while Nairobi is the national capital with a much larger white-collar and professional sector. Interestingly, the child mortality rate in Mombasa fell by 16 per cent between 1969 and 1979 but by only 3 per cent in Nairobi. Overall, child mortality in Nairobi is over 30 per cent *higher* than in the adjacent rural regions, while in Mombasa it is 40 per cent *lower* than in the neighbouring rural area. Moreover, in each region the urban-rural gap in child mortality has been widening.

To explain this paradox, one has to look at the interaction of urban-rural development policies in Kenya. The introduction of individual land tenure and the commercialization of agriculture led to higher agricultural yields but also, as graphically described by Migot-Adholla, 'set off two opposite trends – concentration of land resources in fewer hands, and increased fragmentation, especially among the poorer peasants' (Migot-Adholla, 1979:158). As a result, some of the residents in Central Province became wealthier whereas the landless suffered. The latter, however, did not remain in their homelands but, as noted by Muwonge, 'Particularly in the districts of Muranga, Kiambu, and Nyeri, where a land reform programme was reaching maturity, thousands who lacked minimum land holdings migrated to Nairobi' (Muwonge, 1980:599).

This urban migration was facilitated by the repeal of the colonial migration restrictions to urban areas at the time of independence, but at the same time the new city council raised the standard of minimally acceptable housing. Under colonial rule this had been 'bed space accommodation in a unit built with permanent materials'; the new regulation required a 'two room unit in permanent material together with kitchen, shower and toilet' (Muwonge, 1980:598). While this measure was more socially acceptable, it effectively decreased the stock of existing housing by necessitating the grouping of former single units, and more importantly, by raising the price of the minimum low rent unit far beyond the resources of the newly arriving migrants. The result was squatting, which in turn was complicated because of periodical demolition of 'substandard housing' in the traditional African housing areas. Ultimately the squatters found an uncontrolled area in Mathare Valley and began to settle there in rapidly increasing numbers, growing from less than 5,000 in 1965 to over 150,000 in 1979.

The extensive migration to Nairobi contributed significantly to the 62 per cent increase in the city's population between 1969 and 1979, compared with 38 per cent in Mombasa (Table 3). In the Mathare Valley, 90 to 99 per cent of houses in 1979 had only one room constructed of temporary materials without private toilet facilities or a kitchen, generally averaging three occupants per house (Muwonge, 1980:606-608). This differential in environmental conditions in Nairobi is evident from the

1979 census results which indicated that mortality before age two in the four wealthiest wards ranged from 41 to 51 per 1,000, while in the four poorest wards, the range was from 109 to 152 (Nyamwanga, 1982). This has been a principal cause of the stagnation of mortality decline in the city.

A very different urban-rural mortality pattern has occurred on the east coast. Child mortality in Mombasa is much lower than in Kilifi and Kwale, especially among the uneducated women. With higher education the differentials narrow and even reverse with secondary education. This is in part due to the fact that the rural areas in Coast Province are among the least developed (Table 2). Also in Mombasa, as in Nairobi, municipal services cover a substantial fraction of the population and promote health even among the uneducated. A good example is the municipal malaria control activities which have markedly reduced malaria transmission in urban areas (Vogel *et al.*, 1974).

It is quite likely that the prevention and treatment of malaria by individual families accounts for some of the educational differentials in child mortality even in the rural areas of Coast Province. Evidence for this comes from a series of investigations over a period of 20 years following a temporary malaria control programme carried out between 1954 and 1959 in the Pare area, a rural region of Tanzania (Pringle, 1969; Matola and Magayuka, 1981). Although the densities of the vectors and their infectivity rates returned to the levels prevailing before the control programme and have remained high for the last ten years, there has been a significant decline in malaria in the population. According to the authors, 'the most significant factor in this is probably the increasing awareness and use of antimalarial drugs by the population, stimulated by national propaganda and by the gradual development of health services' (Matola and Magayuka, 1981:813).

This assessment has indicated how government development policies which affect the social and economic circumstances of families at the household level can be directly translated into mortality risks for their offspring. Considering that Nairobi has the largest number of doctors and finest medical facilities in the country (including Kenyatta National Hospital which alone consumes 25 per cent of the national health budget) and yet still has a child mortality rate almost 35 per cent higher than the surrounding rural area, it seems reasonable to conclude that Western hospital-based medicine is not a major variable influencing urban-rural differentials.

While certain natural ecological settings predispose to some diseases more than others – for example, respiratory diseases and accidental burns are relatively more common in the cooler highlands, and malaria and diarrhoea relatively more common in the coastal plains (Republic of Kenya, 1981) – mortality differentials are not primarily due to the natural ecological settings *per se*, but to the knowledge and resources that are available to take effective measures to reduce the risk of exposure to, or effectively treat, the disease conditions. Thus even in the highly malarious coastal region, municipal investments in Mombasa can contribute to reducing mortality among children of uneducated mothers to the same level seen in malaria-free Nairobi. In the malarious rural district, child mortality among better educated mothers has been reduced to only one-third of that among their uneducated counterparts.

These conclusions based on macro or areal analyses using data from the 1979 census are consistent with the findings of a household survey carried out in 1974 by ILO (Anker and Knowles, 1977). This study found that maternal literacy, income and toilet facilities were positively associated with child survival to age three while the use of traditional medicine and mother's illness showed a negative association with this variable. Urban residence appeared to increase the chances of child survival, largely through other variables such as toilet facilities. However, there was no association with use of hospitals. Residence in a malarious region was also shown to have an independent effect.

These observations are not novel in Africa. Even the most macro level analysis shows that literacy and per capita GNP exert the strongest association with child survival while the number of persons per doctor or per bed has no effect (United Nations, 1979). Gaisie (1979) has concluded that the decline in infant mortality in Ghana from 205 to 132 per 1,000 between 1950 and 1970 could not be attributed to health services which had scarcely reached the majority of the population, but must be related to 'general improvements in the standard of living' (Gaisie, 1979). More critically, Caldwell (1979), in his analysis of child mortality differentials in urban and rural Nigeria, concluded that maternal education was probably not operating as a proxy for other social variables but actually was indicative of patterns of maternal behaviour which have a direct bearing on the survival of the child. Among other variables, father's occupation exerted the greatest impact on child survival, while the effect of urban versus rural residence, an indirect indicator of the availability of health services, was negligible.

DETERMINANTS OF CHILD SURVIVAL

This analysis reinforces the basic conclusion that child survival is primarily determined by the social and economic resources of the child's family. Analytically, these family resources are essentially expressed by two indicators – maternal education and some index of the economic circumstances of the household. Correlations between child survival and indicators of social equity are likely to be quite direct.

The analysis of the Kenyan situation goes beyond merely reconfirming a statistical association but rather is an attempt to assess to what extent development policies and strategies in a developing country can be specifically related to trends and differentials in child mortality. The results are quite striking. A full 86 per cent of the decline in childhood mortality between 1962 and 1979 may be 'explained' by the increase in maternal education. The remaining 14 per cent can reasonably be attributed to improvements in the economic situation of households.

While certain modern Western technologies such as antimalarial drugs seem to have had an impact on mortality, at least in some regions, it is virtually impossible to measure any independent impact of the existing formal medical system. This observation, which is hardly unique to Kenya, is of concern to many observers, especially in the medical profession. It may be argued, for example, that maternal education helps to lower child mortality only because the formal medical system exists to make available effective health technologies. This is, of course, true to some degree; conceptually, however, this interpretation places medical technologies as an 'intermediate' rather than a primary variable in mortality decline.

To explore this issue further, a general conceptual model of the factors influencing child mortality will be developed here. The model is based on the following premises:

1. In a well-protected setting, more than 98 per cent of infants can be expected to survive the first five years of life;

2. reduction of this survival probability is due to the operation of social and economic factors as the primary determinants of mortality;

3. these socio-economic determinants must operate through some basic biological mechanisms, or intermediate variable, which will first influence risks of morbidity and secondly the outcome of the morbid process;

4. the states of morbidity (diseases, malnutrition) in the surviving population are not considered as independent variables, but rather biological indicator variables reflecting the operations of the intermediate variables;

5. mortality in infancy and childhood is generally the ultimate consequence of cumulative episodes of morbidity (including their biological synergies) and only infrequently is the result of a single isolated episode of disease.

The key to the conceptual model proposed here is the identification of a set of *intermediate* (biological) *variables* which directly influence the *risk* of morbidity and mortality and through which all social and economic determinants can be shown to operate. Fifteen such variables have been identified and grouped into five categories as follows:

A. Maternal fertility factors:

    1.   Age of childbearing,
    2.   Parity,
    3.   Birth interval;

B. Environmental contamination with infectious agents:

    4.   Contamination of air,
    5.   Contamination of food/water/fingers,
    6.   Contamination of skin/fomites/soil,
    7.   Vectors;

C. Availability of nutrients to the foetus and infant:

    8.   Calories,
    9.   Protein,
    10. Vitamins,
    11. Minerals;

D. Injuries:

    12. Accidents,
    13. Intentional injury;

E. Personal disease control factors:

    14. Personal preventive measures,
    15. Treatment.

Figure 3 illustrates in a simplified form the conceptual model of the determinants of child mortality and identifies the relevant social practices that are related to each of the five categories of intermediate variables. Thus the intermediate variable 'nutrient availability' is modulated by the physiological factors of the host related to appetite, absorption and metabolism. Similarly, the risks related to the intermediate variable 'environmental contamination' are influenced by the hosts' resistance to infection. In this latter case, host resistance may be decreased by injuries, or immaturity at birth, or increased by vaccines. The figure also illustrates (see 'feedback' arrows) the mechanisms that produce the biological synergy with malnutrition and infections; infections reduce appetite and alter physiological functions which aggravate malnutrition, while malnutrition reduces host resistance, increasing the risk to more severe disease manifestations from infections. Finally, the model illustrates that the risks of mortality are moderated by treatments which are a function of sickness care behaviour.

It is also important to consider the concept of social synergy (as distinguished from biological synergy) as a risk factor. Social synergy implies that the same social determinant, e.g., poverty, can operate independently on more than one intermediate variable to influence the risk of infant mortality. The resultant combined risk is greater than the simple sum of the operation of each intermediate variable. This concept has more than theoretical significance. It not only explains why some direct biomedical interventions have a much lesser impact than expected, but also clarifies why basic social changes such as mother's education may considerably influence child survival.

The conceptual framework developed here is built on earlier models (Mosley, 1980; Chen, 1981), although two premises deserve emphasis. Firstly, diseases (e.g., diarrhoea, malaria) or disease states (e.g., malnutrition) are not treated as causal factors, but only as indicator variables. For example, to observe that the high mortality among children in a certain population is correlated with a high frequency of 'malnutrition' as measured by growth failure is only to note the biological process leading to mortality. This observation does not give much more information on the determinants of high mortality than does the observation that a high fertility level is correlated with a high frequency of pregnancies among married women.

FIGURE 3: CONCEPTUAL MODEL OF THE ACTION OF THE FIVE INTERMEDIATE VARIABLES IN CHILD MORBIDITY AND MORTALITY AND THEIR HOUSEHOLD SOCIAL DETERMINANTS

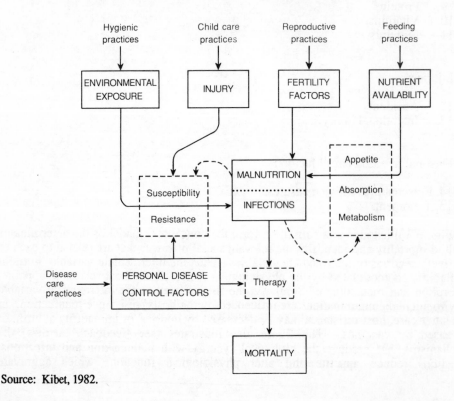

Source: Kibet, 1982.

This conceptual approach complements the utility of specific aetiological studies in establishing the relevant determinants of mortality. A careful definition of biological 'causes' of diseases may be essential to define the operation of some specific intermediate variables and thus point to their determinants. The point being stressed here is that the diseases registered as 'cause of death' are not the same as the determinants of mortality in a population. The failure to appreciate this distinction too often leads to disease-oriented technical intervention programmes that fail to achieve their goals; a good example is the use of supplementary feeding programmes to combat 'malnutrition' (Beaton and Ghassemi, 1982).

The second point to emphasize is that an infant or child death usually does not have a discrete cause, but in most cases is the result of a long series of minor biological insults which cumulatively retard growth, lead to wasting and progressively wear down the resistance of the individual. A minor illness such as respiratory infection or diarrhoea thus often results in death.

This process of retarded growth ultimately leading to death has been well documented in a ten-year longitudinal study in rural Guatemala by Mata (1978a). Typically, faltering growth begins after weaning and is associated with multiple episodes of infection, primarily of the gastro-intestinal and respiratory systems. Although the dietary intake is generally deficient in these children, Mata emphasizes that it is the combined process of poor diet and multiple recurrent infections that leads the child down the 'road to death'. Similar findings have been reported from longitudinal studies in Gambia and Uganda (Cole and Parkin, 1977; Rowland, 1979).

Puffer and Serrano (1973), in their analysis of over 34,000 deaths among children under five years of age from 13 widely separated areas in Latin America, came to much the same conclusion. In discussing diarrhoeal diseases as a 'cause' of death, the authors observed that

in many children there is a history of repeated diarrhoeal disease episodes which combined with inadequate food intake result in nutritional deficiency ... Thus a vicious cycle is often established, and it is difficult to know which of the conditions should be considered as underlying cause (diarrhoeal disease or nutritional deficiency) because of their reciprocal implications (Puffer and Serrano, 1973:140-141).

Even with a more specific disease like measles, nutritional deficiency was found to be a contributory or pre-existing cause in roughly 60 per cent of cases.

Because death is the end result of a cumulative series of pathological processes, the biological status of surviving children reflects their position along the spectrum from good health to life-threatening disability. The simplest indicator of this is growth faltering and body wasting, which can be measured by relating height and weight to age. Direct quantitative verification of this relationship between physical status and probability of death is provided in two prospective studies in Bangladesh and one in India (Sommer and Loewenstein, 1975; Kielmann and McCord, 1978; Chen et al., 1980). These field studies have clearly demonstrated a great increase in the relative risk of death among the more 'malnourished' children in each study population, although the absolute risk of death for any specific level of 'malnutrition' varied from one population to another (Bairagi, 1982). This would appear to reflect differences in availability, quality and effectiveness of curative services which, as the conceptual model illustrates, influence mortality risk. Studies in New Guinea and several Latin American countries which have documented a decline in death rates without any change in nutrition levels among surviving children illustrate how improvements in sickness care can reduce mortality with little alteration in morbidity risks (Malcolm, 1974; Solimano and Vine, 1983).

THE OPERATION OF INTERMEDIATE VARIABLES INFLUENCING MORTALITY

Each of the intermediate variables will now be discussed in turn to investigate how each one operates to directly influence the risk of mortality, and, more importantly, to identify the social and economic factors that may operate through it. This should shed further light on how such determinants as maternal education exert such a profound effect on child mortality, even in poor societies. It should also be possible to infer what might be the potential impact of the introduction of specific health technologies in the absence of other social change.

A. Maternal Fertility Factors

Maternal age, parity, and birth interval, each have an independent effect on the risk of infant mortality (Federici and Terrenato, 1983). Childbearing at very young (under 18) and older (over 35) ages, at high parity (over four) and with short birth intervals (under one year) increase the risk of infant death, especially in the presence of two or more factors, for instance high parity among very young women. Many births to these high-risk mothers are characterized by immaturity and low birthweight. Studies in both developed and developing countries have documented an exponential increase in the risk of infant death for newborns with birthweights below 2,500 grams, reaching almost 100 per cent for infants under 1,000 grams (Puffer and Serrano, 1975). Advanced maternal age is also associated with higher risks of birth trauma.

Among the socio-economic determinants which operate to influence the risk of infant mortality through these intermediate variables are: age at marriage; age at first sexual union; desired family size; beliefs about use of fertility control practices; knowledge of, and access to, methods of contraception; postpartum abstinence; terminal abstinence. Breastfeeding, age of weaning and/or use of bottles also affect postpartum amenorrhoea, and thus birth spacing.

As a medical technical intervention, modern contraceptives can lower infant mortality provided they are widely used and if the users include high-risk mothers in terms of age and parity. Indeed, in several countries such as the USA, Chile and Thailand, a substantial fraction (from 13 per cent to 33 per cent) of the observed decline in infant mortality has been related to changes in the age-parity structure of childbearing (Rohde and Allman, 1981).

B. Environmental Contamination with Infectious Agents

With a few significant exceptions such as tetanus and plague, almost all infectious agents have their reservoir in human hosts and thus the transmission of these diseases depends largely on patterns of human behaviour (Mosley, 1983). Basically, four intermediate variables can be identified through which infectious agents most often enter the human host to produce disease. These routes and major diseases are:

1. Contamination of Air

This is the mechanism for infectious agents which enter the respiratory tract. These include viral diseases such as influenza, viral pneumonia, viral tracheobronchitis, viral meningitis, measles, mumps, chickenpox and smallpox, and bacterial diseases such as whooping cough, diphtheria, streptococcal sore throat, pneumococcal pneumonia, bacterial meningitis and tuberculosis. Beyond improving ventilation and reducing crowding, there is very little that can be done to reduce the level of air contamination.

The major social measures that can be taken act to reduce the number of infectious hosts in the environment. One can isolate infectious cases, as is done for active pulmonary tuberculosis and diphtheria. If effective drugs are available, infectious persons (cases and/or carriers) can be treated to eliminate the agent (tuberculosis, streptococcal pharyngitis, and meningococcal infections). While these measures require the availability of medical technology, knowledge about, access to, and compliance with the medical programme are primarily determined by social and economic circumstances. These same social circumstances that deter use of medical technology are associated with a higher probability of exposure (overcrowding, poor ventilation), and more severe disease (undernutrition). This illustrates how social synergy can operate to multiply the risk of death through the simultaneous operation of several intermediate variables.

Immunization, which eliminates the susceptibles from the environment (infectious agents depend on human hosts for survival), will ultimately eliminate the disease. This has already been accomplished with smallpox and is being approached with measles vaccine in some populations.

Effective treatments and vaccines exist for relatively few viral and bacterial agents that produce respiratory diseases. Furthermore, direct environmental interventions have only a minor effect on the airborne transmission of these agents. Consequently, the incidence (risk) of the common respiratory diseases does not vary much under different social conditions (Parkin, 1975). The severity may vary markedly, however, due to the biological synergy of infections with malnutrition (Scrimshaw et al., 1968). Nonetheless, biological synergy is a secondary phenomenon which can only become manifest because of the operation of several intermediate determinants simultaneously due to social synergy.

2. Contamination of Food and Water

This refers to infectious agents which are acquired by swallowing, primarily with food and water, but also in some cases through hand-to-mouth. These are mostly gastro-intestinal diseases where the agent is excreted by the infectious host in the faeces and include a multitude of diarrhoeal diseases and dysenteries caused by many types of bacteria and viruses, and some parasites. Diseases such as cholera, typhoid, infectious hepatitis and the intestinal parasites (round worm and giardia) are perhaps the best known examples.

These infectious agents can be killed simply by heat and soap and water. For example, if careful attention is given to heating all food just before eating, boiling and properly storing drinking water, and washing hands before eating, the risk of acquiring these infections can be dramatically reduced. In the urban slums of Bangladesh, for example, the provision of soap and water containers and some guidelines about washing hands and clothes reduced the transmission of shigella dysentery by 67 per cent even without attention to cooking food or boiling water (Khan, 1982).

The adverse effects of social behaviour on contamination of food and water are well documented. For example, a series of field investigations in Gambia have demonstrated a marked rise in childhood gastro-enteritis and mortality with the onset of the rainy season (Rowland and McCallum, 1977). The authors observe that at this time

feeding of small children is particularly haphazard ... infants may be left in the compound in the care of a young nursemaid with a supply of porridge or gruel for the next eight to nine hours, and food from the evening meal is sometimes stored overnight (Rowland and McCallum, 1977:200).

In rural Bangladesh, contamination of weaning foods by *E. coli* was found to be positively correlated with the incidence of diarrhoea due to toxigenic *E. coli*, the most frequent pathogen in all causes of diarrhoea (Black *et al.*, 1982). Again, seasonal variations were evident, with the highest contamination in warmer temperatures when bacteria could proliferate to levels 100 times higher than in cooler weather.

It is because of the risks related to poor food handling that bottle feeding may be dangerous to the infant. These risks are of course not unique to the use of bottles; any supplementary or weaning foods can be dangerous if not properly prepared. 'Weaning diarrhoea' among poor populations is a well-known example (Gordon, 1971).

In most developing countries, diarrhoeal diseases are a leading medical cause of death of infants and young children, along with respiratory diseases and malnutrition. The case fatality rate for episodes of childhood diarrhoea (excluding cholera) is, however, quite low. In healthy populations it is much less than 1 in 1,000 and even in the developing world is generally less than 1 per cent. More importantly, episodes of diarrhoea hinder the growth of the infant.

Thus, it is not so much the severity of the diarrhoeal diseases which is important, but rather their frequency. In fact, the frequency may be so high, with only brief periods between episodes, that it is often more practical to count the number of active cases at any point in time (prevalence) rather than to attempt to enumerate the number of episodes (incidence). Prevalence can range from 5 per cent to 25 per cent of children depending on season and other factors. In these circumstances, a strategy which can reduce the incidence of diarrhoea rather than one directed towards treatment of cases is evidently the more appropriate for reducing mortality. The latter is the usual medical approach. Incidence, however, can be substantially reduced with the application of a few hygienic principles and by using resources that are readily available in almost every village to reduce the level of contamination of food and water, at least for the vulnerable infant. Most mothers, even those with limited means, are capable of this provided they have the information and the motivation. Undoubtedly, this is one of the mechanisms by which mothers with even a few years of primary education can contribute to improving child survival. With only slightly more economic resources, the level of contamination could be substantially reduced by having safe water from a well with a pump, and installing wash basins, a toilet, and cement floors. By contrast, where fuel and water must be carried five or even ten kilometres daily, as occurs in many regions of Africa, the time, resources, and energy for preventive health measures are simply not available (White *et al.*, 1972).

3. Contamination of Skin/Fomites/Soil

These infectious agents enter the host through the skin, resulting in primary infections or infestations of the skin such as impetigo, abscesses, wound infection or scabies. For two parasitic infestations – hookworm and schistosomiasis – the larvae enter the skin through the eggs of the agent and are excreted in the faeces or urine.

Except for the special case of venereal diseases, the social determinants that operate through this intermediate variable are primarily those related to poverty. Poor basic hygiene such as rarely bathing or using soap, never washing or changing clothes or bedding, crowded living conditions, lack of water and sanitary facilities, indiscriminate defaecation and urination, are of great consequence. These diseases are rarely fatal, although they are among the most common conditions treated at any rural dispensary in a developing country. Prevention is hindered more by social and economic conditions than by technical constraints.

One particularly important disease in this group is tetanus of the newborn, which is contracted at the time of delivery when the umbilical stump is contaminated with tetanus spores from the soil. Because tetanus organisms are widely found in soil and in the intestinal tracts of humans and domestic animals, man is not the primary source of general environmental contamination (Bytchenko, 1966). However, in a rural setting where people are in close contact with animals and where manure is used in the fields, and in particular where cowdung is used to plaster the floor and walls of houses, and as a fuel, neonatal tetanus will be more prevalent. Prevention by immunizing childbearing women is technically feasible. However, in rural Bangladesh where mortality from neonatal tetanus is very high (up to 25 per thousand births), the majority of pregnant women refused to accept vaccine, even when it was taken to their home (Rahman *et al.*, 1981). Here again is a case of social synergy where the same traditions promoting a high risk to disease exposure (cowdung is traditionally used for fuel and constructing houses and almost all births are attended by untrained persons) are coupled with an unwillingness to accept modern technical innovation for disease prevention.

4. Vector Transmission

This group includes vector-borne diseases such as yellow fever, filariasis, river blindness, sleeping sickness, plague, typhus, and especially malaria. Environmental control of malaria represents one situation where a modern health technology can be applied involuntarily and has been found in small-scale studies to reduce infant mortality by 50 per cent in areas hyperendemic for *falciparum* malaria. At the national level, Gray (1974) has reported that roughly 25 per cent of the total decline of mortality in Sri Lanka between 1930-45 and 1946-60 could be attributed to the malaria control activities. Similar observations have been reported from Guyana, Mauritius and Venezuela (Gray, 1974:226-227).

In recent years national malaria eradication campaigns have received less emphasis, largely for political and economic reasons, although technical constraints have also played a role (Farid, 1980). This has led to a resurgence of malaria transmission in many areas, so far without a major mortality impact. For example, the revival of malaria in Sri Lanka in 1968-70 (over 1,000,000 cases were reported) had such a marginal effect on mortality in the affected areas that 'the increases and decreases are too small to be attributed with any certainty to a specific cause' (Meegama, 1981). The wider availability and more effective utilization of drug therapy has undoubtedly contributed to this attenuation of mortality, as was noted earlier in the Pare region of Tanzania (Matola and Magayuka, 1981).

Although PHC can help to lower mortality from the vector-borne diseases by encouraging the use of prophylactic medication and effective treatment at the periphery, their long-term control requires a high level of technical expertise coupled with a strong community involvement and sustained financial resources. Conversely, families may reduce the risk of infection from the intestinal and skin diseases with relatively simple means.

C. Availability of Nutrients

Each of the four classes of nutrients – calories, protein, vitamins and minerals – may show isolated deficiencies in different ecological settings, but for brevity, primary attention will be focused on protein-calorie-malnutrition (PCM). Any PHC programme based on the narrow technical or 'selective' approach requires that there be no absolute poverty or severe food shortage in the population. In many African countries, however, rapid population growth and political mismanagement, aggravated by weather conditions, have led to declines in per capita food production, and, in the more extreme cases, to starvation and famine. Even Kenya, which enjoyed political stability until 1982, has neglected food production to the extent that it moved from a food surplus to a food deficit nation in 1980, with very little possibility of reversing the situation in the next decade (Government of Kenya, 1981).

The mortality impact of gross food shortages in a subsistence level agrarian population can be substantial. The Bangladesh famine of 1974, for example, resulted in a 45 per cent rise in the crude death rate in the Matlab area (Chen, Chakraborty et al., 1981). Similarly, infant mortality in the estate population in Sri Lanka rose by 70-80 per cent following the food shortages of 1974 (Meegama, 1981). Not surprisingly, these crises do not affect all segments of the population equally, but are selectively much more severe among the landless poor, as reported by McCord (1975) in Bangladesh. Interestingly, in a further study of the same population, higher family income was found to be only associated with a better nutritional status among children of illiterate mothers (Bairagi, 1980).

Inequities in food availability are not limited to macro-economic factors; micro-economic and social factors are at least as important in most developing countries. Inequalities in the intrafamilial allocation of such resources as food, health care and education which impact directly on mortality levels in the population have been widely documented (Safilios-Rothschild, 1980; Engle, 1981). In general, women and children are the most disadvantaged groups. Thus in rural Bangladesh, discrimination against females in food allocation and health care may lead to post-neonatal and child mortality rates among females that are 20-50 per cent higher than for males (D'Souza and Chen, 1980; Chen et al., 1981).

Because of the critical role of the mother, particularly in the early months of life when breastmilk is fundamental to survival, her participation in work outside the home may have a significant impact on infant nutrition and mortality (Popkin, 1975). Indeed, Taylor et al. (1971) observed that in rural Punjab in India, medical and nutrition interventions were often ineffective because of the numerous competing claims on the overworked mother's time and attention, particularly in the harvest season (Taylor et al., 1971). A similar connection between women's seasonal agricultural activity and seasonal episodes of childhood malnutrition, diarrhoea and mortality has been documented in the Gambia (Rowland and McCallum, 1977; Rowland, 1979). Income earned by women is also of importance for child survival. For example, Kumar (1977) has demonstrated that in Kerala, whereas the more time a woman spent in outside employment was associated with poorer child nutrition, the increased income she earned was correlated with better child nutrition. Thus the relationahip between female labour force participation and infant mortality is not a straightforward one.

A mother's own nutritional status also directly affects infant survival through foetal nutrition. There are two facets of this: an intergenerational effect and the effects of diet during pregnancy. Mothers of short stature due to chronic childhood malnutrition are more likely to have 'small for date' newborns with a higher risk of infant death (Committee on Maternal Nutrition, 1970; Mata, 1978b). Regarding the second factor, numerous studies of developing societies have demonstrated that the level of calorie intake during pregnancy is associated with the birthweight of newborns and thus with mortality risks (Mata, 1978b; Lechtig et al., 1975; Roberts et al., 1982; Iyangar, 1974). Only about 5 per cent of newborns in developed countries have a low birthweight (under 2,500 grams), compared with 13 to 28 per cent as reported for many developing countries (Rosa and Turshen, 1970). In rural Guatemala, one project with good medical care revealed that the risk of death for babies weighing less than 2,500 grams at birth was four times higher compared with heavier babies born in the same community (Habicht et al., 1975).

These social and economic factors which operate through nutrient availability are the reason why direct PHC interventions may be relatively ineffective in many developing countries. The general ineffectiveness of food supplementation programmes in combating malnutrition is a well-known case (Beaton and Ghassemi, 1982). At the same time, one may also appreciate how maternal education and economic development can have such a profound impact on child mortality by improving food availability in the family and by transforming the social and economic dynamics within the household (Caldwell and McDonald, 1981).

D. Injuries

Accidents and injuries account for only a relatively small fraction of deaths in developing countries compared with malnutrition and infections. There are exceptions such as in societies where infanticide and child neglect – more often directed against females – is commonly practised to control family size or sex composition (Scrimshaw, 1978). Trauma related to childbirth can also be a significant cause of death. This risk can be greatly reduced by PHC programmes which assure that all pregnant mothers get qualified antenatal and delivery care. Perhaps the most important contribution of this intermediate variable to mortality is through the breakdown in host resistance that occurs from burns and cuts which then become sites for life-threatening infections.

E. Personal Disease Control Factors

Western-trained physicians commonly distinguish between preventive measures for the healthy and therapeutic measures for the sick. The first set of activities are largely delegated to the public sector, while reserving the second, more profitable activity for themselves. Unfortunately, this dichotomy is also evident in health care systems in most developing countries. A much more relevant distinction is between 'illness' and 'disease' as introduced by Fabrega (1972). Illness refers to the local cultural definition of a bodily condition, which then determines the choice of healing strategies by a given population. Disease refers to the biomedical definition as given by modern scientific medicine, and which has universal validity. While Western medicine incorporates much of universal scientific validity, it also includes many popular beliefs and folk practices of Western culture.

Two points of importance for the potential effectiveness of PHC strategies operating through these intermediate variables may be made here. The first relates to traditional health beliefs and choices of actions to be taken.[2] In traditional culture there is no dichotomy between preventive and therapeutic measures. In reality, prevention is usually accorded much higher priority. Every stage of life, and often almost every daily activity is accompanied by rituals and actions to assure health and welfare. Furthermore, life may be filled with all sorts of taboos, many related to diet, to avoid illnesses.

When an illness is recognized, therapy will be selected based on the presumed cause. In most traditional systems, the physical symptoms, unless for a well-recognized disease like smallpox, usually do not give a clue to the 'cause', and the choice of therapy – for example, sacrificing to a certain spirit – will be dictated by the subsequent course of the illness. Often this trial and error approach will involve several different traditional measures successively and even simultaneously, including Western medicine when available. But, because the Western curative system is alien to the local culture, there will be underutilization of modern facilities except by the educated (Westernized) clients. As a consequence, the mortality gap between (Western) educated and traditionally educated families widens since Western medicine offers not only some very effective preventive and therapeutic technologies, but also the scientific conception of disease causation.

The effectiveness of a PHC programme is thus very much dependent upon the degree to which the population accepts the scientific basis of disease causation. The exceptions are technologies which can be applied involuntarily (malaria spraying), or by force and compulsion (smallpox vaccination), or which are automatically accepted because of other perceived social benefits (a water system).

---

[2]See various articles in Kleinman et al., 1975.

The second point concerns the distinction between the 'clinical effectiveness' of modern technologies in preventing diseases and deaths, and the 'demographic effectiveness' of these measures at a population level in terms of saving lives. Western medicine may offer very effective therapies like penicillin that are almost 100 per cent effective in curing specific diseases, yet their introduction in an underdeveloped society may have little or no effect on mortality. The classical example of a 'technological misfit' between Western concepts of medical care and health realities in the Third World was the Many Farms project among Navahos in the 1950s (McDermott, 1966). More recent examples are to be found in Gambia and Guatemala (Rowland and McCallum, 1977; Mata, 1978a).

Even vaccines which may be almost 100 per cent effective for a specific disease are unlikely to exert a demographic impact which is proportional to the contribution of that disease to all 'causes' of death (Rohde, 1982). Measles is a good example. Measles is very rarely fatal in a well-nourished population, with a case fatality rate of about 0.03 per cent. In the Western world, measles was virtually eliminated well before vaccine became available, through improved nutrition which reduced the severity without changing the incidence of the disease (McKinlay and McKinlay, 1977).

In many developing countries, particularly in Africa, the case fatality rate for measles ranges from 5 to 25 per cent, with the disease claiming 10 per cent or more of all childhood deaths (Morley, 1973). However, the introduction of the measles vaccine will not automatically reduce childhood deaths by 10 per cent because of three factors related to social synergy and bilogical synergy. First, unless immunization is compulsory and can be enforced, the self-selection of acceptors means that the most disadvantaged segment of the population which is at highest risk of death will remain unimmunized. Secondly, even when a child is successfully immunized, the protection is only against one specific agent. The child remains at risk for all other causes of death and, all other things being equal, a certain proportion will die from these 'competing' causes. Thus the eradication of smallpox in Brazil, Nigeria and India resulted in a gain in life expectancy at birth ranging from 0.09 to 0.81 years (Namfua et al., 1978).

However, those children whose deaths might be prevented by measles vaccine are at risk of dying, not because of the severity of measles per se, but because their nutritional status is so poor that they are more likely to die of any infectious disease. Thus preventing a measles death among these children may not necessarily save a life, but only change the biological cause of death (Chen, Chakraborty et al., 1981).

This is not to suggest that preventive and curative technical interventions by PHC programmes are ineffective. Indeed, a recent analysis of the results of ten PHC projects in different cultural settings suggests that direct interventions can reduce infant and child mortality by one-third to one-half (Gwatkin et al., 1980b). What distinguished the more successful projects was their lesser reliance on hospital-based, high technology medical services in favour of approaches more appropriate to village conditions. In particular, various nutrition strategies were implemented which were designed to overcome existing social and cultural practices promoting malnutrition. A second factor associated with the more successful projects was 'the unusual effectiveness with which the programmes were organized, administered and directed' (Gwatkin et al., 1980b:22). The primary determinants of programme success, therefore, would appear to be the effectiveness of the project in introducing relevant social change in village settings rather than the biological effectiveness of the technologies themselves. Rather, these technologies operate as intermediate variables in lowering mortality.

CONCLUSION

For many years there has been a debate about the relative contribution of modern scientific medicine versus social and economic development in contributing to mortality decline (McKeown, 1976, 1978; Preston, 1980). The extremely rapid decline in mortality in developing countries this century, and particularly after World War II, suggests that the introduction of medical technology in the absence of much social change was a key factor (Davis, 1956; Arriaga and Davis, 1969). However, the recent stagnation of mortality decline at relatively high levels has promoted a re-examination of this thesis (Mosley, 1979; Gwatkin, 1980). The resolution of this debate is obviously critical for the PHC strategy.

The conceptual model presented in this paper should help to better understand the issue. Fifteen intermediate variables that directly influence the biological risk of morbidity and mortality are identified. The utility of the framework is that it not only indicates how various patterns of social behaviour and biomedical interventions affect levels of infant and child mortality, but it also defines indicators to assess the operation of these variables.

A key element in this analytical model is the concept of social synergy: that is, how a single social determinant, such as women's education, can operate to influence the risk of death through several intermediate variables simultaneously. Consequently, social changes, particularly those that incorporate the scientific concept of disease causation, may be expected to produce very marked improvements in child survival. The conceptual approach also clarifies why many modern medicine technologies such as antibiotics and vaccines which are highly effective in a clinical setting may be relatively ineffective at a population level. These disease-specific technologies eliminate only one of a multiplicity of conditions that operate simultaneously and synergistically to influence the risk of death. Only in cases where a specific disease has a high prevalence and a high fatality among otherwise healthy persons, will a disease-specific intervention (for example, maternal immunization to prevent neonatal tetanus, malaria control programmes) have a noticeable demographic impact.

One may also contrast the factors affecting the historical decline in infant and child mortality in developed countries with the current strategies being advocated in PHC programmes for developing countries. Before disease-specific technologies were available for conditions such as measles and diarrhoeal disease, mortality control was achieved primarily by social changes relating to improved nutrition and family hygiene which led to greater host resistance. The effect was to reduce the incidence of diarrhoeal diseases and reduce the severity of measles. The current technologic approach to PHC concentrates on measles immunization and oral rehydration for diarrhoeal diseases. This is intended to reduce the severity of diarrhoea, leaving the incidence unchanged, and to reduce the incidence of measles. However, measles mortality is much more a consequence of the severity of the disease in the presence of malnutrition rather than incidence. Similarly, diarrhoea kills primarily because of its frequent recurrence leading to debilitating malnutrition. Hence the technologic approach may have limited effectiveness in isolation from more fundamental social changes.

China is a classical example of the effective application of the PHC strategy on a national scale through a holistic or 'causal web' approach. According to Worth, '... their apparent success in these battles can largely be attributed to their pattern of attacking simultaneously on several fronts, usually in a labour intensive pattern, without a great deal of prior attention being paid to which aspect of the attack will be most effective' (Worth, 1975). Such disease control programmes were based on modern scientific information; however, the key element to their success was mass mobilization, health education, and 'social engineering'.

For non-communist developing countries, there is a critical need for a scientific basis to determine the most cost-effective set of specific interventions given the limited resources for PHC programmes (Evans *et al.*, 1981). Perhaps the most ambitious field experiment to date to test the Western model of PHC is the Lampang Province Health Development Project (1981) designed to cover 600,000 people in Northern Thailand between 1974 and 1981. This project, supported with a major increment in financial resources and the guidance of leading health professionals from Thailand and abroad, was forced to conclude after seven years that in terms of demographic impact 'it appears difficult to discern health status changes that were not already underway when the Project began and to differentiate between changes in health status in the Project areas that are different from changes in the control areas' (p.137). Broadly, the reason given for lack of a discernible impact in spite of such innovations as the recruitment and training of over 6,000 additional PHC workers to deliver basic services was that the 'system has not sufficiently emphasized all areas where needs may be greatest – nutrition, child health, water supply and sanitation. The modified system tends to reemphasize medical care, which ultimately has less influence on health status' (p.98). Their overall conclusion, reflecting the thesis of the chapter, was that 'The results compel health workers to recognize that their efforts are only part of the range of social and economic factors that interplay to affect the population's health' (p.138).

The results of a multiple regression analysis of data from a sample of married couples in Chiang Mai and Chiang Rai provinces, also in Northern Thailand, confirm these findings (Frenzen and Hogan, 1982). Infant survival was affected by demographic factors such as age, parity, birth intervals, length of gestation and a history of pregnancy loss, as well as by social factors such as mother's education, father's occupation, and place of residence. Contact with a health professional showed an independent effect on child survival. Similarly, a study contrasting mortality levels in Kerala and West Bengal observed that while both states have similar levels of medical facilities, it is the differential use of the facilities that contributes to the difference in life expectancy between the two areas (Nag, 1982). This in turn was attributed less to differences in economic development than to different social development including political institutions that promote social services, education, health services and transportation, as well as encouraging awareness about the need and right to use these facilities.

The two studies in Thailand cited above exemplify the current difficulties with PHC. An enormously ambitious and costly medical intervention research project was undertaken by biomedical scientists with little attention to, and virtually no research on, the social determinants of child survival. At the same time, social scientists were studying the social determinants of infant mortality in other localities without paying adequate attention to the biological intermediate variables that influence disease. Obviously, a multidisciplinary approach is needed to develop the sound knowledge base which is a prerequisite for healthy policy and health programmes.

Elaborate strategies to study the interaction of social determinants with biological intermediate variables have already been established for fertility (Bongaarts, 1978). Admittedly, the analytical framework is much simpler for fertility than for mortality inasmuch as all intermediate variables relate to a single biological event, the initiation of pregnancy, with a known probability of successful outcome. Mortality research requires more complex models since multiple biological processes are involved with different, and in some cases, variable, probabilities of death. The simple conceptual model presented here has attempted to define some key variables and specify some aspects of their operation. Hopefully, it will prove a useful tool to stimulate more critical research into the determinants of child mortality that will lead to more rational health programmes in the future.

SUMMARY

The strategy for primary health care defined at the Alma Ata Conference involved five basic aspects: community participation, strategy adapted to the local context, multisectoral approach, health programmes largely operated by paramedical personnel, and use of simple technologies. A few years later, it now seems that health programmes are retaining only the last two objectives as the others seem in practice to have been abandoned.

An analysis of recent trends in infant and child mortality in Kenya reveals that the decline observed over the past 20 years can be largely attributed to progress in the field of female education (Table 1). Regional variations in child mortality are strongly correlated with the income level of household (Table 2 and Figure 2). Under these conditions, medical techniques are no more than an intermediate variable, not a primary determinant of child mortality.

To enable a better definition of primary health care strategy, a general conceptual model of the factors influencing infant and child mortality is proposed (Figure 3).

The key to this model is the notion of social synergy: a single social determinant can influence the risk of death by operating independently on several intermediate variables, which amplifies its action. Fifteen biological intermediate variables through which the socio-economic determinants operate are classified into five categories: maternal fertility factors, environmental contamination with infectious agents, availability of nutrients to the foetus and infant, injuries, and personal disease control factors. The ways in which each variable acts upon morbidity and mortality and the socio-economic factors which operate through it are systematically examined.

The success of primary health care programmes calls for a better knowledge of the determinants of infant and child mortality. The development of models such as the one presented here should throw light on the sometimes paradoxical results obtained from previous health programmes.

REFERENCES

Ahluwalia, R. and Mechen, B. (1980), *Traditional Medicine in Zaire: Present and Potential Contribution to Health Services*, IDRC, Ottawa.

Akpovi, S.U., Johnson, D.C., and Brieger, W.R. (1982), 'Guinea worm control: testing the efficacy of health education in primary care', *International Journal of Health Education*, 25:229-237.

Anker, R. and Knowles, J.C. (1977), *An Empirical Analysis of Mortality Differentials in Kenya at the Macro and Micro Level*, Population and Employment Working Paper No. 60, International Labour Office, Geneva.

Arriaga, E. and Davis, K. (1969), 'The patterns of mortality change in Latin America', *Demography*, 6:223-242.

Assad, M. and Katsha, S. (1981), 'Villagers' participation in formal and informal health services in an Egyptian delta village', *Regional Paper*, Population Council, Arab Republic of Egypt.

Bairagi, R. (1980), 'Is income the only constraint on child nutrition in rural Bangladesh?', *World Health Bulletin*, 58:767-772.

Bairagi, R. (1982), 'On the best cutoff point for nutritional monitoring', *American Journal of Clinical Nutrition*, 35:769-770.

Barkan, J.D. (1979), 'Comparing politics and public policy in Kenya and Tanzania', in Barkan and Okumu, 1979, pp. 16-19.

Barkan, J.D. and Okumu, J.J. (eds) (1979), *Politics and Public Policy in Kenya and Tanzania*, Heinemann Educational Books, Nairobi.

Barnum, H., Barlow, A., Fajardo, L. and Pradilla, A. (1980), *A Resource Allocation Model for Child Survival*, Oelgeschlager, Gunn & Hain, Cambridge, Mass.

Beaton, G.H. and Ghassemi, H. (1982), 'Supplementary feeding programmes for young children in developing countries', *American Journal of Clinical Nutrition*, 35(Supplement):864-916.

Bidwell, E.S. (1980), 'Let's not forget the traditional healers', *World Health Forum*, 1:161-162.

Black, R.E., Brown, K.H., Becker, S., Alim, A.R.M.A. and Merson, M.H. (1982), 'Contamination of weaning foods and transmission of enterotoxigenic *E.coli* diarrhoea in children in rural Bangladesh', *Transactions of the Royal Society of Tropical Medicine*, 76:259-264.

Bongaarts, J. (1978), 'A framework for analyzing the determinants of fertility', *Population and Development Review*, 4:105-132.

Bytchenko, B. (1966), 'Geographical distribution of tetanus in the world, 1951-60: a review of the problem', *World Health Bulletin*, 34:71-104.

Caldwell, J.C. (1979), 'Education as a factor in mortality decline: an examination of Nigerian data', in *Proceedings of the Meeting on Socio-economic Determinants and Consequences of Mortality*, U.N., New York, and WHO, Geneva.

Caldwell, J.C. and McDonald, P. (1981), 'Influence of maternal education on infant and child mortality – levels and causes', in IUSSP, 1981, pp.79-96.

Central Bureau of Statistics (1969), *Population Census, Vol.4: Analytical Report*, Ministry of Finance and Planning, Government of Kenya.

Central Bureau of Statistics (1979a), *Statistical Abstract*, Table 105, Government of Kenya.

Central Bureau of Statistics (1979b), 'The implications of Kenya's high rate of population growth', *Social Perspectives*, 4.

Central Bureau of Statistics, Ministry of Economic Planning and Development (1980a), *Economic Survey 1980*, pp.1-6.

Central Bureau of Statistics (1980b), *Kenya Fertility Survey, 1977-78: First Report*, Ministry of Economic Planning and Finance, Nairobi.

Central Bureau of Statistics (1980c), *Economic Survey*, Government of Kenya.

Chen, L.C. (1981), 'Child survival: levels, trends and determinants', in *Determinants of Fertility in Developing Countries: A Summary of Knowledge*, National Academy of Sciences, Washington, D.C.

Chen, L.C., Chakraborty, J., Sadar, A.M., and Yunus, M. (1981), 'Estimating and partitioning the mortality impact of several modern medical technologies in basic health services', in IUSSP, 1981, pp.113-142.

Chen, L.C., Chowdhury, A.K.M.A. and Huffman, S.L. (1980), 'Anthropometric assessment of energy-protein malnutrition and subsequent risk of mortality among preschool aged children', *American Journal of Clinical Nutrition*, 33:1836-1845.

Chen, L.C., Huq, E. and D'Souza, S. (1981), 'Sex bias in family allocation of food and health care in rural Bangladesh', *Population and Development Review*, 7:55-70, (Chapter 8 of this book).

Choffat, F. (1980), 'Fracture treatment by Moroccan bone setters', *World Health Forum*, 1:181-182.

Chowdhury, A.O. (1981), 'Gonoshasthaya Kendra (Peoples Health Center)', *Link*, 1:3-5.

Cole, T.J. and Parkin, J.M. (1977), 'Infection and its effect on the growth of young children: a comparison of The Gambia and Uganda', *Transactions of the Royal Society of Medicine and Hygiene*, 71:196-198.

Committee on Maternal Nutrition (1970), *Maternal Nutrition and the Course of Pregnancy*, National Academy of Sciences, Washington, D.C.

D'Souza, S. and Chen, L. (1980), 'Sex differentials in mortality in rural Bangladesh', *Population and Development Review*, 6:257-270.

Davis, K. (1956), 'The amazing decline of mortality in underdeveloped areas', *American Economic Review*, 46:305-318.

El Dareer, A. (1981), 'An epidemiological study of female circumcision in Sudan', Thesis, Department of Community Medicine, University of Khartoum.

Engle, P.L. (1981), 'Maternal care, maternal substitutes, and children's welfare in the developed and developing countries', paper prepared for the International Center for Research on Women: Policy Round Table, Washington, D.C., 10 December.

Evans, J., Hall, K.L. and Warford, J. (1981), 'Shattuck Lecture – health care in the developing world: problems of scarcity and choice', *New England Journal of Medicine*, 305:1117-1127.

Fabrega, H. (1972), 'Medical anthropology', in B. Siegel (ed.), *Biennial Review of Anthropology*, Stanford University Press, Stanford, pp. 167-229.

Family Health Institute (1978), *A Working Paper on Health Services Development in Kenya: Issues, Analyses and Recommendations*, Washington, D.C.

Farid, M.A. (1980), 'The malaria programme – from euphoria to anarchy', *World Health Forum*, 1:8-21.

Federici, J. and Terrenato, L. (1983), 'Biological determinants of early life mortality', in Preston, 1983, pp.331-358.

Frenzen, P.D. and Hogan, D. (1982), 'The impact of class, education and health care on infant mortality in a developing society: the case of rural Thailand', *Demography*, 19:391-408.

Gaisie, S.K. (1979), 'Some aspects of socioeconomic determinants of mortality in tropical Africa', in *Proceedings of the Meeting on Socio-economic Determinants and Consequences of Mortality*, U.N., New York, and WHO, Geneva.

Gish, O. (1982), 'Appropriate choice in health technology', *Tropical Doctor*, 12:223-227.

Gordon, J.E. (1971), 'Diarrhoeal disease of early childhood – worldwide scope of the problem', *Annals of the New York Academy of Science*, 176:9-15.

Government of Kenya (1981), 'National food plan', *Sessional Paper No 4*.

Government of Kenya, *Development plan 1979-1983*, P.l., p.145.

Gray, R.H. (1974), 'The decline of mortality in Ceylon and the demographic effects of malaria control', *Population Studies*, 28,2:205-229.

Grosse, R.N. (1980), 'Interrelation between health and population: observation derived from field experiences', *Social Science and Medicine*, 14c:99-120.

Gwatkin, D.R. (1980), 'Indication of change in developing country mortality trends: the end of an era?', *Population and Development Review*, 6:615-644.

Gwatkin, D.R., Wilcox, J.R., and Wray, J.D. (1980a) 'The policy implications of field experiments in primary health and nutrition care', *Social Science and Medicine*, 14c:121-128.

Gwatkin, D.R., Wilcox, J.R., and Wray, J.D. (1980b), *Can Health and Nutrition Interventions Make a Difference?*, Overseas Development Council, Washington, D.C.

Habicht, J.P., Lechtig, A., Yarbrough, C., and Klein, R.E. (1975), 'Maternal nutrition, birth weight, and infant mortality', in *Size at Birth*, CIBA Foundation Symposium 27 (New Series), Elsevier – Excerpta Medica, Amsterdam.

Haliman, A. (1981), 'Banjarnegara health development program and its impact on disadvantaged groups', paper presented at ESCAP Workshop on Integrated Rural Development Projects, 27-30 October.

Hamamsy, L. (ed.) (1973), *The Daya of Egypt: Survival in a Modernizing Society*, Caltech Population Program Occasional Papers, Series 1, No. 8, Pasadena.

Hickman, G.M., Dickens, W.H.G. and Woods, E. (1973), *The Lands and People of East Africa*, Longman and Harlow, London.

Hill, K. and Trussell, J. (1977), 'Further developments in indirect mortality estimation', *Population Studies*, 31:313-334.

International Union for the Scientific Study of Population (IUSSP) (1981), *International Population Conference, Manila, 1981*, Vol.2, IUSSP, Liège.

Iyangar, L. (1974), 'Influence of diet on the outcome of pregnancy in Indian women', in *Proceedings of the 9th International Conference of Nutrition, Mexico, 1972*, Karger, Basel, pp.48-53.

Kapur, R.L. (1980), 'Traditional healers in mental health care in India', *World Health Forum*, 1:182-184.

Khan, M.U. (1982), 'Interruption of Shigellosis by hand washing', *Transactions of the Royal Society of Tropical Medicine and Hygiene*, 76:164-168.

Kibet, M. (1982), 'District level mortality differentials in Kenya based on 1979 census data', Thesis, Population Studies and Research Institute, University of Nairobi.

Kielmann, A.A. and McCord, C. (1978), 'Weight for age as an index of risk of death in children', *Lancet*, 1:1247-1250.

Kleinman, A., Kunstadter, P., Alexander, E.P. and Cole, J.L. (eds.) (1975), *Medicine in Chinese Cultures: Comparative Studies of Health Care in Chinese and Other Societies*, Fogerty International Center, US Government Printing Office, Washington, D.C.

Kochar, V., Marwah, S.M. and Udupa, K.N. (1977), 'Strengthening the folk health system: proposed link between the health needs of the rural population and limitation of the formal health system in remote rural areas', in *Alternative Approaches to Health Care*, Indian Council for Medical Research, New Delhi.

Kumar, S.K. (1977), 'Composition of economic constraints in child nutrition: impact of maternal incomes and employment in low income households', Thesis, Cornell University.

Lampang Province Health Development Project (1981), *Summary Final Report of the Lampang Health Development Project*, Volume 1, Ministry of Public Health, Thailand.

Lechtig, A., Habicht, J.P., Delgado, H., Klein, R.E., Yarbrough, C. and Martorell, R. (1975), 'Effect of food supplementation during pregnancy on birthweight', *Pediatrics*, 56:508-520.

Malcolm, L.A. (1974), 'Ecological factors relating to child growth and nutritional status', in F. Falkner and A.F. Roche (eds.), *Nutrition and Malnutrition: Identification and Measurement*, Plenum Press, New York, London.

Marera, R.A., Levine, A. and Ray, D.K. (1980), '"Crash" health manpower planning: a method for developing countries', *World Health Forum*, 1:34-44.

Mata, L. (1978a), *The Children of Santa Maria Cauque: A Prospective Field Study of Health and Growth*, MIT Press, Cambridge, Mass.

Mata, L. (1978b), 'Maternal factors and fetal growth', in Committee on Maternal Nutrition, *Maternal Nutrition and the Course of Pregnancy*, National Academy of Sciences, Washington, D.C.

Matola, Y.A. and Magayuka, S.A. (1981), 'Malaria in the Para area of Tanzania. V: Malaria 20 years after the end of residual insecticide spraying', *Transactions of the Royal Society of Tropical Medicine and Hygiene*, 75:811-813.

McCord, C. (1975), 'Campanigong Health Project', unpublished report.

McDermott, W. (1966), 'Modern medicine and the demographic disease pattern of overly traditional societies: a technological misfit', *Journal of Medical Education*, 41:138-162.

McKeown, T. (1976), *The Modern Rise of Population*, Arnold, London.

McKeown, T. (1978), 'Fertility, mortality and causes of death: an examination of issues related to the modern rise of population', *Population Studies*, 32:535-543.

McKinlay, J.B. and McKinlay, S.M. (1977), 'The questionable contribution of medical measures to the decline of mortality in the United States in the twentieth century', *Milbank Memorial Fund Quarterly*, 55:405-428.

Meegama, S.A. (1981), 'The decline in mortality in Sri Lanka in historical perspective', in IUSSP, 1981, pp.143-164.

Migot-Adholla, S.E. (1979), 'Rural development policy and equality', in Barkan and Okumu, 1979, pp.154-178.

Montoya-Aquilar, C. (1977), 'Health goals and political will', *WHO Chronicle*, 30:441.

Morley, D. (1973), *Paediatric Priorities in the Developing World*, Butterworth, London.

Mosley, W.H. (1979), 'Health, nutrition and mortality in Bangladesh', *Research in Human Capital and Development*, 1:77-94.

Mosley, W.H. (1980), 'Social determinants of infant and child mortality: some considerations for an analytical framework', discussion paper for Population Council Conference on Health and Mortality in Infancy and Early Childhood, Cairo, 18-20 May.

Mosley, W.H. (1983), 'Biological contamination of the environment', in S.H. Preston (ed.), *Biological and Social Aspects of Mortality and the Length of Life*, Ordina Editions, Liège, pp.39-68.

Mott, F.L. (1982), 'Infant mortality in Kenya: evidence from the Kenya fertility survey', World Fertility Survey, *Scientific Reports*, No. 32, WFS, London.

Muwonge, W. (1980), 'Urban policy and patterns of low-income settlement in Nairobi, Kenya', *Population and Development Review*, 6:595-614.

Nadim, W.El M. (1980), *Rural Health Care in Egypt*, IDRC, Ottawa.

Nag, M. (1982), 'Impact of social development and economic development on mortality: a comparative study of Kerala and West Bengal', *Working Paper* No. 78, Population Council, New York.

Namfua, P., Kim, Y.K. and Mosley, W.H. (1978), 'An estimation of the impact of smallpox eradication on the expectation of life in selected less developed countries', *World Health Statistics Quarterly*, 31:110-119.

Nyamwanga, F. (1982), 'Correlates of child mortality differentials in the Nairobi metropolitan area', Thesis, Population Studies and Research Institute, University of Nairobi.

Parker, R.L. (1982), 'Selected health components of community-based distribution programs', paper prepared for Workshop on Family Planning and Health Components in Community-based Distribution Projects, Charlottesville, 12-14 January.

Parkin, J.M. (1975), 'A longitudinal study of village children in Uganda: pattern of illness during the second year of life', in R. Owar, V.L. Ongom and B.G. Keraja (eds), *The Child in the African Environment*, East African Literature Bureau, Nairobi, pp.193-195.

Popkin, B.M. (1975), 'Income, time, the working mother and child nutrition', *Discussion Paper*, No. 75-9, Institute of Economic Development and Research, University of the Philippines.

Population Reference Bureau (1980), *World Population Data Sheet*, Washington, D.C.

Preston, S.H. (1980), 'Causes and consequences of mortality declines in less developed countries during the twentieth century', in A. Easterlin (ed.), *Population and Economic Change in Developing Countries*, University of Chicago Press, Chicago, pp.289-360.

Preston, S.H. (ed.), (1983), *Biological and Social Aspects of Mortality and the Length of Life*, Ordina, Liège.

Pringle, G. (1969), 'Experimental malaria control and demography in a rural East African community: a retrospect', *Transactions of the Royal Society of Tropical Medicine and Hygiene*, 63:S2-S18.

Puffer, R.R. and Serrano, C.V. (1973), *Patterns of Mortality in Childhood*, PAHO, Washington, D.C.

Puffer, R.R. and Serrano, C.V. (1975), *Birthweight, Maternal Age and Birth Order: Three Important Determinants in Infant Mortality,* Scientific Publication, No. 294. PAHO, Washington, D.C.

Rahman, M. *et al.* (1981), *Factors Related to Acceptance of Tetanus Toxoid Immunization among Pregnant Women in a Maternal-Child Health Programme in Rural Bangladesh,* Scientific Report No. 43, ICDDR,B, Dakha.

Republic of Kenya (1981), *Status of Health 1979*, Ministry of Health, Draft Report.

Rienks, A. and Iskandar, P. (1981), 'Primary and indigenous health care in rural central Java: a comparison of process and contents', *Hedera Report* No. 4, Faculty of Medicine, Gadjah Mada University, Yogyakarta.

Roberts, S.B., Paul, A.A., Cole, T.J. and Whitehead, R.G. (1982), 'Seasonal changes in activity, birth weight, and lactational performance in rural Gambian women', *Transactions of the Royal Society of Tropical Medicine and Hygiene*, 76:668-678.

Rohde, J. (1982), 'Why the other half dies: the science and politics of child mortality in the Third World', Leonard Parsons Lecture, University of Birmingham, (mimeograph).

Rohde, J. and Allman, J. (1981), 'Infant mortality in relation to the level of fertility control practice in developing countries', in IUSSP, 1981, pp.97-112.

Ronaghy, H.A. and Solter, S. (1974), 'Is the Chinese "Barefoot Doctor" exportable to Iran?', *Lancet*, 1:1331-1333.

Rosa, F.W. and Turshen, M. (1970), 'Fetal nutrition', *World Health Bulletin*, 43:785-795.

Rowland, M.G.M. (1979), 'Dietary and environmental factors in child mortality in the Gambia and Uganda', paper presented at Conference on the Medical Aspects of Demography, Peterhouse, Cambridge, 17-18 September.

Rowland, M.G.M. and McCallum, J.P.K. (1977), 'Malnutrition and gastroenteritis in The Gambia', *Transactions of the Royal Society of Tropical Medicine and Hygiene*, 71:199-203.

Safilios-Rothschild, C. (1980), 'The role of the family: a neglected aspect of poverty', in *Implementing Programs of Human Development*, World Bank Staff Working Paper, No. 403, World Bank, Washington, D.C.

Scrimshaw, N.S., Taylor, C.F. and Gordon, J.E. (1968), *Interaction of Nutrition and Infection*, Monograph Series No. 28, WHO, Geneva.

Scrimshaw, S.C.M. (1978), 'Infant mortality and behavior in the regulation of family size', *Population and Development Review*, 4:383-404.

Senga, W.M., Faruqee, R. and Ateng, B.A. (1980), *Population Growth and Agricultural Development in Kenya*, Occasional Paper No. 40, Institute for Development Studies, University of Nairobi.

Solimano, G.R. and Vine, M. (1983), 'Malnutrition, infection and infant mortality', in Preston, 1983, pp.83-112.

Sommer, A. and Loewenstein, M.S. (1975), 'Nutritional status and mortality: a prospective validation of the QUAC stick', *American Journal of Clinical Nutrition*, 28:287-292.

Taylor, C.E. (1982), 'Experiences from the worldwide primary health care movement relevant to Indonesia', Paper given at Seminar on Health for All by the Year 2000, University of Indonesia, Jakarta.

Taylor, C.E. *et al.* (1971), 'Malnutrition, infection, growth and development: the Narangwal experience', Department of International Health, Johns Hopkins University, Baltimore (mimeograph).

United Nations Economic Commission for Africa (1979), 'Mortality differentials and their correlates in Africa', in *Proceedings of the Meeting on Socio-economic Determinants and Consequences of Mortality*, U.N., New York, and WHO, Geneva, pp.208-235.

University of Ghana and UCLA (1979), *The Danfa Comprehensive Rural Health and Family Planning Project, Ghana, Final Report*, University of Ghana Medical School, Accra and UCLA School of Public Health, Los Angeles.

Unschuld, P.U. (1975), 'Medico-cultural conflicts in an Asian setting: an explanatory theory', *Social Science and Medicine*, 9:303-312.

Vogel, L.C. *et al.* (1974), *Health and Disease in Kenya*, East African Literature Bureau, Nairobi.

Walsh, J.A. and Warren, K.S. (1980), 'Selective primary health care: an interim strategy for disease control in developing countries', *Social Science and Medicine*, 14c:145-163.

Weiss, E. (1982), 'The Calabar Rural Maternal and Child Health – Family Planning Project: the evaluation and research component', *Working Paper* No. 16, Population Council, New York.

Were, M.K. (1979), 'People's participation in their health care', Department of Community Health, Faculty of Medicine, University of Nairobi.

White, G.F., Bradley, D.J. and White, A.U. (1972), *Drawers of Water: Domestic Water Use in East Africa*, University of Chicago Press, Chicago.

World Bank (1980), 'Policies of developing countries', in *Health Sector Policy Paper*, Washington, D.C.

World Bank (1981), *World Development Report 1981*, Washington, D.C.

World Health Organization (1978), *The Promotion and Development of Traditional Medicine*, Technical Report Series No. 662, WHO, Geneva.

World Health Organization and UNICEF (1978), *Alma Ata 1978: Primary Health Care*, WHO, Geneva.

Worth, R.M. (1975), 'The impact of new health programs on disease control and illness patterns in China', in *Medicine in Chinese Cultures*, Fogerty International Center, US Government Printing Office, Washington, D.C., pp.477-485.

Wright, S. (1982), 'Kenya: what went wrong with the picture of success', *South: The Third World Magazine*, 26:33-38.

APPENDIX I

WHAT WE KNOW ABOUT HEALTH TRANSITION: THE PROCEEDINGS OF AN INTERNATIONAL WORKSHOP, CANBERRA, MAY 1989.

Edited by

John Caldwell, Sally Findley, Pat Caldwell, Daphne Broers-Freeman and Wendy Cosford

Contents

CHAPTER 3.
Johansson, Sheila R.
(University of California
at Berkeley)

Cultural software, institu-
ional hardware and health
information processing in
social systems.

CHAPTER 4.
Potter, Joseph
(Harvard School of Public Health)

Parallels between the health
transition and the fertility
transition.

CHAPTER 5.
Kunitz, Stephen
(University of Rochester Medical
Center)

The value of particularism in
the study of the cultural,
social, and behavioural determinants of mortality.

B. HISTORICAL EXPERIENCE OF THE WEST

CHAPTER 6.
Woods, Robert
(University of Liverpool)

The role of public health
initiatives in the nineteenth
century mortality decline.

CHAPTER 7.
Ewbank, Douglas
and Sam Preston
(University of Pennsylvania)

Personal health behaviour and
the decline in infant and
child mortality: the United States,
1900-1930.

CHAPTER 9.
van de Walle, Etienne and
Francine van de Walle
(University of Pennsylvania)

The private and the public child.

CHAPTER 10.
Riley, James
(Indiana University)

Long-term morbidity and mortality
trends: inverse health transitions.

C. HEALTH TRENDS IN THE DEVELOPING WORLD

CHAPTER 11.
Palloni, Alberto
(University of Wisconsin)

Timing and speed of the decline
in infant mortality in Latin
America, 1900-1985.

CHAPTER 12.
Kunstadter, Peter and Sally
Kunstadter (San Francisco
Medical Center)

Health transitions in Thailand.

CHAPTER 13.
Cantrelle, Pierre and Thérèse
Locoh (ISD, Paris)

Social and cultural factors related
to health in West Africa.

CHAPTER 14.
Zimmet, Paul, S. Serjeantson,
G. Dowse and C. Finch
(WHO Centre on the Epidemiology
of Diabetes, Melbourne)

Killed by the 'good life': the
chronic disease epidemic – adverse
effects of lifestyle change in
developing Pacific nations.

D. SOCIO-POLITICAL ELEMENTS OF HEALTH

CHAPTER 15.
Millard, Ann V. (Michigan
State University)

Agricultural development and
malnutrition: a causal model
of child mortality.

CHAPTER 16.
Findley, Sally E.
(Rockefeller Foundation)

Social reflections of changing
morbidity patterns in the
health transition.

CHAPTER 17.
Behrman, Jere R. and Anil B.
Deolalikar (University of
Pennsylvania)

Health, nutrition and macro
economic adjustment with a
human face: the analytical
basis for the UNICEF advocacy
and a case comparison.

CHAPTER 18.
Nag, Moni
(Population Council)

Political awareness as a factor in
accessibility of health
services: a case study of
rural Kerala and West Bengal.

CHAPTER 19.
Gray, Alan
(ANU)

Australian Aboriginal families
and the health care system.

E. RELATIONSHIP BETWEEN EDUCATION AND HEALTH-RELATED
BEHAVIOUR

CHAPTER 20.
Cleland, John (London School of
Hygiene and Tropical Medicine)

Maternal education and child
survival: further evidence and
explanations.

CHAPTER 21.
LeVine, Robert and Suzanne
Dixon (Harvard University)

Education-health care linkages in
East Africa.

CHAPTER 22.
Lindenbaum, Shirley (New School
for Social Research, New York)

Maternal education and health care
processes in Bangladesh: the
health and hygiene of the
middle classes.

CHAPTER 23.
Das Gupta, Monica
(NCAER, Delhi)

Death clustering, maternal
education and the determinants of
child mortality in rural Punjab,
India.

CHAPTER 24.
Bhuiya, Abbas, Kim Streatfield
and Paul Meyer
(ANU)

Mothers' hygienic awareness,
behaviour, and knowledge of major
childhood diseases in Matlab,
Bangladesh.

CHAPTER 25.
Ewan, Christine
(University of Wollongong)

Lay knowledge and beliefs about
heart disease and risk.

F. CULTURAL ATTITUDES TO SICKNESS AND HEALTH – A CASE STUDY OF INDONESIA

CHAPTER 26.
Hull, Terence H.
(ANU)

Roots of primary health care
institutions in Indonesia.

CHAPTER 27.
Widyantoro, Ninuk and
Sarsanto W. Sarwano
(Indonesian Planned Parenthood
Assoc.)

Cultural dimensions of an
Indonesian family planning
service.

CHAPTER 28.
Sarlito Wirawan Sarwono
(University of Indonesia)

Social psychological aspects
of health and health care.

CHAPTER 29.
Raharjo, Yulfita
and Lorraine Corner
(Indonesian Institute of
Sciences)

Cultural attitudes to health
and sickness in public health
programs: a demand-creation
approach using data from West
Aceh, Indonesia.

G. SOCIAL AND CULTURAL CONTEXT OF HEALTH RELATED BEHAVIOUR

CHAPTER 30.
Caldwell, John C., Pat Caldwell,
Indra Gajanayake, I.O. Orubuloye,
Indrani Pieris and P.H. Reddy
(ANU)

Cultural, social and
behavioural determinants of
health and their mechanisms:
a report on related research
programs.

CHAPTER 31.
Basu, Alaka
(National Council of Applied
Economic Research, Delhi)

Cultural influences on child health
in a Delhi slum and in what way is
urban poverty preferable to rural
poverty?

CHAPTER 32.
Bledsoe, Caroline
(Northwestern University)

Differential care of children of previous unions within Mende households in Sierra Leone.

CHAPTER 33.
Powles, John
(Monash University, Melbourne)

The best of both worlds: attempting to explain the persisting low mortality of Greek migrants to Australia.

CHAPTER 34.
Reddy, P.H.
(Population Centre, Karnataka, India)

Dietary practices during pregnancy, lactation and infancy.

CHAPTER 35.
Underwood, Peter and Dennis Gray
(University of Western Australia)

Barriers to health in North Yemen: what is the 'evidence' and what 'evidence' is wanted?

CHAPTER 36.
Gaisie, Sam K.
(University of Gambia)

Culture and health in Sub-Saharan Africa

CHAPTER 37
Visaria, Leela
(Gujarat Inst. for Area Planning, Ahmedabad)

Socio-cultural determinants of health in rural Gujarat: results of a longitudinal study.

CHAPTER 38.
Eisenbruch, Maurice
(Department of Psychiatry, Royal Children's Hospital, Melbourne)

The role of cultural bereavement in health transition in a multi-cultural society.

H. WOMEN'S EMPOWERMENT AND HEALTH

CHAPTER 39.
Finerman, Ruthbeth
(Memphis State University)

Who benefits from health care decisions? Family medicine in an Andean Indian community.

CHAPTER 40.
Cosminsky, Sheila
(Rutgers University)

Women's health care strategies: a Guatemalan plantation.

CHAPTER 41.
Popkin, Barry
and Rebecca Miles Doan
(University of N. Carolina)

Women's roles, time allocation and health.

I. THE STRUCTURE AND PROVISION OF HEALTH SERVICES

CHAPTER 42.
Janzen, John
(University of Kansas)

Strategies of health-seeking and structures of social support in Central and Southern Africa.

CHAPTER 43.
Denoon, Donald
(ANU)

Creating medical issues: how do physical conditions become medical problems?

CHAPTER 44.
Gadomski, Anne, Robert Black and W. Henry Mosley
(Johns Hopkins University)

Constraints to the potential impact of the direct interventions for child survival in developing countries.

CHAPTER 45.
Higginbotham, Nick and Linda Connor
(University of Newcastle)

Culture accommodation of primary health care: a framework for assessing the contribution of patient-provider fit to health transitions.

CHAPTER 46.
Nations, Marilyn and Monica Facanha Farrias
(Project Hope, Ceara, Brazil)

Jeitinho Brasileiro: Cultural creativity and making the medical system work for poor Brazilians.

J. THE RECEIPT OF HEALTH SERVICES

CHAPTER 47
Maddocks, Ian
(Flinders University)

What makes a patient good?

CHAPTER 48.
Sushama, P.N.
(ANU)

Social context of health behaviour in Kerala.

CHAPTER 49.
Shariff, Abusaleh
(Gujarat Inst. for Area Planning, Ahmedabad)

A few cultural concepts and socio-behavioural aspects of human health in India.

CHAPTER 50.
Streatfield, Kim, Lamtiur H. Tampubolon and Charles Surjadi
(ANU)

Child health among the Jakarta poor.

CHAPTER 51.
Gifford, Sandy
(Monash University)

Cultural barriers to participating in cancer screening programs: a case study of breast and cervical screening among older Macedonian and Italian women living in Victoria, Australia.

K. SOCIAL AND BEHAVIOURAL ASPECTS OF SPECIFIC DISEASES

CHAPTER 52.
Aaby, Peter
(University of Copenhagen)

Social and behavioural factors affecting transmission and severity of measles infection.

CHAPTER 53.
van Ginneken, Jeroen
(Netherlands Central Bureau of Statistics)

Behavioural factors affecting transmission and treatment of acute respiratory infections.

CHAPTER 54.
Smith, Barry
(ANU)

The Victorian poliomyelitis epidemic, 1937-38.

CHAPTER 55.
Douglas, Bob
(ANU)

Acute respiratory infections: history, medicine and behaviour.

CHAPTER 56.
Hetzel, Basil
(ICCIDD, Adelaide)

Communication and social marketing in controlling iodine deficiency disorders.

L. WHAT TO TELL METHODOLOGISTS

CHAPTER 57.
Palloni, Alberto
(University of Wisconsin)

Methodological problems in the study of the health transition.

CHAPTER 58.
Diamond, Ian and
Patty Solomon
(ANU)

Some contributions of statistics to the study of health transitions.

CHAPTER 59.
Lindenbaum, Shirley
(New School for Social Research, New York)

The view from anthropology.

CHAPTER 60.
Maddocks, Ian
(Flinders University)

What to tell epidemiologists.

CHAPTER 61.
Berman, Peter   What to tell methodologists.
(Ford Foundation, Delhi)

M. WHAT TO TELL POLICY MAKERS

CHAPTER 62.
McNicoll, Geoffrey   Comments on policy aspects of
(ANU)   health transition research.

CHAPTER 63.
Douglas, Bob   What to tell the policy makers.
(ANU)

CHAPTER 64.
Hetzel, Basil   A case study in the development of
(ICCIDD, Adelaide)   health policy.

N. OVERVIEW

CHAPTER 65.
Simons, John   Themes and issues for a sociology of
(London School of Hygiene   the health transition.
and Tropical Medicine)

APPENDIX II

HEALTH TRANSITION WORKSHOP, LONDON, JUNE 1989

MEASUREMENT OF HEALTH TRANSITION CONCEPTS

List of Papers Presented

Adjei, Sam

Ways in which the design and delivery of health services may influence uptake: methods of enquiry.

Akin, John S.
(University of North Carolina)

Estimating the impacts of socio-economic and biomedical factors on child health – the Cebu study.

Assogba[1], Laurent N.M.,
Oona M. Campbell[2] and
Allan G. Hill[2]
([1]University of Lome, [2]London School of Hygiene and Tropical Medicine)

Advantages and limitations of large-scale health interview surveys for the study of health and its determinants.

Behrens, R.H.
(London School of Hygiene and Tropical Medicine)

Biomedical methods for the assessment of nutritional status in the individual and in communities.

Bledsoe, Caroline
(Northwestern University)

Unravelling the trickle-down model within households: foster children and the phenomenon of scrounging.

Briceno-Leon, Roberto
(University of Central Venezuela)

The four dimensions of Chagas disease.

Crook[1], Nigel,
Radhika Ramasubban[2] and
Bhanwar Singh[2]
([1]University of London,
[2]Centre of Social and Technological Change, Bombay)

A multi-dimensional approach to the social analysis of the health transition in Bombay.

DaVanzo, Julie and
Paul Gertler
(The Rand Corporation)

Household production of health: a microeconomic perspective of health transitions.

Dyson, Tim and
Michael Murphy
(London School of Economics)

Macro-level study of socio-economic development and mortality: adequacy of indicators and methods of statistical analysis.

Findley, Sally E.
(Rockefeller Foundation)

Community influences on health transition processes: toward a contextual model.

Foster[1], Stanley O. and
Jason S. Weisfeld[2]
([1]Atlanta, USA, [2]Kaduna, Nigeria, Centers for Disease Control)

Practical epidemiologic methods for managing the health transition.

Gray, Alan
(ANU)

Discovering determinants of Australian Aboriginal population health.

Hammad, A. El Bindari
and C.A. Mulholland
(World Health Organization)

The health status of vulnerable groups: a valuable indicator for national development.

Heggenhougen, Kris
(London School of Hygiene and Tropical Medicine)

Perceptions of health care options and therapy seeking behaviour.

Manton[1], Kenneth G.,
Max Woodbury[1] and
John E. Dowd[2]
([1]Duke University, [2]World Health Organization)

Methods to identify geographic and social clustering of disability and disease burden.

Myntti, Cynthia
(London School of Hygiene and Tropical Medicine)

The anthropologist as storyteller: picking up where others leave off in public health research.

Palloni, Alberto
(University of Wisconsin)

Review of data sources and methods for assessment of mortality trends, age patterns, differentials and causes in the Third World.

Paolisso[1], Michael,
Duncan Ngaré[2] and
Judith Timyan[1]
([1]International Center for Research on Women, [2]Kenyan Medical Research Institute, Nairobi)

Behavioural research on household activity pattern, resource allocation and care practice.

Randall, Sara
(NEF, Douentza, Mali)

Multi-method perspectives of Tamasheq illness: care, action and outcome.

Scrimshaw, Susan C.M.
(University of California,
Los Angeles)

Combining quantitative and
qualitative methods in the study
of intrahousehold resource
allocation.

Simons, John
(London School of Hygiene
and Tropical Medicine)

The measurement of subjective
rationales for health-related
behaviour.

Stolnitz, George J.
(Indiana University)

How do we evaluate the effects
of different social policies
on health?

Streatfield[1], Kim,
Lamtiur H. Tampubolon[2]
and Charles Surjadi[2]
([1]ANU, [2]Atma Jaya
University, Jakarta)

Investigating health beliefs
and related health seeking
behaviour among the urban poor
of Jakarta.

Yoder, P. Stanley
(University of Pennsylvania)

Cultural conceptions of illness
and the measurement of changes
and differentials in morbidity.